Life on Earth

RED FOX, JAPAN

David Attenborough
Life on Earth
A NATURAL HISTORY

The augmented and enlarged edition.
Published by The Reader's Digest Association Limited
in conjunction with William Collins
and the British Broadcasting Corporation

This edition of LIFE ON EARTH
was designed by
The Reader's Digest Association Limited
London

Published by
The Reader's Digest Association Limited
25 Berkeley Square
London W1X 6AB
in conjunction with
William Collins Sons & Co. Limited
14 St James's Place, London SW1A 1PS
and The British Broadcasting Corporation
35 Marylebone High Street
London W1M 4AA

Typesetting
Jolly & Barber Limited, Rugby
Colour separations
Gilchrist Bros Limited, Leeds
Mullis-Morgan Limited, London
Printing and binding
Arnoldo Mondadori Editore, Verona, Italy

Printed in Italy

Consultant biologist
Andrew Laurie

Picture researcher
Naomi Narod

Artists
Tom Adams
Peter Barrett
Hargrave Hands
Jeffery Matthews
Charles Pickard
Charles Raymond
Harry Titcombe
Michael Woods

SEA-LIONS, GALAPAGOS ISLANDS

ANT ON LESSER STITCHWORT, WALES

Contents

Introduction

Twenty-five years ago, I went to the tropics for the first time. I still recall, with great clarity, the shock of stepping out of the plane and into the muggy, perfumed air of West Africa. It was like walking into a steam laundry. Moisture hung in the atmosphere so heavily that my skin and shirt were soaked within minutes. A hedge of hibiscus bordered the airport buildings. Sunbirds, glittering with green and blue iridescence, played around it, darting from one scarlet blossom to another, hanging on beating wings as they probed for nectar. Only after I had watched them for some time, did I notice, clasping a branch within the hedge, a chameleon, motionless except for its goggling eyes which swivelled to follow every passing insect. Beside the hedge, I trod on what appeared to be grass. To my astonishment, the leaflets immediately folded themselves flat against the stem, transforming green fronds into apparently bare twigs. It was sensitive mimosa. Beyond lay a ditch covered with floating plants. In the spaces between them, the black water wriggled with fish, and over the leaves walked a chestnut-coloured bird, lifting its long-toed feet with the exaggerated care of a man in snow-shoes. Wherever I looked, I found a prodigality of pattern and colour for which I was quite unprepared. It was a revelation of the splendour and fecundity of the natural world from which I have never recovered.

Almost every year since that first trip, I have managed, one way or another, to get back to the tropics. Usually my purpose has been to make a film about some corner of that infinitely varied world. So I have had the luck to journey for months with the sole object of

finding and filming a rare creature that few people have seen in the wild, and to gaze on some of the most marvellous spectacles that the wild places of the world have to offer – a tree full of displaying birds of paradise in New Guinea, giant lemurs leaping through the forest of Madagascar, the biggest lizards in the world prowling, like dragons, through the jungle of a tiny island in Indonesia.

The films we made tried to document the lives of particular animals showing how each found its food, defended itself and courted, and the ways in which it fitted into the community of animals and plants around it. One element, however, was missing. We seldom examined the basic character of its anatomy. The quintessence of, for example, a lizard is only fully understandable in the light of the particular possibilities and limitations dictated by its reptilian nature and that, in turn, only becomes comprehensible in the light of its past.

So the idea formed that a group of us might make a series of films that portrayed animals in a slightly different way from any we had attempted before. Such films would be concerned not only with natural history in the sense that those two words are normally used, but with the history of nature. They would try to survey the whole animal kingdom and consider each great group of animals in the light of the part it has played in the long drama of life from its beginnings until today. This book stems from the three years of travelling and research that went into the making of those films.

The condensation of three thousand million years of history into three hundred pages, the

description of a group of animals containing tens of thousands of species within one chapter, compels vast omissions. My method has been to try to perceive the single most significant thread in the history of a group and then concentrate on tracing that, resolutely ignoring other issues, no matter how enticing they may seem.

This, however, risks imposing an appearance of purpose on the animal kingdom that does not exist in reality. Darwin demonstrated that the driving force of evolution comes from the accumulation, over countless generations, of chance genetical changes sifted by the rigours of natural selection. In describing the consequences of this process it is only too easy to use a form of words that suggests that the animals themselves were striving to bring about change in a purposeful way – that fish *wanted* to climb on to dry land and to modify their fins into legs, that reptiles *wished* to fly, strove to change their scales into feathers and so ultimately became birds. There is no objective evidence of anything of the kind and I have endeavoured, while describing these processes in a reasonably succinct way, not to use any phrases that might suggest otherwise.

To a surprising degree, nearly all the major events in this history can be told using living animals to represent the ancestral creatures which were the actual protagonists. The lungfish today shows how lungs may have developed; the mouse deer represents the first hoofed mammals that browsed in the forests of fifty million years ago. But misunderstandings can come unless the nature of this impersonation is made quite clear. In rare

instances, a living species seems to be identical
with one whose remains are fossilised in rocks
several hundred million years old. It happens
to have occupied a niche in the environment
that has existed unchanged for such vast
periods of time and suited it so ideally that it
had no cause to change. In most cases,
however, living species, while they may share
essential characters with their ancestors, differ
from them in many ways. The lungfish and
the mouse deer are fundamentally similar to
their ancestors, but they are by no means
identical. To underline this distinction each
time with a phrase like 'ancestral forms that
closely resemble the living species' would be
unnecessarily clumsy and literal-minded, but
that qualifying phrase must be taken as read
whenever I have referred to an ancient
creature by the name of a living one.

I have used familiar English names rather
than scientific Latin ones so that when an
animal makes its appearance in this history, it
is quickly recognised for what it is. I have
expressed age in absolute terms of millions of
years rather than use the adjectival names of
periods coined by classical geology. Lastly, I
have made no reference by name to those
many scientists whose work has provided the
facts and theories on which the following
pages are based. This has been done solely to
try to maintain clarity in the narrative. I
intend no minimisation of the debt owed to
them by all of us who take pleasure in
watching animals. They and their researches
have provided us with that most valuable of
insights, the ability to perceive the continuity
of nature in all its manifestations and to
recognise our place within it.

GOLIATH HERON, TANZANIA

1. THE INFINITE VARIETY

Some four million different forms of life exist on earth today. How can such diversity be explained?

It is not difficult to discover an unknown animal. Spend a day in the tropical forest of South America, turning over logs, looking beneath bark, sifting through the moist litter of leaves, followed by an evening shining a mercury lamp on a white screen, and one way and another you will collect hundreds of different kinds of small creatures. Moths, caterpillars, spiders, long-nosed bugs, luminous beetles, harmless butterflies disguised as wasps, wasps shaped like ants, sticks that walk, leaves that open wings and fly – the variety will be enormous and one of these creatures will almost certainly be undescribed by science. The difficulty will be to find specialists who know enough about the groups concerned to be able to single out the new one.

No one can say just how many species of animals there are in these greenhouse-humid dimly lit jungles. They contain the richest and the most varied assemblage of animal and plant life to be found anywhere on earth. Not only are there many major categories of creatures – monkeys, rodents, spiders, hummingbirds, butterflies – but most of those types exist in many different forms. There are over forty different species of parrot, over seventy different monkeys, three hundred hummingbirds and tens of thousands of butterflies. If you are not careful, you can even be bitten by a hundred different kinds of mosquito.

In 1832 a young Englishman, Charles Darwin, twenty-four years old and naturalist on HMS *Beagle*, a brig sent by the Admiralty in London on a surveying voyage round

---

Darwin's 'imps of darkness', the marine iguanas of the Galapagos
Darwin found these strange reptiles swarming in herds, thousands strong, over the black lava rocks of several of the Galapagos Islands. They are, clearly, very like the common iguana of the mainland of South America and, like it, they are vegetarian. But here in the Galapagos there is little vegetation and they have developed unique ways of finding food. They browse on seaweed as the Pacific surf crashes about them and even swim out to sea and dive down to graze on the sea floor. They are just one of the unique creatures of the Galapagos that set Darwin pondering on the way that species originate.

Long necks on dry land, short necks on wet
Some of the Galapagos Islands are dry; others are comparatively well watered. The giant tortoises of the Galapagos have necks that match their circumstances. On the dry islands, they are long-necked so that they can reach up and browse leaves from trees. On other islands, where there is so much water that the tortoises can even wallow, they can usually find ground vegetation and their necks are short.

the world, came to such a forest outside Rio de Janeiro. In one day, in one small area, he collected sixty-eight different species of small beetle. That there should be such a variety of species of one kind of creature astounded him. He had not been searching specially for them so that, as he wrote in his journal, 'It is sufficient to disturb the composure of an entomologist's mind to look forward to the future dimensions of a complete catalogue'. The conventional view of his time was that all species were immutable and that each had been individually and separately created by God. Darwin was far from being an atheist – he had, after all, taken a degree in divinity in Cambridge – but he was deeply puzzled by this enormous multiplicity of forms.

During the next three years, the *Beagle* sailed down the east coast of South America, rounded Cape Horn and came north again up the coast of Chile. The expedition then sailed out into the Pacific until, 600 miles from the mainland, they came to the lonely archipelago of the Galapagos. Here Darwin's questions about the creation of species recurred, for in these islands he found fresh variety. He was fascinated to discover that the Galapagos animals bore a general resemblance to those he had seen on the mainland, but differed from them in detail. There were cormorants, black, long-necked diving birds like those that fly low along Brazilian rivers, but here in the Galapagos, their wings were so small and with such stunted feathers that they had lost the power of flight. There were iguanas, large lizards with a crest of scales along their backs. Those on the continent climbed trees and ate leaves. Here on the islands, where there was little vegetation, one species fed on seaweed and clung to rocks among the surging waves with unusually long and powerful claws. There were tortoises, very similar to the mainland forms except that these were many times bigger, giants that a man could ride. The English Vice-Governor of the Galapagos told Darwin that even within the archipelago, there was variety: the tortoises on each island were slightly different, so that it was possible to tell which island they came from. Those that lived on relatively well-watered islands where there was ground vegetation to be cropped, had a gently curving front edge to their shells just above the neck. But those that came from arid islands and had to crane their necks in order to reach branches of cactus or leaves of trees, had much longer necks and a high peak to the front of their shells that enabled them to stretch their necks almost vertically upwards.

The suspicion grew in Darwin's mind that species were not fixed for ever. Perhaps one could change into another. Maybe, thousands of years ago, birds and reptiles from continental South America had reached the Galapagos, ferried on the rafts of vegetation that float down the rivers and out to sea. Once there, they had changed, as generation succeeded generation, to suit their new homes until they became their present species.

The differences between them and their mainland cousins were only small, but if such changes had taken place, was it not possible that over many millions of years, the cumulative effects on a dynasty of animals could be so great that they could bring about major transformations? Maybe fish had developed muscular fins and crawled on to land to become amphibians; maybe amphibians in their turn had developed water-tight

A finch becomes a 'woodpecker'

Only one kind of finch reached the Galapagos from the mainland. Eventually, different populations of finch became adapted to different environments and today there are 13 different species in the archipelago. This one (below) plays the role of woodpecker, feeding on insects in tree bark. Instead of developing the long probing tongue of a true woodpecker, it has learned to pick out the insects with a long thorn.

skins and become reptiles; maybe, even, some ape-like creatures had stood upright and become the ancestors of man.

In truth the idea was not a wholly new one. Many others before Darwin had suggested that all life on earth was interrelated. Darwin's revolutionary insight was to perceive the mechanism that brought these changes about. By doing so he replaced a philosophical speculation with a detailed description of a process, supported by an abundance of evidence, that could be tested and verified; and the reality of evolution could no longer be denied.

Put briefly, his argument was this. All individuals of the same species are not identical. In one clutch of eggs from, for example, a giant tortoise, there will be some

Cormorants that have lost the power of flight

Sometimes a new environment demands not more talents but fewer. These cormorants, at first sight, seem very like their cousins that nest around the coasts of South America. But these birds live on the Galapagos and they are, in one crucial way, quite different. When cormorants come ashore after swimming and feeding, they habitually hold their wings out to dry in the sun (left). When the Galapagos cormorant does so, it reveals that its wings are not like those of other cormorants. Its feathers are tattered and stunted. Before man arrived on the islands there were no predators, so these cormorants had no need to fly to escape from enemies. Over many generations, their wing feathers degenerated and the cormorants of the Galapagos Islands are now quite incapable of using their wings for flight.

THE MANY WAYS IN WHICH FOSSILS ARE FORMED

Any evidence in rocks testifying to the past existence of a living organism can justifiably be called a fossil. Sometimes it may be no more than a faint track made originally in mud; sometimes it may be the body of an animal that has been changed, molecule by molecule, into stone.

Some 2 million years ago, in Siberia, mammoths occasionally fell into ravines and died. Their bodies were quickly covered by snow and by the gravels brought down by rivers in the short Arctic spring. Thereafter, the gravels consolidated and the biting frost kept the corpses in cold storage. When scientists excavated them, they found the bodies complete with flesh, hair and internal organs. In some cases, they even discovered recognisable fragments of vegetation on the huge teeth and in the stomach and so were able to deduce what the animal had been chewing for its last meal.

Total preservation like this, however, is a very exceptional form of fossilisation. Usually the soft parts of an animal rot and disappear, so the vast majority of fossils consist of no more than the hard parts of the body – teeth, bones or shells. Even these, if they are to survive, must be buried in some way. Occasionally, this may happen on land – in a sand-dune or down a cave – but much more commonly, it occurs at the bottom of a swamp or a lake or in the sea. When the sediments enclosing the bone or shell become compressed by the weight of the deposits accumulating above, and when, over millions of years, earth movements raise and fold them, then the shells and bones may themselves be turned to stone. Solutions of minerals, such as silica or lime, may permeate the rock and replace the substances formed by the animal.

Often, this process results in a solid cast in the new mineral of the original shape, but sometimes the petrifaction happens so slowly and with such delicacy that even the internal structure is faithfully reproduced. So a fossil tooth, in section, may reveal the layered construction and internal canals of its original, and the skull of a 400-million-year-old fish show the intricate pathways of the nerves and blood vessels that once surrounded and supplied it.

Fossils that consist of an empty space

Under some circumstances, the processes of petrifaction work in the opposite way. Then the liquids in the rocks do not replace the shells and bones, but dissolve them, leaving behind no more than an empty space. But even these can reveal a great deal about the shape and character of the original creature. The impression of the outside surface of a shell may be almost as informative as the shell itself.

In some circumstances, sediments seep inside a shell or bone and, when that is dissolved away, a cast of the

An ancient coral *Corals are perfect candidates for fossilisation, for they build skeletons of lime or silica and these, being already stone, can survive unaltered in the rocks. This one (left), sectioned and polished, shows all the details of its internal structure, although it is some 400 million years old.*

Three ways of leaving a mark *The actual shell of some of these cockles has survived. Where it has disappeared, however, the cockle has still left a sign of its existence as an internal cast (bottom right) or as an imprint of its exterior (middle right).*

interior is left. A corkscrew of limestone can reveal the internal shape of a vanished whelk; sandstone that once filled a deer skull may show the shape of the brain and so provide evidence of the behaviour of that long-dead creature.

Some shapes in the rocks that fully justify the name of fossil may never have been part of the animal at all. A horseshoe crab, as it crawls over a sandy beach, leaves behind it a line of tracks. If the gently lapping waves of the returning tide fill such tracks with a dusting of fine sediment, then there will be a difference in the substance and texture of the two layers. If the beach sands become sandstone, the rock will have a tendency to erode or cleave along this line of discontinuity. So tens of millions of years later, the weather or the tap of the fossil-hunter's hammer may reveal the ancient tracks once more.

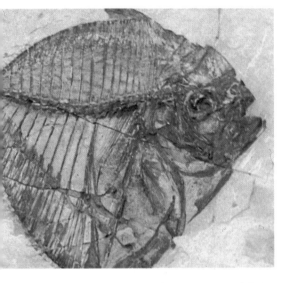

A fragile skeleton
The perfection with which this small fish has been fossilised makes it clear that its body drifted down in water, where there was little current to disturb the delicate remains and a swift deposition of mud to cover them.

An internal cast
Sometimes the chemical conditions during rock formation dissolve lime and so remove all traces of shells. But the solidified sediment that once filled them may remain and be quite sufficient to identify the organism that once existed.

hatchlings which, because of their genetic constitution, will develop longer necks than others. In times of drought they will be able to reach leaves and so survive. Their brothers and sisters, with shorter necks, will starve and die. So those best fitted to their surroundings will be selected and be able to transmit their characteristics to their offspring. After a great number of generations, tortoises on the arid islands will have longer necks than those on the watered islands. And so one species will have given rise to another.

This concept did not become clear in Darwin's mind until long after he had left the Galapagos. For twenty-five years he painstakingly amassed evidence to support it. Not until 1859, when he was forty-eight years old, did he publish it and even then he was driven to do so only because another younger naturalist, Alfred Wallace, working in Southeast Asia, had formulated the same idea. He called the book in which he set out his theory in detail, *The Origin of Species by Means of Natural Selection or the Preservation of Favoured Races in the Struggle for Life.*

Since that time, the theory of natural selection has been debated and tested, refined, qualified and elaborated. Later discoveries about genetics, molecular biology, population dynamics and behaviour have given it new dimensions. It remains the key to our understanding of the natural world and it enables us to recognise that life has a long and continuous history during which organisms, both plant and animal, have changed, generation by generation, as they colonised all parts of the world.

The direct, if fragmentary, evidence for this history lies in the archives of the earth, the sedimentary rocks. The vast majority of animals leave no trace of their existence after their passing. Their flesh decays, their shells and their bones become scattered and turn to powder. But very occasionally, one or two individuals out of a population of many thousands have a different fate. A reptile becomes stuck in a swamp and dies. Its body rots but its bones settle into the mud. Dead vegetation drifts to the bottom and covers them. As the centuries pass and more vegetation accumulates, the deposit turns to peat. Changes in sea level may cause the swamp to be flooded and layers of sand to be deposited on top of the peat. Over great periods of time, the peat is compressed and turned to coal. The reptile's bones still remain within it. The great pressure of the overlying sediments and the mineral-rich solutions that circulate through them cause chemical changes in the calcium phosphate of the bones. Eventually they are turned to stone, but they retain not only the outward shape that they had in life, albeit sometimes distorted, but on occasion even their detailed cellular structure is preserved so that you can look at sections of them through the microscope and plot the shape of the blood vessels and the nerves that once surrounded them.

The most suitable places for fossilisation are in seas and lakes where sedimentary deposits like sandstones and limestones are slowly accumulating. On land, where for the most part rocks are not built up by deposition but broken down by erosion, deposits, such as sand dunes, are only very rarely created and preserved. In consequence, the only land-living creatures likely to be fossilised are those that happen to fall into water. Since this is exceptional fate for most of them, we are never likely to know from fossil

A chronicle of life in the Grand Canyon

The topmost rocks of the Grand Canyon were laid down some 200 million years ago. The fossil remains they contain reveal what kind of creatures had come into existence by that time. Amphibians, like huge newts, waddled over estuaries leaving their footprints impressed in the sand (top); insects, related to the dragonflies of today (middle), whirred through the branches of tall, fern-like trees (bottom). But a few hundred metres farther down the Canyon, all signs of trees, insects and back-boned creatures disappear.

evidence anything approaching the complete range of land creatures that has existed in the past. Water-living animals, such as fish, molluscs, sea urchins and corals, are much more promising candidates for preservation. Even so, very few of these perished in the exact physical and chemical conditions necessary for fossilisation. Of those that did, only a tiny proportion happen to lie in the rocks that outcrop on the surface of the ground today; and of these few, most will be eroded away and destroyed before they are discovered by fossil hunters. The astonishment is that, in the face of these adverse odds, the fossils that have been collected are so numerous and the record they provide so detailed and coherent.

How can we date them? Since the discovery of radioactivity scientists have realised that rocks have a geological clock within them. Several chemical elements decay with age, producing radioactivity in the process. Potassium turns into argon, uranium into lead, rubidium into strontium. The rate at which this happens can be estimated. So if the proportion of the secondary element to the primary one in a rock is measured, the time at which the original mineral was formed can be calculated. Since there are several such pairs of elements decaying at different speeds, it is possible to make cross-checks. This technique, which requires extremely sophisticated methods of analysis, will always remain the province of the specialist. But anyone can date many rocks in a relative way by simple logic and by doing so put into order the major events of fossil history. If rocks lie in layers, and are not grossly disturbed, then the lower layer must be older than the upper. So we can follow the history of life through the strata and trace the lineages of animals back to their beginnings by going deeper and deeper into the earth's crust.

A mule ride down a calendar of fossils

The deepest cleft that exists in the earth's surface is the Grand Canyon in the western United States. The rocks through which the Colorado River has cut its way still lie roughly horizontally, layer upon layer, red, brown and yellow, sometimes pink in early light, sometimes blue in the shadowed distance. The land is so dry that only isolated juniper trees and low scrub freckle the surface of the cliffs and the rock strata, some soft, some hard, are clear and stark. Most of them are sandstones or limestones that were laid down at the bottom of the shallow seas that once covered this part of North America. When they are examined closely, breaks in the succession can be detected. These represent times when the land rose, the seas drained away and the sea-bed became dry so that the deposits that had accumulated on it were eroded away. Subsequently, the land sank again, seas flooded back and deposition restarted. In spite of these gaps, the broad lines of the fossil story remain clear.

A mule will carry you in an easy day's ride from the rim to the very bottom of the Canyon. The first rocks you pass are already some 200 million years old. There are no remains of mammals or birds in them, but there are traces of reptiles. Close by the side of the trail, you can see a line of tracks crossing the face of a sandstone boulder. They were made by a small four-footed creature, almost certainly a lizard-like reptile,

A vertical mile of rock: 2000 million years of history

Fossils are not abundant in every one of the layers of the Grand Canyon, but the order of the layers and the characteristics of their rocks make it possible to identify the same sequences outcropping in the gorges and mountains near by. There they may be richer in fossils which will fill in gaps in the story. Many of the more recent layers of rocks that once lay above the present-day surface around the rim of the Canyon have been eroded away. But the Canyon's highest sequence can be recognised in the base of a nearby mountain and there the later layers still remain, forming the mountain face. These continue the record for another 30 million years. Between them, they provide detailed evidence of the order in which different kinds of animals and plants appeared through 2000 million years of history.

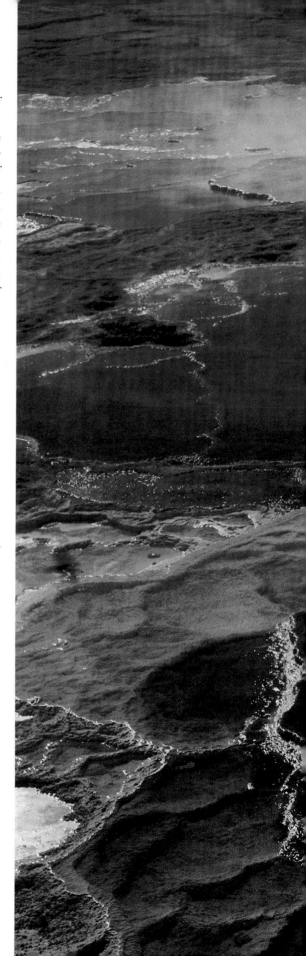

running across a beach. Other rocks at the same level elsewhere, contain impressions of fern leaves and the wings of insects.

Halfway down the Canyon, you come to 400-million-year-old limestones. There are no reptiles to be found here, but there are the bones of strange armoured fish. An hour or so later – and a hundred million years earlier – the rocks contain no sign of backboned animals of any kind. There are a few shells and worms that have left behind a tracery of trails in what was the muddy sea floor. Three-quarters of the way down, you are still descending through layers of limestone, but now there is no sign of life whatever. By the late afternoon, you ride at last into the lower gorge where the Colorado River runs green between high rock walls . You are now a vertical mile below the rim and the rocks have been dated to the immense age of 2000 million years. Here you might hope to find evidence for the very beginnings of life. But there are no organic remains of any kind. The dark fine-grained rocks lie not in horizontal layers like all those above, but are twisted and buckled and riven with veins of pink granite.

The earliest signs of life

Are signs of life absent because these rocks and the limestones directly above are so extremely ancient that all such traces have been crushed from them? Could it be that the first creatures to leave any sign of their existence were as complex as worms and molluscs? For many years these questions puzzled geologists. All over the world, rocks of this antiquity were carefully searched for organic remains. One or two odd shapes were found, but most authorities dismissed these as patterns produced by the physical processes of rock formation that had nothing whatever to do with living organisms. Then during the 1950s, the searchers began to use high-powered micro-scopes on some particularly enigmatic rocks.

A thousand miles northeast of the Grand Canyon, ancient rocks of about the same age as those beside the Colorado River outcrop on the shores of Lake Superior. Some of them contain seams of a fine-grained flint-like substance called chert. This was well known during the last century because the pioneers used it in their flintlock guns. Here and there, it contains strange white concentric rings a metre or so across. Were these merely eddies in the mud on the bottom of the primeval seas or could they have been formed by living organisms? No one could be sure and the shapes were given the non-committal name of stromatolite, a word derived from Greek meaning no more than 'stony carpet'. But when researchers cut sections of these rings, ground them down into slices so thin that they were translucent and examined them through the microscope, they found, preserved in the chert, the shapes of simple organisms, each no more than one or two hundredths of a millimetre across. Some resembled filaments of algae; others, while they were unmistakably organic, had no parallels with living organisms; and some looked to be identical with the simplest form of life existing today, bacteria.

It seemed almost impossible to many people that such tiny things as micro-organisms could have been fossilised at all. That relics of them should have survived for such a vast period of time seemed even more difficult to believe. The solution of silica

which had saturated the dead organisms and solidified into chert was clearly as fine-grained and durable a preservative as exists. The discovery of the fossils in the Gunflint Chert stimulated further searches not only in North America but all over the world and other micro-fossils were found in cherts in Africa and Australia. Some of these, astonishingly, pre-dated the Gunflint specimens by a thousand million years. But if we want to consider how life arose, we have to look back a further thousand million years beyond even the earliest micro-fossils, to a time when the earth was completely lifeless and still cooling after its birth.

The steaming world where life began

The planet then was radically different in almost every way from the one we live on today. The clouds of water vapour that had surrounded it had condensed to form seas, but they were still hot. We are not sure how the land masses lay, but they certainly bore no resemblance in either form or distribution to modern continents. Volcanoes were abundant, spewing ash and lava. The atmosphere was very thin and consisted of swirling clouds of hydrogen, carbon monoxide, ammonia and methane. There was little or no oxygen. This mixture allowed ultraviolet rays from the sun to bathe the earth's surface with an intensity that would be lethal to modern animal life. Electrical storms raged in the clouds, bombarding the land and the sea with lightning.

Laboratory experiments were made in the 1950s to discover what might happen to these particular chemical constituents under such conditions. Such gases, mixed with water vapour, were subjected to electrical discharge and ultraviolet light. After only a week of this treatment complex molecules were found to have formed in the mixture, including sugars, nucleic acids and amino acids, the building blocks of proteins. There seems no doubt that molecules such as these could have formed in the seas of the earth at the very beginning of its history.

DNA, and the start of evolution

As the millions of years passed, the concentrations of these substances increased and the molecules began to interact with one another to form even more complex compounds. It may even be that some ingredients were added from outer space, brought by meteorites. Eventually, among a great variety of substances, there appeared one that was to be crucial for the further development of life. It is called deoxyribonucleic acid, or DNA for short. Its structure endows it with two key properties. First, it can act as a blueprint for the manufacture of amino acids; and second, it has the capacity to replicate itself. With this substance, molecules had reached the threshold of something quite new, for these two characteristics of DNA are also those of living organisms such

The oldest organisms of all

The scalding hot springs of Yellowstone Park in North America seem very unlikely places in which to find life of any kind. Yet in many ways they reproduce the conditions in which the first life came into existence some 3000 million years ago. So these are the places to search to discover the kind of organisms that evolved at the beginning of life's history. And they exist here in surprising variety – bacteria and simple algae, forming skins and curds which contribute to the colour of a pool, sometimes causing it to change with the season as the colonies wax and wane. 19

HISTORY OF LIFE IN A SINGLE YEAR

The very simplest forms of life appeared between 3000 and 4000 million years ago. Such a vast period of time is beyond imagination, but to appreciate the *relative* times at which different kinds of life appeared, the history of life on earth can be compared to a single year in which one day represents ten million years.

Life arose in the sea at the beginning of January and remained restricted to the simplest of forms until some time in August, when simple worms and other multi-celled creatures appeared. It was not until the beginning of November that fossilised remains appear in the rocks in sufficient quantity to enable us to chart developments in detail. Thereafter, developments took place with increasing speed.

2nd WEEK NOVEMBER	Small-shelled molluscs begin to flourish; corals and a few jawless proto-fish appear.
3rd WEEK NOVEMBER	Jawless fish become abundant; the first small plants colonise the land.
4th WEEK NOVEMBER	Bony fish proliferate, including air-breathing forms; amphibians clamber on to land.
1st WEEK DECEMBER	Sharks swim in the sea; tall forests of tree ferns and club mosses spread over the land, inhabited by insects and early reptiles.
DECEMBER 8th	Dinosaurs and huge sea-going reptiles develop.
DECEMBER 12th	Small mammals appear among the dinosaurs; pterodactyls and toothed birds fly in the sky.
DECEMBER 17th	True beaked birds take to the air; plants develop flowers.
DECEMBER 24th	Dinosaurs and other giant reptiles disappear.
DECEMBER 25th	Mammals develop into a wide variety of forms; snakes appear.
DECEMBER 30th	Mammals proliferate, establishing many modern families.
DECEMBER 31st	In the evening ape-men appear; modern man arrives a few minutes before midnight.

as bacteria. And bacteria, besides being the simplest form of life we know, are also among the oldest fossils we have discovered.

The ability of DNA to replicate itself is a consequence of its unique structure. It is shaped like two intertwined helices. During cell division, these unzip, splitting the molecule along its length into two separate helices. Each then acts as a template to which other simpler molecules become attached until each has once more become a double helix.

The simple molecules from which DNA is mainly built are of only four kinds, but they are grouped in trios and arranged in a particular and significant order on the immensely long DNA molecule. This order specifies how the twenty or so different amino acids are arranged in a protein, how much is to be made, and when. A length of DNA bearing the information for an unbroken sequence of manufacture is called a gene.

Occasionally, the DNA copying process involved in reproduction may go wrong. A mistake may be made at a single point or a length of DNA may become temporarily dislocated and be reinserted in the wrong place. The copy is then imperfect and the proteins it will create may be entirely different. When this occurred in the first organisms on earth, evolution began, for such mistakes in copying are the source of variations from which natural selection can produce evolutionary change. And we know from micro-fossils that there were already several distinct forms of bacteria-like organisms as long ago as 3000 million years.

Such vast periods of time baffle the imagination, but we can form some idea of the relative duration of the major phases of the history of life if we compare the entire span, from these first beginnings until today, with one year. Since we are unlikely yet to have discovered the oldest fossils of all, we can reckon that life started well before 3000 million years ago and as a rough guide, it will serve to let one day represent ten million years. On such a calendar, the Gunflint fossils of algae-like organisms, which seemed so extremely ancient when they were first discovered, are seen to be quite late-comers in the history of life, not appearing until the second week of August. In the Grand Canyon, the oldest worm trails were burrowed through the mud in the second week of November and the first fish appeared in the limestone seas a week later. The little lizard will have scuttled across the beach during the middle of December and man did not appear until the evening of 31 December.

But we must return to January. The bacteria fed initially on the various carbon compounds that had taken so many millions of years to accumulate in the primordial seas. But as they flourished, so this food must have become scarcer. Any bacterium that could tap a different source of food would obviously be very successful and eventually some did. Instead of taking ready-made food from their surroundings, they began to manufacture their own within their cell walls, drawing the necessary energy from the sun. This process is called photosynthesis. One of the ingredients it requires is hydrogen, a gas that is produced in great quantities during volcanic eruptions.

Conditions very similar to those in which the early photosynthesising bacteria lived can be found today in such volcanic areas as Yellowstone in Wyoming. Here a great

The Morning Glory Pool

A resemblance to the blue trumpet-shaped flower of the morning glory plant gives this spectacular pool its name. The intense blue of its centre comes from minerals dissolved by the super-heated water on its way up to the surface. Here it is too hot for any living organism, but towards the edge of the basin, where it is just a little cooler, skins of brown algae and bacteria form over the rocks of the bottom

mass of molten rock, lying only a few thousand feet down in the earth's crust, heats the rocks on the surface. In places, the ground water is well above boiling point. It flows up channels through the rocks under decreasing pressure until suddenly it flashes into steam and water spouts high into the air as a geyser. Elsewhere, the water wells up into steaming pools. As it trickles away and cools, the salts it gathered from the rocks on its way up, together with those derived from the molten mass far below, are deposited to form rimmed and buttressed basins, surrounded by tiers of terraces. In these scalding mineral-laden waters, bacteria flourish. Some grow into matted filaments and curds, others into thick leathery sheets. Many are brilliantly coloured, their intensity of hue varying during the year as the colonies wax and wane. The names given to these pools

give a hint of the variety of the bacteria and the splendour of the effects they produce – Emerald Pool, Sulphur Cauldron, Beryl Spring, Firehole Falls, Morning Glory Pool and – a particularly rich one with several species of bacteria – Artists' Paintpots.

The organisms that produced oxygen from water

When you wander through this amazing landscape, you can smell sulphuretted hydrogen, the unmistakable stench of rotting eggs, produced by the reaction of ground water with the molten rock far beneath. This is the source from which many of the bacteria here obtain their hydrogen and as long as bacteria were dependent upon volcanic action for it, they could not spread widely. But other forms eventually arose which were able to extract hydrogen from a very much more widespread source – water. This development was to have a profound effect on all life to come, for if hydrogen is removed from water, the element that remains is oxygen. The organisms that did this are a little more complex in structure than bacteria. They used to be called blue-green algae because they appeared to be close relatives of the green algae that are common in ponds, but now that their very primitive character is recognised, they are referred to as cyanophytes or simply, blue-greens. The chemical agent which they contain, making it possible for them to use water in the photosynthetic process, is chlorophyll, which is also possessed by true algae and the higher plants.

Blue-greens are found wherever there is constant moisture. You can often see mats of them, beaded with silver bubbles of oxygen, blanketing the bottoms of ponds. In Shark Bay, on the northwest coast of tropical Australia, they have developed in a particularly spectacular and significant form. Hamelin Pool, one small arm of this vast inlet, has its entrance blocked by a sand bar covered with eel grass. The flow of water in and out of the Pool is so greatly impeded that evaporation under the grilling sun has made the waters very salty indeed. As a result, marine creatures such as molluscs which would normally feed on blue-greens and keep them in check, cannot survive. The blue-greens, therefore, flourish uncropped just as they did when they were the most advanced form of life anywhere in the world. They secrete lime, forming stony cushions near the shores of the Pool and teetering columns at greater depths. Here is the explanation of those mysterious shapes seen in section in the Gunflint Chert. The blue-green pillars of Hamelin Pool are living stromatolites and the groups of them standing on the sun-dappled sea-floor are as close as we may ever get to a scene from the world of 2000 million years ago.

The arrival of the blue-greens marked a point of no return in the history of life. The oxygen they produced accumulated over the millennia to form the kind of oxygen-rich atmosphere that we know today. Our lives, and those of all other animals, depend on it. We need it not only to breathe but to protect us. Oxygen in the atmosphere forms a screen, the ozone layer, which cuts off most of the ultraviolet rays of the sun. These were the very rays which provided energy to synthesise amino acids and sugars in the primordial oceans, so the arrival of the blue-greens ruled out the possibility that life on earth could ever begin in the same way again.

The simple blue-greens

Some blue-greens, like Spirulina and Phormidium which live in mud, are thread-like. Gloeotrichia is feathery and floats about in water. Others, such as Microcystis, form clumps. Blue-greens have no visible internal structures like those in other single-celled organisms. Photosynthesis is carried on, not by separate granules, but throughout the cell. Nor is their genetic material gathered together in a nucleus, so cells cannot exchange DNA as other organisms do during sexual reproduction. Instead, blue-greens reproduce themselves by fragmenting.

MICROCYSTIS ($\times$ 110)   PHORMIDIUM ($\times$ 240)

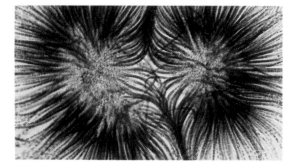

GLOEOTRICHIA ($\times$ 90) (ABOVE)

SPIRULINA ($\times$ 450) (BELOW)

The controversial circles

The rocks on the shores of Lake Superior, in the middle of the North American continent (below), have long been known to be among the most ancient in the world. They were formed from beds of sand laid down in a sea. During their immensely long history of about 1900 million years, they have been compressed and contorted to form extremely hard rock, called Gunflint Chert. Yet the first geologists to examine them found strange white rings. The geologists called these formations stromatolites, and some even claimed that they were the relics of the earliest living organisms.

Living relics from geological history

The shores of Hamelin Pool, in Western Australia (right), are lined with pillars built by colonies of lime-producing algae and bacteria. These organisms cannot survive for long out of water, so near the shore their colonies are short with flat tops. A little farther out, in deeper water, they grow into pillars 2–3 metres tall. It was growths like these, cut horizontally, that formed the rings in the Gunflint Cherts.

Life remained at this stage of development for a vast period. Eventually, however, a further huge jump was made. Exactly how it happened we still do not know for sure but you can find examples of the kind of organisms it produced in almost any patch of fresh water.

Life becomes more complicated

A drop from a pond, viewed through a microscope, swarms with tiny organisms, some spinning, some crawling, some whizzing across the field of vision like rockets. As a group they are called the Protista. They are all single cells, yet within their cell walls, they contain much more complex structures than any bacterium possesses. One central

A shell made of plant skeletons

Difflugia bacillifera (× 1400) is a kind of amoeba that builds itself a shell from the empty skeletons of microscopic plants, cementing them together in the same kind of way that the larva of a caddis fly does.

Budded colonies

Zoothamnium geniculatum (× 600) forms colonies by budding. When the big reproductive cell swims off to found a new colony, the others die.

An amoeba with spiky armour

Euglypha ciliata (× 1400), another amoeba, armours itself with long spines of silica. Those around the mouth on the left resemble small teeth, but what function they or those on the body serve is unknown.

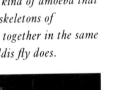

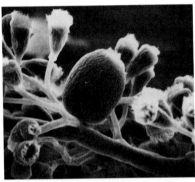

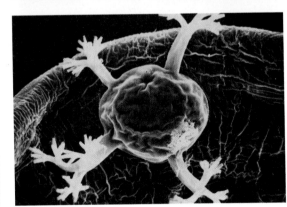

Scavenger with a ring of teeth

Trichodina pediculus (× 2500) scavenges over the surface of tadpoles and water organisms. It propels itself by beating the cilia on its back, and grips its host by a ring of movable teeth on its lower surface.

A shrimp's passenger

Spirochona gemmipara (× 850) attaches itself to the gills of freshwater shrimps and feeds by sucking water through its trumpet-shaped mouth.

A mouth on every tentacle

Dendrocometes paradoxus (× 800) has many mouths, each at the tip of one of its sticky tentacles. Its offspring form internally and are born through a split in the parent's body.

Protistans under an electron microscope

A drop of pond water, seen by an electron microscope, reveals myriads of single-cell organisms called protistans. Some of them live in delicate shells of silica or lime, produced in an endless variety of shapes (below). The electron microscope which produced the pictures of protistans on these two pages uses beams of electrons rather than rays of light, and so can detect details invisible to an optical microscope.

packet, the nucleus, is full of DNA. This appears to be the organising force of the cell. Elongated bodies, the mitochondria, provide energy by burning oxygen in much the same way as many bacteria do. Many cells have a thrashing tail attached to them and this resembles a filamentous bacterium called a spirochaete. Some protistans also contain chloroplasts, packets of chlorophyll which, like blue-greens, use the energy of sunlight to assemble complex molecules as food for the cell. Each of these tiny organisms thus appears to be a committee of simpler ones. Some researchers believe that this is exactly what they are. It may be that one cell which habitually fed by flowing round other particles, took some bacteria and blue-greens within it and these, instead of being digested, survived to collaborate in a communal life of hitherto unparalleled

intimacy. However it took place, micro-fossils indicate that cells of this complexity first appeared about 1200 million years ago – say early September in the year of life.

The dawning of sexuality

Protistans reproduce by splitting into two, as bacteria do, but their internal design is much more complex and their division, not surprisingly, is an elaborate business. Most of the separate structures, the members of the committee, themselves split. Indeed, the mitochondria and chloroplasts, each with their own DNA, often do so independently of the division of the main cell. The DNA within the nucleus replicates in a particularly complex manner which ensures that all its genes are copied and that each daughter cell receives a complete duplicate set. There are, however, several other methods of reproduction practised by various protistans on occasions. The details vary. The essential feature of all the techniques is that a shuffling of genes is involved. In some cases this takes place when two cells join up and exchange genes before breaking apart and then undergoing cell division some time later. In other cases, cells normally contain two complete sets of genes which, after shuffling, divide to make new cells with only one set. These cells are of two types – a large comparatively immobile one, and a smaller active one, driven by a flagellum. The first is called an egg and the second a sperm – for this is the dawning of sexuality. When the two types unite in a new amalgamated cell the genes are once again in two sets but in new combinations with genes from not just one parent but two. This may well be a unique combination which will produce a slightly different organism with new characteristics. Since sexuality increased the possibilities of genetic variation, it also greatly accelerated the rate at which evolution could proceed as organisms encountered new environments.

There are about 10,000 species of protistans. Some are covered by a mat of flailing threads or cilia, which with a coordinated beat drive the creature through the water. Others, including the amoeba, move by bulging out fingers from the main body and then flowing into them. Many of those that live in the sea secrete shells with the most elaborate structure of silica or lime. These are among the most exquisite objects that the microscope-borne explorer will ever encounter. Some resemble minuscule snail shells, some ornate vases and bottles. The most delicate of all are of shining translucent silica, concentric spheres transfixed by needles, gothic helmets, rococo belfries and spiked space capsules. The inhabitants of these shells extend long threads through pores with which they trap particles of food.

Other protistans feed in a different way, photosynthesising with the aid of their packets of chlorophyll. These can be regarded as plants; the remainder of the group, which feed on them, as animals. The distinction between the two at this level, however, does not have as much meaning as such labelling might suggest, for there are many species that can use both methods of feeding at different times.

Some protistans are just large enough to see with the naked eye. With a little practice, the creeping grey speck of jelly which is an amoeba can be picked out in a drop of pond water. But there is a limit to the growth of a single-celled creature, for as size increases,

Giants of the single-cell world

These tiny globes, named Volvox, are common in freshwater ponds. Each is about a millimetre across and only just visible to the naked eye, but in the world of single-celled organisms, they are giants. Their walls are constructed from single cells which have joined to form a lattice. The smaller balls within each globe are offspring colonies. In due course, the parent's wall will tear and they will swim free.

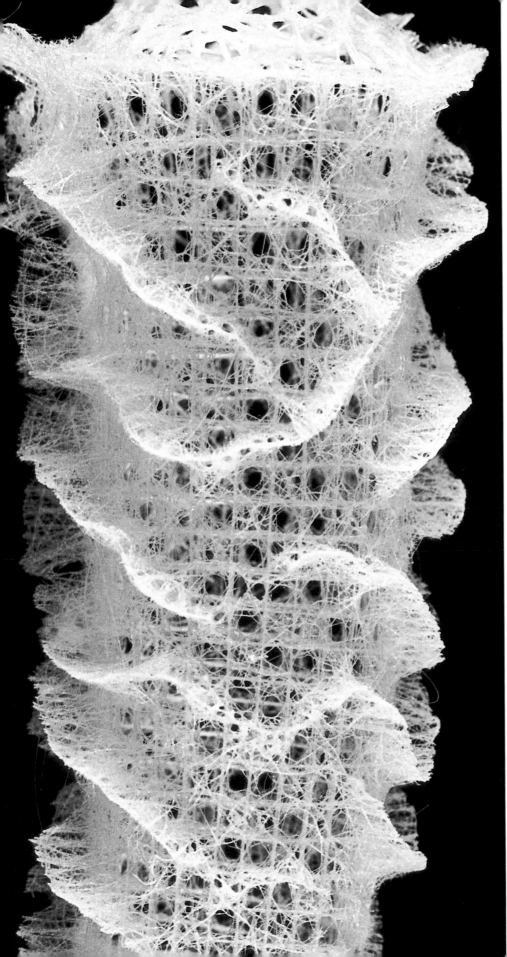

The mysterious architecture of a sponge

Venus' Flower Basket (left) builds its skeleton from tiny interlocking needles of silica. The living cells form a wall around the inside of this delicate structure. Few people have seen the creature alive for it lives in depths of about 300 metres, but occasionally fishermen trawling around Japan and the Philippines bring up one of these astonishing skeletons. They are usually about 30 centimetres long.

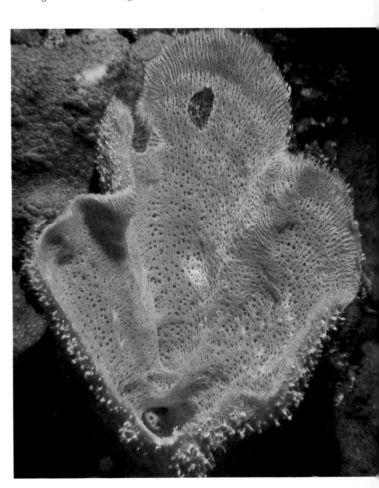

How a sponge feeds

A living sponge (above) has a maze of channels lined with beating hairs which create a current, drawing in water. Edible particles are absorbed, then the water is expelled from vents on the surface (right).

the chemical processes inside the cell become difficult and inefficient. Size, however, can be achieved in a different way – by grouping cells together in an organised colony.

One species that has done this is Volvox, a hollow sphere, almost the size of a pin-head, constructed from a large number of cells, each with a flagellum. The striking thing about these units is that they are virtually the same as other single cells that swim by themselves and have separate existences. The constituent cells of Volvox, however, are coordinated, for all the flagella around the sphere beat in an organised way and drive the tiny ball in a particular direction.

Sponges - miraculous colonies of cells

This kind of coordination between constituent cells in a colony was taken a stage further, probably between 800 to 1000 million years ago – some time in October in our calendar – when sponges appeared. Sponges can grow to a very considerable size. Some species form soft shapeless lumps on the sea floor two metres or so across. Their surfaces are covered with tiny pores through which water is drawn into the body by flagella, and then expelled through larger vents. The sponge feeds by filtering particles from this stream of water passing through its body. The colonial bonds between its constituents are very loose. Individual cells may crawl about over the surface of the sponge like amoebae. If two sponges are growing close to one another, they may, as they grow, come into contact and eventually merge into one huge organism. If a sponge is forced through a fine gauze sieve so that it is broken down into separate cells, these will eventually reorganise themselves into a sponge, each kind of cell finding its appropriate place within the body. Most remarkable of all, if you take two sponges and treat them both in this extreme way and then mix cells from the two, they will reconstitute themselves into a single mixed-parentage entity.

Some sponges produce a soft flexible substance around their cells which supports the whole organism. This, when the cells themselves have been killed by boiling and washed away, is what we use in our baths. Other sponges secrete tiny needles, called spicules, either of lime or silica, which mesh together to form a scaffold in which the cells are set. How one cell orientates itself and produces its spicule so that it fits perfectly into the overall design is totally unknown. When you look at a complex sponge skeleton such as that made of silica spicules which is known as Venus' Flower Basket, the imagination is baffled. How could quasi-independent microscopic cells collaborate to secrete a million glassy splinters and construct such an intricate and beautiful lattice? We do not know. But even though sponges can produce such miraculous complexities as this, they can hardly be counted as properly integrated multicellular animals. They have no nervous system, no muscle fibres. The simplest creatures to possess these physical characteristics are the jellyfish and their relatives.

The arrival of nerves and muscles

A typical jellyfish is a saucer fringed with stinging tentacles. This form is called a medusa after the unfortunate woman in a Greek myth who was loved by the god of the

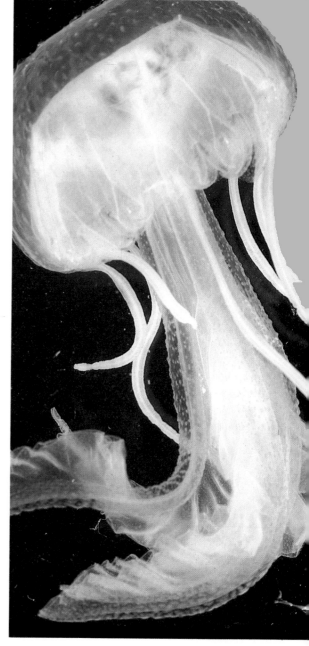

PELAGIA NOCTILUCA

The symmetrical jellyfish

Jellyfish swim by convulsive contractions of their bells but they are largely at the mercy of the ocean currents. Many feed on the organic particles that float around them as they drift through the sea. Others capture small fish that blunder into them. Since food may come to them from any direction, both adult and young usually have a symmetrical ring of tentacles with which to intercept and convey the food to the central mouth. Each species has evolved its own variation of this basic radial pattern.

SCYPHOMEDUSAN LARVA (LEFT)

A RHIZOSTOME JELLYFISH

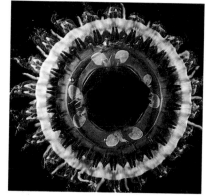

ATOLLA

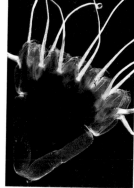

PERIPHYLLA

PORPITA

PHYSOPHORA HYDROSTATICA (ABOVE)

CARYBDEA RASTONI (BELOW)

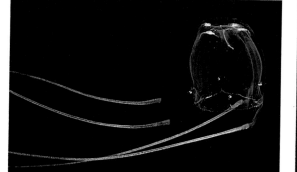

POLYORCHIS (LEFT)

AEQUOREA CAPTURING A COMB JELLY (ABOVE)

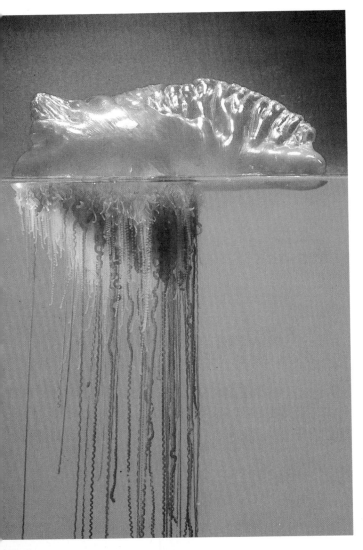

sea and as a result had her hair changed by a jealous goddess into snakes. Jellyfish are constructed from two layers of cells. The jelly which separates them gives the organism a degree of rigidity needed to withstand the buffeting of the sea. They are quite complex creatures. Their cells, unlike those of the sponge, are incapable of independent survival. Some are modified to transmit electric impulses and are linked into a network which amounts to a primitive nervous system; others are able to contract in length and so can be considered as simple muscles. There are also stinging cells with coiled threads inside them, the unique possessions of the jellyfish tribe. When food or an enemy comes near, the cell discharges the thread which is armed with spines like a miniature harpoon and often loaded with poison. It is these cells in the tentacles that will sting you if you unluckily brush against a jellyfish when swimming.

Jellyfish reproduce by releasing eggs and sperm into the sea. The fertilised egg does not develop into another jellyfish directly but becomes a free-swimming creature quite different from its parents. It eventually settles down on the bottom of the sea and grows into a tiny flower-like organism called a polyp. In some species, this sprouts, through branching twigs, into other polyps. They filter-feed with the aid of tiny beating cilia. Eventually, the polyps bud in a different way and produce miniature medusae which detach themselves and wriggle away to take up the swimming life once more.

This alternation of form between generations has allowed all kinds of variations within the group. The true jellyfish spend most of their time as free-floating medusae with only the minimum period fixed to the rocks. Others, like the sea anemones, do the reverse. For all their adult lives they are solitary polyps, glued to the rock, their tentacles waving in the water ready to trap prey that may touch them. Yet a third kind are colonies of polyps but ones that have, confusingly, given up their attachment to the sea bottom and sail free like medusae. The Portuguese Man O'War is one of these. Chains of polyps dangle from a float filled with gas. Each chain has a specialised function. One kind produces reproductive cells; another absorbs sustenance from captured prey; another, heavily armed with particularly virulent stinging cells, trails behind the colony for up to fifty metres, paralysing fish that blunder into it.

Stranded on a beach, 650 million years ago

It seems an obvious assumption that these relatively simple organisms appeared very early in the history of life, but for a long time there was no proof that they actually did so. Such hard evidence could only come from the rocks. Even if micro-organisms can be preserved in chert, it is difficult to believe that a creature as large but as fragile and insubstantial as a jellyfish could retain its shape long enough to be fossilised. But in the 1940s some geologists noticed very odd shapes in the ancient Ediacara Sandstones of the Flinders Ranges in southern Australia. These rocks, now thought to be about 650 million years old, were believed to be completely unfossiliferous. Judging from the size of the sand grains of which they are composed and the ripple marks on the surface of their bedding planes, they had once formed a sandy beach. Very occasionally, flower-like impressions were detected on them, some the size of a buttercup, some as big as a

A lethal sailor

The Portuguese Man O'War has no swimming bell. Instead it is propelled by a bladder, about 20 centimetres long, filled with gas, which catches the wind. Its immensely long tentacles, armed with poison stings, trail behind (detail left).

The hungry flowers of the sea

The sticky tentacles of a beadlet anemone (above) have caught a prawn that wandered too close to them. Their taste cells have confirmed that their capture is edible and their sting cells have been fired into it so that it is paralysed. Slowly the tentacles close around the prawn and drag it down into the anemone's bag-like stomach. There it will be rapidly dissolved by powerful digestive juices. The few inedible remains will later be pushed out again through the central mouth.

The travelling young

Sea anemone eggs develop into creatures like tiny jellyfish (left and below) which float in the upper waters of the sea. Most will be eaten by bigger animals, but some survive. A few may be carried great distances and settle down on rocks far away from their parents.

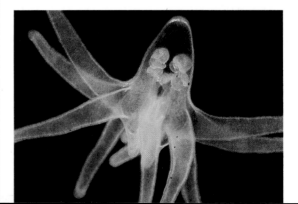

The infinite variety

rose. Could these be the marks left by jellyfish stranded on the beach, baked in the sun and then covered by a wash of fine sand by the next tide? Eventually, enough of these shapes were collected and studied for it to be undeniable that this is just what they must be.

At least sixteen different species have now been recognised. Some were floating medusae. Some appear to have had gas bladders like the Portuguese Man O'War. Among the most spectacular of these extraordinary fossils are colonial forms that lived fixed to the sea floor and which lie in the dusty brown sandstone like long feathers. The barbs can be seen to be separate branches lined with polyps. They must have been washed up on this ancient beach after being torn from their moorings, perhaps by a storm. Several of them have a vague impression of a coin-like disc near the base. At first this was interpreted as a separate medusa-like form, but it appears in a number of specimens in just such a position and some now think that it may have been a holdfast.

You do not have to go far to find a living parallel for these organisms. Closely similar creatures called sea pens grow in the sea within a hundred miles of the Flinders Ranges. Sea pens were given their names when people wrote with quills, and very apt it must have seemed, for not only are they shaped like feathers but their skeleton is flexible and horny. They grow sticking up vertically on sandy sea floors, some only a few centimetres long, some half as tall as a man. At night they are particularly spectacular for they glow with a bright purple luminescence and if you touch them, ghostly waves of light pulsate along their slowly writhing arms.

Coral – the ideal fossil maker

Sea pens are also called soft corals. Stony corals, their relatives, often grow alongside them and they too are colonial creatures. Their history is not as ancient as that of the sea pens – none have been found on the Ediacara beaches – but once they had appeared, they flourished in immense numbers. An organism that produces a skeleton of stone and lives in an environment where deposits of ooze and sand are being laid down, is an ideal subject for fossilisation. Huge thicknesses of limestone in many parts of the world consist almost entirely of coral remains and they provide a detailed chronicle of the development of the group.

The coral polyps secrete their skeletons from their bases. Each is connected with its

Stranded creatures on a 650-million-year-old beach
Fossils in the ancient sandstones of the Ediacara Hills in Australia are extremely rare. This is a particularly fine slab. Its face, now vertical, once formed the horizontal surface of a sandy beach. Ripple marks can just be detected stretching across it. A segmented worm (Spriggina) curves across the top. Below lie two superbly preserved colonial organisms (Charniodiscus) that look remarkably like the living sea pen (left). Beside the one on the right is a disc-shaped mark that may be its holdfast. The larger disc farther right is a segmented worm. On the opposite page are photographs of three other fossils from these immensely old rocks.

The float of an ancient Man O'War
This specimen seems to have been the gas-filled float of a jellyfish like the Portuguese Man O'War. Its presence argues that the Ediacara creatures were preceded by millions of years of jellyfish evolution.

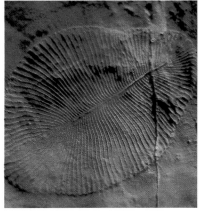

A leaf-shaped worm
A segmented worm about 10 centimetres long. The way different specimens are puckered and folded makes it clear they were creatures with thin, flexible bodies.

Fossil of a jellyfish
Flower-like impressions, such as this one, are the least rare of the Ediacara fossils and were the first to be accepted as the fossilised remains of living creatures. It is now agreed that they are the impressions of jellyfish.

The infinite variety

Coral that sways like ocean plants

Not all corals build stony skeletons and form reefs. A whole group are soft and flexible with only a few needles of lime scattered through their bodies to stiffen them. The polyps of Xenia (below) have particularly elaborate arms which can be watched opening and closing as the colony feeds in the shallow water of a tropical lagoon. The orange sea fan (below right) is common off European shores and grows in dense swaying shrubberies.

neighbours by strands that extend laterally. As the colony develops, new polyps form, often on these connecting sections and their skeletons grow over and stifle earlier polyps. So the limestone the colony builds is riddled with tiny cells where polyps once lived. The living ones form only a thin layer on the surface. Each species of coral has its own pattern of budding and so erects its own characteristic monument.

Corals are very demanding in their environmental requirements. Water that is muddy or fresh will kill them. Nor will they grow at depths beyond the reach of sunlight for they are dependent upon single-celled algae that grow within their bodies. The algae photosynthesise food for themselves and in the process absorb carbon dioxide from the water. This assists the corals in the building of their skeletons, and releases oxygen which helps the corals respire.

The first time you dive on a coral reef is an experience never to be forgotten. The

The infinite variety

sensation of moving freely in three dimensions in the clear sunlit water that corals favour is, in itself, a bewitching and other-worldly one. But there is nothing on land that can prepare you for the profusion of shapes and colours of the corals themselves. There are domes, branches and fans, antlers delicately tipped with blue, organ pipes that are blood red. Some seem flower-like yet when you touch them they have the incongruous scratch of stone. Often different coral species grow beside one another, mingled with sea pens arching above and beds of anemones that wave long tentacles in the current. Sometimes you swim over great meadows that consist entirely of one kind of coral; sometimes in deeper water you discover a coral tower hung with fans and sponges that extends beyond your sight into depths of darkest blue.

But if you swim only during the day, you will hardly ever see the organisms that have created this astounding scene. At night, with a torch in your hand, you will find the

The night-flowering coral

The tube coral is colonial. Each polyp is connected to its neighbours by filaments running through minute holes in its massive limestone skeleton. During the day, it looks like a rounded boulder punctured by tiny holes, but at night (below) polyps like tiny flowers emerge from the tubes and wave their tentacles to catch drifting food.

A coral polyp that lives alone

The polyp of the mushroom coral lives a solitary life, lying loose on the sandy bottom. By day, its stony blades (left) look like the gills of a huge mushroom. At night (above), huge tentacles totally obscure the skeleton.

35

coral transformed. The sharp outlines of the colonies are now misted with opalescence. Millions of tiny polyps have emerged from their limestone cells to stretch out their minuscule arms and grope for food.

Coral polyps are each only a few millimetres across but, working together in colonies, they have produced the greatest animal constructions the world had seen before man began his labours. The Great Barrier Reef, running parallel to the eastern coast of Australia for over a thousand miles, can be seen from the moon. So if, some 500 million years ago, an astronaut from some other planet passed near the earth, he could easily have noticed in the blue seas a few new and mysterious turquoise shapes; and from them he might have guessed that life on earth had really started.

A deceptive softness
The polyps of reef-building coral usually emerge only at night, but occasionally colonies will feed during the day and then the flower-like polyps transform their familiar sharp outlines and give them a deceptively soft appearance. When those of the leather coral (left) retract, they reveal a fleshy yellowish rind that covers the whole surface of the boulder-shaped colony, but if you touch it, you can feel the prickles of its stony skeleton beneath.

The great builders
Stony corals rely on tiny green algae growing within them to help in the process of extracting lime from the sea-water for their skeletons. They can therefore only grow where there is some sunlight, and cannot construct reefs in the black depths of the ocean floor. The island of Bora-Bora (right), near Tahiti in the central Pacific, was once an active volcano that erupted from the ocean bed and built up a huge cone of lava and ash that eventually rose thousands of feet above the surface of the ocean. After it had ceased to be active, corals began to grow in a girdle around it, at the depths that best suited them. But, in addition to needing sunlight, corals do not flourish in brackish or muddy water, and the fresh-water streams flowing down the flanks of the island carried with them silt and mud produced by the erosion of the island's rocks. The corals therefore grew much more vigorously on the outer face of the reef, in the clear unsullied ocean waters, than on the inside. So the reef has grown steadily outwards, leaving behind it a shallow lagoon floored by its own dead skeletons.

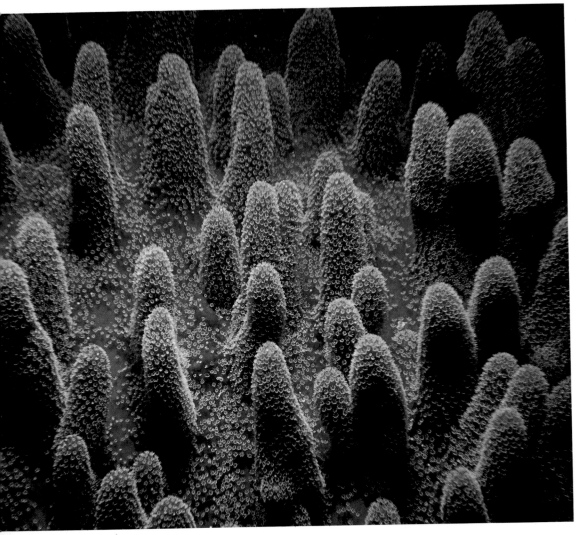

2. BUILDING BODIES

Six hundred million years ago, three kinds of animal appeared in the seas – shelled worms, segmented creatures and others with five rays. Each established a great group of today's animals

The Great Barrier Reef swarms with life. The tides surging through the coral heads charge the water with oxygen and the tropical sun warms it and fills it with light. All the main kinds of sea animals seem to flourish here. Phosphorescent purple eyes peer out from beneath shells; black sea urchins swivel their spines as they slowly perambulate on needle tip; starfish of an intense blue spangle the sand; and patterned rosettes unfurl from holes in the smooth surface of coral. Dive down through the pellucid water and turn a boulder. A flat ribbon, striped yellow and scarlet, dances gracefully away and an emerald green brittle star careers over the sand on writhing catherine-wheel arms to find a new hiding place.

The variety at first seems bewildering, but leaving aside primitive creatures like jellyfish and corals which we have already discussed, and the much more advanced backboned fish, nearly all can be allocated to one of three main types: shelled animals, like clams, cowries and sea snails; radially symmetrical creatures like starfish and sea urchins; and elongated animals with segmented bodies varying from wriggling bristle worms to shrimps and lobsters.

The principles on which these three kinds of bodies are built are so fundamentally different that it is difficult to believe that they can be related to one another except right at the very roots of the evolutionary tree. The fossil record bears this out. All three groups, being sea-dwellers, have left behind abundant remains and the details of their separate dynastic fortunes can be traced through the rocks for hundreds of millions of years. The walls of the Grand Canyon show that animals without backbones, in-vertebrates, came into existence long before the vertebrates such as fish. But just below

A sheltered life

Protection from other hungry creatures is a major need for animals with soft bodies. The molluscs solve the problem by building shells from calcium carbonate which they extract from the surrounding water. Here a clam cautiously draws apart the two valves of its shell and explores its surroundings with its tentacles.

39

Building bodies

the layer of gently folded limestones that contains the earliest of the invertebrate fossils, the strata change radically. Here the rocks are highly contorted. They had once formed mountains. These were eroded and eventually covered with the sea that deposited the limestone now lying above them. The episode occupied many millions of years and during all that time there were no deposits. As a consequence, this junction in the rocks represents a huge gap in the record. To trace the invertebrate lines back to their origins, we must find another site where rocks were not only deposited continuously throughout this critical period, but have survived in a relatively undistorted condition.

Such places are few, but one lies in the Atlas Mountains of Morocco. The bare hills behind Agadir in the west are built of blue limestones so hard that they ring under the fossil-hunter's hammer. The beds of rock are slightly tilted but otherwise undistorted by earth movements. On the crest of the passes, the rocks yield fossils. They are not very many, but if you look hard enough you can collect quite a range of species. All fossils found anywhere in the world in rocks of this age can be placed in one or other of those three main groups we identified on the reef. There are tiny shells, the size of your little finger nail, called brachiopods; radially symmetrical organisms looking like stalked flowers called crinoids; and trilobites, segmented creatures that resemble woodlice.

The limestones at the top of the Moroccan succession are about 560 million years old. Beneath them lie more layers extending downwards for thousands of feet, seemingly unchanged in character. In them, surely, must be evidence about the origins of those three great invertebrate groups.

But it is not so. As you clamber down the mountainside over the strata, the fossils suddenly disappear. The limestone seems to be exactly the same as that at the head of the pass, so the seas in which it was laid down must surely have been very similar to those that produced fossiliferous rocks. There are no signs of a revolutionary change in physical conditions. It is simply that at one time the ooze covering the sea floor contained shells of animals – and before that did not.

This abrupt beginning to the fossil record is not just a Moroccan phenomenon, though you can see it here more vividly than in most places. It occurs in almost all the rocks of this age throughout the world. The micro-fossils from the cherts of Lake Superior and South Africa show that life had started long, long before. In the theoretical year of life, shelled fossils do not appear until early November. So the bulk of life's history is undocumented in the rocks. Only at this late date, about 600 million years ago, did several separate groups of organisms begin to leave records of any abundance by secreting shells. Why this sudden change should have come about we do not know. Perhaps before this time the seas were not at the right temperature or did not have the chemical composition to favour the deposition of the lime from which most marine shells and skeletons are constructed. Whatever the reason we have to look elsewhere for evidence of the origins of the invertebrates.

Forests of sea-lilies

The earliest crinoids, which appeared for the first time in rocks 560 million years old, are very uncommon. They were comparatively simple in shape with a long slender stem and five pairs of short arms sprouting from a bud-like structure at the top. As time passed, however, they developed into complex and luxuriant forms, like these from south Germany, 180 million years old.

The simple flatworms

We can find some living clues back on the reef. Fluttering over the coral heads, hiding in the crevices or clinging to the underside of rocks, are flat leaf-shaped worms. Like jellyfish, they have only one opening to their gut through which they both take in food and eject waste. They have no gills and breathe directly through their skin. Their underside is covered with cilia which by beating enable them to glide slowly over surfaces. Their front end has a mouth below and a few light-sensitive spots above so that the animal can be said to have the beginnings of a head. The flatworm is the simplest creature to show signs of such a thing.

The eye-spots, to be of any use, must be linked to muscles so that the animal can react to what it senses. In flatworms all that exists is a simple network of nerve fibres. There are a few thickenings in some of them, but these can hardly be described as brains. Yet the flatworms have surprising powers. One freshwater species, for example, can learn. Individuals have been trained to find their way through a simple maze, selecting white-painted passages and avoiding dark-painted ones by being given slight electric shocks when they made a wrong decision. Even more surprisingly, that memory has been

The primordial patterns

Two kinds of organism appear much more abundantly than crinoids in the very early fossil-bearing rocks. There are small creatures that protected themselves with two-valved shells, the brachiopods (above left); and also much more complex animals with segmented bodies, numerous legs and well-developed eyes, the trilobites (above right). Each of these pioneered a pattern of bodily organisation that was to be inherited by one of the great divisions of the animal kingdom. 41

Building bodies

The flamboyant flatworm

Flatworms, like this one, are among the most brilliant of marine creatures, yet the function of their colours is still unknown and the animals themselves, with only simple eyes, cannot see them.

PRIMITIVE INVERTEBRATES

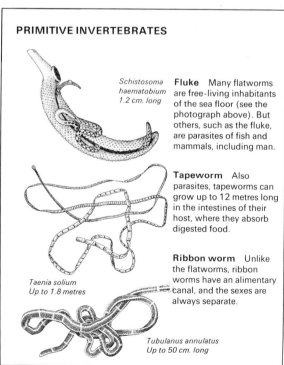

Schistosoma haematobium 1.2 cm. long

Fluke Many flatworms are free-living inhabitants of the sea floor (see the photograph above). But others, such as the fluke, are parasites of fish and mammals, including man.

Tapeworm Also parasites, tapeworms can grow up to 12 metres long in the intestines of their host, where they absorb digested food.

Ribbon worm Unlike the flatworms, ribbon worms have an alimentary canal, and the sexes are always separate.

Taenia solium Up to 1.8 metres

Tubulanus annulatus Up to 50 cm. long

shown to reside in a substance, for if a worm that has learned the maze is killed and its flesh fed to another worm, the new one will run the maze correctly without training.

Today there are some 3000 species of flatworm in the world. Most are tiny and water-living. You can find freshwater ones in most streams simply by dropping in a piece of raw meat or liver. If the underwater vegetation is thick, flatworms are likely to glide out in dozens and settle on the bait. Some species manage to live on land in humid tropical forests, undulating on mucus that they secrete from their undersides. One of these grows to a length of about 60 centimetres. Other flatworms have taken to the parasitic life and live unseen within the bodies of other animals, including man's, and in astronomic numbers. The liver flukes still retain the typical flatworm form. Tapeworms are also members of the group, though they look very different for after burying their heads in the walls of their host's gut, they bud off egg-bearing sections from their tail end. These segments remain attached while they mature, eventually forming a chain that may be as much as 10 metres long. The whole creature, as a result, looks as though it is divided into segments, but in fact these separate living packets of eggs are quite different from the permanent internal compartments of a truly segmented creature like an earthworm.

Flatworms are very simple creatures. Members of one free-swimming group lack a gut altogether and look very like the tiny free-swimming coral organisms before they settle down to a sedentary life. So there is little difficulty in believing those researchers who conclude from a study of the detailed structure of both adult and larva that the flatworms are descended from simpler organisms like corals and jellyfish.

In the period when these first marine invertebrates were evolving, between 600 and 1000 million years ago, erosion of the continents was producing great expanses of mud and sand on the sea bed around the continental margins. This environment must have contained abundant food in the form of organic detritus falling from the waters above. It also offered concealment and protection for any creature that lived within it. The flatworm shape, however, is not suited to burrowing. A tubular form is much more effective and eventually worms with such a shape appeared. Some became active burrowers, tunnelling through the mud in search of food particles. Others lived half-buried with their mouthparts above the sediment. Cilia around their mouths created a current of water and from it they filtered their food.

Worms with shells

Some of these creatures lived in a protective tube. In time, the shape of the top of this was modified into a collar with slits in it. This improved the flow of water over the tentacles. Further modification and mineralisation eventually produced two flat protective shells. These were the first brachiopods. One of them, named Lingulella, gave rise to a line of descendants that still live today, virtually unchanged; they are what are often called living fossils.

Examples of such immensely long-lived species occur several times in the history of life. A creature appears and spreads widely. As time passes, conditions in parts of its range alter and some of its descendants evolve into slightly different forms enabling them to survive more efficiently in their new circumstances. But in a few places conditions remain unaltered and they suit the original design to perfection. No variants appear which exploit this environment more effectively. So the ancient species, encountering no change, makes no change and plods on across the millennia, generation after generation, an ultra-conservative.

The descendants of Lingulella, slightly larger and called Lingula, are found today in, among other places, the coastal waters of Japan, burrowing in the sand and mud of estuaries. In form they look like long worms with two small horny shells at one end. The body, however, is quite complicated. It has a digestive tract that ends in an anus and a

The floating larva of a brachiopod

The tiny young brachiopod has a shell so thin as to be transparent. The muscle holding the two halves together forms a solid mass in the centre. On either side are tentacles which filter edible particles from the water.

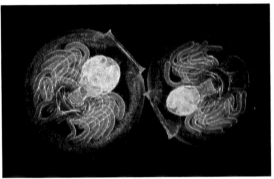

One of the most ancient of living organisms

Shells similar to these Lingula occur in rocks 570 million years old. Today the creature lives in mud or sand, with its two shells projecting above the surface collecting food, a way of life so effective that no other more efficient creature has yet managed totally to displace it.

group of tentacles around the mouth, enclosed within the two shell valves. These tentacles are covered with beating cilia which create water currents. As food particles are swept by, they are caught by the tentacles and passed by them down to the mouth. In this process, the tentacles serve another and important function, for the water brings with it dissolved oxygen which Lingula needs in order to respire. The tentacles absorb it and so, in effect, they become gills. The valves enclosing the tentacles not only give protection to these soft delicate structures, but concentrate the water into a steady stream so that it flows more effectively over them.

The brachiopods elaborated this design considerably over the next hundred million years or so. Some became larger with heavy lime shells. The tentacles inside grew so big they required the support of a delicate spiral of lime. Many species developed a hole at the hinge end of one of the valves through which the worm-like stalk emerged to fasten the animal into the mud. This gave the shell the look of an inverted Roman oil lamp, with the stalk as the wick, and so the group as a whole gained the name of lamp-shells.

The most successful shelled worms – the molluscs

The brachiopods are by no means the only shelled worms whose fossils are found in these ancient rocks. Another kind developed in which the elaborated worm did not attach itself to the sea floor but continued to crawl about and secreted a small conical tent of shell under which it could huddle when in danger. This was the ancestor of the most successful group of all these shelled worms, the molluscs, and it too has a living representative, a tiny organism called Neopilina, which was dredged up in 1952 from the depths of the Pacific. Today there are about 60,000 different species of molluscs.

The lower part of the molluscan body is called the foot. Its owners move themselves about by protruding it from the shell and rippling its undersurface. Many species carry a small disc of shell on the side of it which, when the foot is retracted, forms a close-fitting lid to the entrance. The upper surface of the body is formed by a thin sheet that cloaks the internal organs and is appropriately called the mantle. In a cavity between it and the central part of the body, most species have gills which are continually bathed by a current of oxygen-bearing water, sucked in at one end of the cavity and expelled at the other.

The shell is secreted by the upper surface of the mantle. One whole group of molluscs have single shells. The limpet, like Neopilina, produces shell at an equal rate right round the circumference of the mantle and so builds a simple pyramid. In other species, the front of the mantle secretes faster than the rear and creates a shell in a flat spiral, like a watch spring. In yet others, maximum production comes from one side so that the shell develops a twist and becomes a turret. The cowrie concentrates its secretion along the sides of the mantle, forming a shell like a loosely clenched fist. From the slit along the bottom, it protrudes not only its foot but two sections of its mantle which extend over each flank of the shell and meet at the top. These lay down the marvellously patterned and polished surface characteristic of cowries.

The single-shelled molluscs feed not with tentacles within the shell like the

A killer shellfish
The cone shell stores specially long teeth grown on its tongue, in a kind of quiver within the shell. It is able to shoot them out through a long protrusible trunk and so harpoon molluscs, worms and even small fish. These weapons carry a venom so potent that it can kill anyone who incautiously picks up a living cone. There are several hundred species of cone shells, each with its own favoured prey. These are textile cones, and one female has just deposited a ribbon of eggs.

brachiopods but with a radula, a ribbon-shaped tongue, covered with rasping teeth. Some use it to scrape algae from the rocks. Whelks have developed a radula on a stalk which they can extend beyond the shell and use to bore into the shells of other molluscs. Through the holes they have drilled, they poke the tip of the radula and suck out the flesh of the victim. Cone shells also have a stalked radula but have modified it into a kind of gun. They slyly extend it towards their prey – a worm or even a fish – and then discharge a tiny glassy harpoon from the end. While the tethered victim struggles they inject a poison so virulent that it kills a fish instantly and can even be lethal to a man. They then haul the prey back to the shell and slowly engulf it.

Neopilina

A tiny mollusc only 2 millimetres across. It has the simplest of molluscan bodies, with a round muscular foot surrounded by stalk-like gills. It feeds on mud.

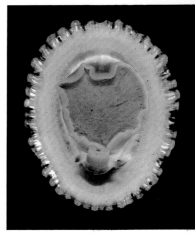

The glossy cowrie

The cowrie protrudes not only its mouth and tentacles (right), but also its mantle, which it can extend right over its shell like a furry cape (above). The mantle of a mollusc contains its shell-producing glands, so the cowrie is able to build up its shell from both sides and makes the outer surface of its shell as glossy and as beautifully coloured as its interior.

The limpet

This is a more complicated creature than Neopilina. It has two tentacles with which to feel its way (above), and its gills are no longer visible from beneath (right) for they are enclosed in the space between the upper surface of the foot and the mantle which lines the shell. It has a file-like 'tongue' with which it scrapes algae from rocks as it crawls round its tiny territory.

45

A kaleidoscope of sea slugs

The sea slugs are all small, only a few centimetres long. Lacking a shell or a mantle cavity, they cannot breathe by pumping a current of oxygen-bearing water over gills. Instead they breathe through a profusion of tentacles covering their backs. The colours and patterns of these vary widely, not only between different species but even between young and adult of the same species. Mysteriously, many of the most spectacularly coloured ones live in depths where the colour is invisible anyway.

Shedding a shell for mobility – the sea slugs

For active hunting, a heavy shell must be something of a handicap and some carnivorous molluscs have taken to a faster if riskier life by doing without it altogether and reverting to the life-style of their flatworm-like ancestors. These are the sea slugs and they are among the most beautiful and highly coloured of all invertebrates in the sea. Their long soft bodies are covered on the upper side with waving tentacles of the most delicate colours, banded, striped and patterned in many shades. Though they lack a shell, they are not entirely defenceless, for some have acquired secondhand weapons. These species float near the surface of the water on their feathery extended tentacles and hunt jellyfish. As the sea slug slowly eats its way into its drifting helpless prey, the stinging cells of the victim are taken into its gut, complete and unsprung. Eventually they migrate within the sea slug's tissues and are concentrated in the tentacles on its back. There they give just the same protection to their new owners as they did to the jellyfish that developed them.

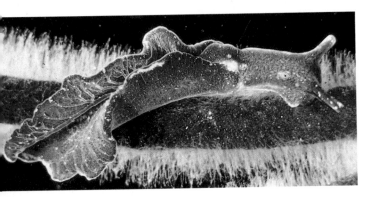

ELYSIA VIRIDIS

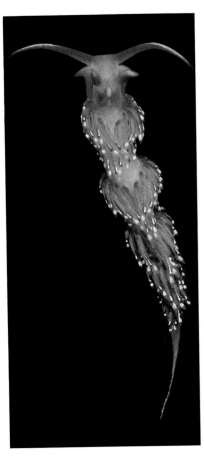

NEMBROTHA

ANALOGIUM STRIATUM

FACELINA CORONATA

TRIDACHIELLA DIOMEDEA

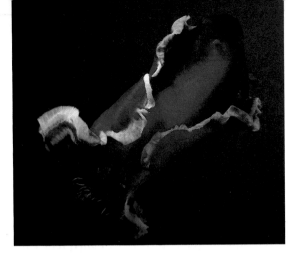

HEXABRANCHUS SANGUINEUS

SACOGLOSSUM

HERMISSENDA CRASSICORNIS (ABOVE)

AEOLID (BELOW)

The slug that eats jellyfish stings

*Glaucus, a sea slug, floats on the surface supported by tentacles that are expanded into lateral fins.
There it preys on Porpita, a surface-living colonial jellyfish (above), eating the sting cells that
would paralyse other organisms, and storing them, undischarged, in its own tentacles ready for use
against any predator that may attack it.*

47

The biggest of all molluscs

Giant clams are so huge that once they have settled down and begun to grow, they cannot move. Very exceptional specimens measure over a metre across and weigh over 200 kilograms. Such monsters are of great age, and coral has usually grown up around them so that little more than the edge of the shells, filled with brilliantly coloured mantle, project above the surface of the reef.

Giant clams and other bivalves

Other molluscs, like mussels and clams, have shells divided into two valves. These creatures are much less mobile. The foot is reduced to a protrusion that they use to pull themselves down into the sand. For the most part, they are filter-feeders, lying with valves agape, sucking water in through one end of the mantle cavity and squirting it out through a tubular siphon at the other. Since they do not need to move, great size is of no disadvantage. Giant clams on the reef may grow to be a metre long; they lie embedded in the coral, their mantles fully exposed, a zigzag of brilliant green flesh spotted with black, which pulsates gently as water is pumped through it. They can certainly be quite big enough for a diver to put his foot into, but he would have to be very incautious indeed to get trapped. Powerful though the clam's muscles are, it cannot slam its valves

The watchful eyes of the scallop
The scallop has a line of small brilliant eyes, each about a millimetre across, along the edge of its mantle. With these it can perceive not only the difference between light and shade, but also movement. So it can detect the slow approach of an enemy like a starfish and take to flight by clapping its valves and leaping.

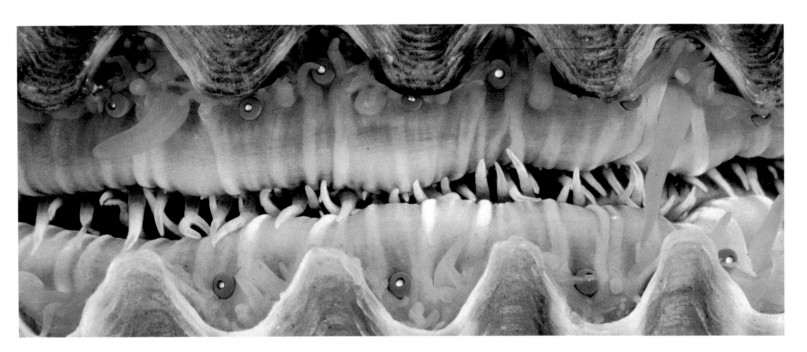

SHELLFISH THAT BORE INTO ROCKS

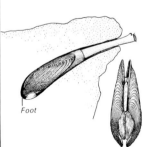

Foot

The common piddock is a mollusc shaped like a narrow mussel, with a sucker-like foot at one end. The shell around the foot is armed with rasp-like teeth, and by opening and closing it the piddock bores its way into a rock. From this safe refuge its 'siphon' sticks out to feed on detritus in the water.

shut, only heave them slowly together, so it gives plenty of notice of its intentions. What is more, even when the valves of a really large specimen are fully closed, they only meet at the spikes on the edge. The gaps between them are so big that if you plunge your arm through into the mantle, the clam is quite unable to grip it – though the experiment is a little less unnerving if it is tried first with a post.

Some filter-feeders like the scallops do manage to travel: they clap their valves together convulsively and so make curving leaps, but by and large adult bivalves live rather static lives and the spreading of the species into distant parts of the sea bed is carried out by the young. The molluscan egg develops into a larva, a minuscule animated globule striped with a band of cilia, which is swept far and wide by ocean currents before, after several weeks, it changes its shape, grows a shell and settles down.

The drifting phase of its life puts it at the mercy of all kinds of hungry animals, from other stationary filter-feeders to fish, so in order that its species shall survive, a mollusc must produce great numbers of eggs. And indeed it does. One individual may discharge as many as 400 million.

The shellfish with jet-propulsion and buoyancy tanks

One branch of the molluscs, very early in the group's history, found a way of becoming highly mobile and yet retaining the protection of a large and heavy shell – they developed gas-filled flotation tanks. The first such creature appeared about 550 million years ago. Its flat-coiled shell was not completely filled with flesh as is that of a snail, but had a hinder end walled off to form a gas chamber. As the animal grew, new chambers were added to provide sufficient buoyancy for the increasing weight. This creature was the nautilus and we can get an accurate idea of how it and its family lived for one species was destined, like Lingula and Neopilina, to become a living fossil.

The species that survives today, the pearly nautilus, grows to about 20 centimetres across. A tube runs from the back of the body chamber into the flotation tanks at the rear so that the animal can flood them and adjust its buoyancy to float at whatever level it wishes. The nautilus feeds not only on carrion but on living creatures such as crabs. It moves by jet-propulsion, squirting water through a siphon in a variation of the current-creating technique developed by its filter-feeding relatives. It searches for its prey with the help of small stalked eyes and tentacles that are sensitive to taste. Its molluscan foot has become divided into some ninety long grasping tentacles with which it grapples with its prey. In the centre of them it has a horny beak, shaped like that of a parrot, capable of delivering a shell-cracking lethal bite.

After some 140 million years of development, the nautiluses gave rise to a variant group with many more flotation chambers to each shell, the ammonites. These became enormously successful. In some rocks their shells lie so thickly that they form solid bands. Those of some species grew as big as lorry wheels. When you find one of these giants embedded in the honey-coloured limestones of central England or the hard blue rocks of Dorset, you might think that such immense creatures could do little but lumber massively along the sea bed. But where erosion has removed the outer shell, the elegant curving walls of the flotation chambers that are revealed remind you that these creatures may well have been virtually weightless in water. Several species have what looks to be a cut-water on the keel of the shell and may even have sailed like galleons across the surface of the prehistoric oceans.

About one hundred million years ago, for reasons that we do not understand, the ammonite dynasty began to dwindle. Many species died out. Other lines gave rise to forms in which the shells were loosely coiled or almost straight. One group took the same path as the sea slugs did in more recent times and lost their shells altogether. Eventually all the shelled forms except the pearly nautilus disappeared. But the shell-less ones survived and they became the most sophisticated and intelligent of all the molluscs, the squids and octopus.

The floating life of the nautilus

The nautilus (right) swims majestically at all levels through the tropical waters of the Indian and Pacific Oceans. The bulk of its body extends beyond its shell and is covered by a fleshy lid formed by an extension of its mantle. The shell's function is not primarily to provide shelter but buoyancy, and it is filled with gas. As the animal grows, the mantle at the back of the shell regularly constructs a new partition, so creating an extra gas-filled compartment to compensate for the increased weight of flesh. Exactly the same flotation technique was used by the nautilus' huge extinct relatives, the ammonites (above), as can be seen when the fossil of one is sectioned.

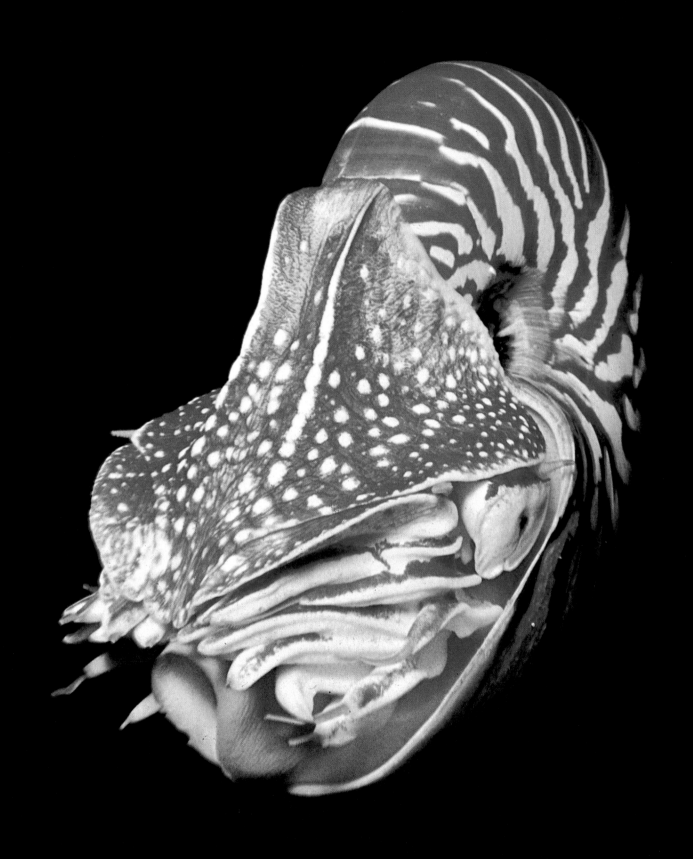

Building bodies

Eight arms and no shell

The octopus has lost its shell altogether. It has no need of one as protection, for it lives among rocks on the sea floor and can hide in holes and crevices if need be. It can, however, defend itself very well with its eight arms. They carry powerful suckers to grapple with an enemy and drag it into its formidable beaked jaws. Nor, being a bottom-liver, does the octopus need a gas-filled shell for buoyancy. It clambers over the rocks of the bottom with the help of the adhesive suckers on its arms, and when it swims it does so by jet-propulsion, squirting water from its mantle-cavity through a nozzle.

The relics of the squid's ancestral shell can be found deep within it. This is the flat leaf of powdery chalk, the cuttle bone, that is often washed up on the seashore. The octopus has no trace of a shell within the flesh of its body, but one species, the argonaut, secretes from one of its arms a marvellous paper-thin version shaped very like a nautilus shell but without chambers, which it uses not as a home for itself but as a delicate floating chalice in which to lay its eggs.

The squid has many fewer tentacles than the nautilus – only ten – and the octopus, as its name makes obvious, has only eight. Of the two creatures, the squids are much the more mobile and have lateral fins running along their flanks which undulate and so propel the animal through the water. Both creatures can, like the nautilus, use jet propulsion on occasion.

Their eyes are very elaborate. In some ways they are even better than our own, for a squid can distinguish polarised light which we cannot do and their retinas have a finer structure which means, almost certainly, that they can distinguish finer detail than we can. To deal with the signals produced by these sense organs they have considerable brains and very quick reactions.

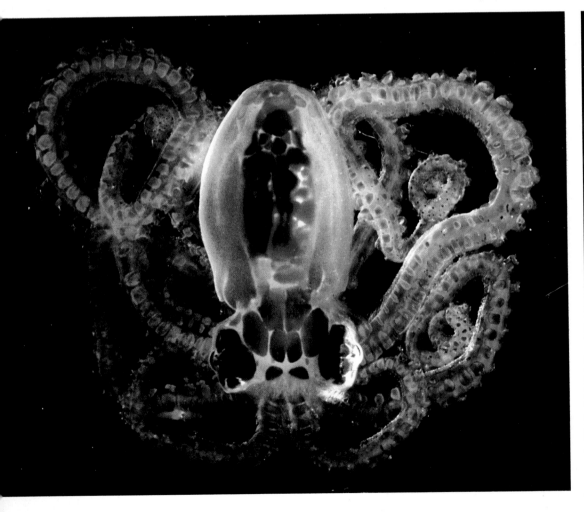

A shell as a cradle

The female argonaut, or paper-nautilus (left), builds a paper-thin shell, not from her mantle but from two of her arms. She clasps it to her body and lays eggs in it (above).

Squids grow to an immense size. In 1954 one was washed ashore in Norway that measured 9 metres from the end of its body to the tip of its outstretched tentacles and weighed about a ton. Even this was not the largest. In 1933, in New Zealand, one was recorded that was 21 metres long with eyes 40 centimetres across, the largest known eyes in the whole animal kingdom. Even now we are unlikely to have discovered the biggest that exists. Squids are so intelligent and swift-moving that they must find little difficulty in avoiding man's clumsy deep-sea dredges. Sperm whales frequently dive to search for squid and they are much more agile than any of our hunting devices. Some return to the surface with scars on their snouts which suggest that they have been battling with creatures possessing suckers 13 centimetres across, and squid beaks even bigger than that of the Norwegian giant have been found in their stomachs. So it is by no means impossible that the kraken and the other legendary sea monsters that are said to be able to rise from the deep and wrap ships in their tentacles, really exist. Even those of which we have evidence are very daunting creatures — and the most surprising descendants to have sprung from the simple little shells that first appeared 600 million years ago.

The squid with a luminous body

It is difficult to make head or tail of a squid, for it moves with equal ease in either direction, its tentacles either held out in front of it or trailing behind. It propels itself by undulating a flap along each side. Squids swim in schools, and often follow the shoals of fish on which they prey. They all have large and very efficient eyes near the base of their tentacles. Many are luminous. This one has a belt of light-producing organs around its body which shine through its transparent mantle. Such lights may help in recognition, for each species has its own pattern.

Building bodies

Variations on a pentagonal theme

All echinoderms have their organs in groups of five, and all possess tube feet operated by water pressure.

ASTERIAS RUBENS DIAMETER 15 CM.

STARFISH *Five arms are usual, but some species have as many as 50. They use their tube feet (below) not only for moving about but for wrenching apart molluscs to reach the flesh.*

FEATHER STARS *Like their close relatives, the crinoids, feather stars begin life on long stalks. But they eventually break away from the upper end of the stalk and swim away, waving their arms, which are fringed with side branches so they look like feathers (right). They grasp rocks on the sea floor, and lie with their arms uppermost, catching food particles.*

ANTEDON BIFIDA DIAMETER 20 CM.

The fivefold symmetry of the 'spiny skins'

But what of the second great category, the one represented in ancient rocks by the flower-like crinoids? As these are traced upwards through the rocks, they become more elaborate and their structure becomes clearer. Each has a central body, the calyx, rising from a stem like the seed-head of a poppy. From this sprout five arms which, in some species, branch repeatedly. The surface of the calyx is made up of closely fitting lime plates, the stems and branches of bead-like discs of the same material. Lying in the rocks, the stems look like broken necklaces, their individual beads sometimes scattered, sometimes still in loose snaking columns as though their thread had only just snapped. Occasionally gigantic specimens are found with stems 20 metres long. These creatures,

like the ammonites, have had their day, but a few species known as sea-lilies still survive in the ocean depths.

They show that the lime plates, in life, are embedded just under the skin. This gives their surface a curious prickly feel. In related families, the skin has spines and needles attached to it so the creatures are known as echinoderms, 'spiny skins'. The basic architectural module on which the echinoderm body is built has a fivefold symmetry. The plates on the calyx are pentagons, five arms extend from it, and all the internal organs are in groups of five. Their bodies work by a unique exploitation of hydrostatic principles. Feet, each a thin tube ending in a sucker and kept firm by the pressure of water within, wave and curl in rows along the arms. The water for this system circulates

SEA CUCUMBERS *Tube feet project from the lower flank of the sea cucumber, which moves on its side. If provoked, as the one below has been, it defends itself by extruding sticky tubules from its anus. These enmesh and doubtless confuse the attacker.*

CUCUMARIA FRONDOSA
LENGTH 20 CM.

If the provocation continues, the sea cucumber will eject all its entrails and abandon them. It grows more in a few weeks.

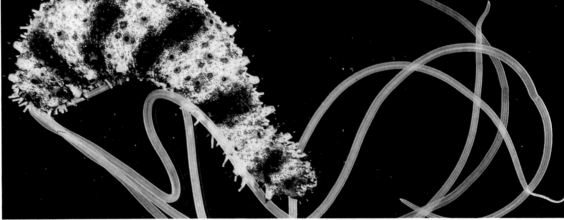

SEA URCHINS *In the sea urchins (above), the original five arms have been transformed into five connected ribs, forming a globular shell covered with spines. Some of the spines have minute teeth and a poisonous mucus.*

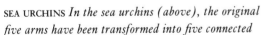

ECHINUS ESCULENTUS
DIAMETER 13 CM.

THE BRITTLE STARS *The most active of the echinoderms move with considerable speed on their spiralling arms (right). If handled roughly, they will shed one or more of their arms, while they scuttle to safety.*

OPHIOTHRIX FRAGILIS DIAMETER 13 CM.

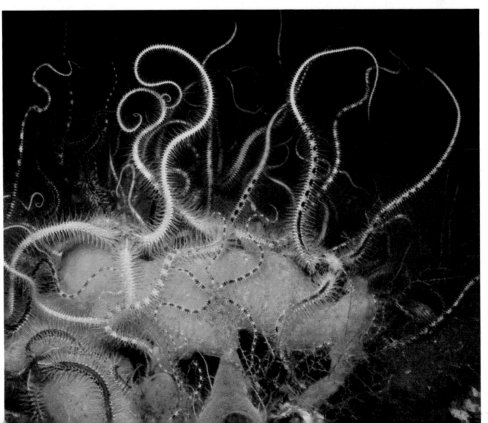

quite separately from that in the body cavity. It is drawn through a pore into a channel surrounding the mouth and circulated throughout the body and into the myriads of tube feet. When a drifting particle of food touches an arm, tube feet fasten on to it and pass it on from one to another until it reaches the gutter that runs down the upper surface of the arm to the mouth at the centre.

Though stalked sea-lilies were the most abundant crinoid in fossil times, the commonest forms today are the stalkless feather stars. Instead of stalks, they have a cluster of curling roots with which they attach themselves to coral or rocks. In places on the Barrier Reef, they swarm in huge numbers, covering the floor of the tidal pools with a tufted coarse carpet of brown.

The fivefold symmetry and the hydrostatically operated tube feet are such distinctive characters that they make members of the group very easy to recognise. The starfish and their more sprightly cousins, the brittle stars, both possess them. These creatures appear to be crinoids that have neither stalk nor rootlets and are lying in an inverted position with their mouths on the ground and their five arms outstretched. Sea urchins are obviously related. They seem to have curled their arms up from the mouth as five ribs and then connected them by more plates to form a sphere.

The sausage-like sea cucumbers that sprawl on sandy patches in the reef are also echinoderms, which lie neither face-up nor face-down, but on their sides. At one end is an opening called the anus, though the term is not completely appropriate for the animal uses it not only for excretion but for breathing as well, sucking water gently in and out over tubules just inside the body. The mouth at the other end is surrounded by tube feet that have become enlarged into short tentacles. These fumble about in the sand or mud, particles adhere to them and the sea cucumber slowly curls them back into its mouth to suck them clean with its fleshy lips. If you pick up a sea cucumber, do so with care, for they have an extravagant way of defending themselves. They simply extrude their internal organs. A slow but unstoppable flood of sticky tubules pours out of the anus, fastening your fingers together in an adhesive tangle of threads. When an inquisitive fish or crab provokes them to such action, it finds itself struggling in a mesh of filaments while the sea cucumber slowly inches itself away on the tube feet that protrude from its underside. Over the next few weeks it will slowly grow itself a new set of entrails.

The echinoderms may seem, from a human point of view, to be a blind alley of no particular importance. Were we to suppose that life was purposive, that everything was part of a planned progression due to culminate in the appearance of man or some other creature that might rival him in dominating the world, then the echinoderms could be dismissed as of no consequence. But such trends are clearer in the minds of men than they are in the rocks. The echinoderms appeared early in the history of life. Their hydrostatic mechanisms proved a serviceable and effective basis for building a variety of bodies, but not susceptible in the end to spectacular development. In the areas that suit them, they are still highly successful. A starfish on the reef can crawl across a clam, fasten its tube feet on either side of its gape and slowly wrench the valves apart to feed

A hydrostatic system
Five rows of tube feet meet at the top of the sea urchin's shell (right). The bead close to their junction contains a pore through which water is drawn for pumping into the feet to keep them firm. Some of the feet (above) are feathery and serve as gills.

How a sea urchin travels

A sea urchin moves with the help of its spines, which are fixed to its shell by ball-and-socket joints, and also by reaching forward with its tube feet and fastening their suckers on objects ahead (right).

on the flesh within. The crown-of-thorns starfish occasionally proliferates to plague proportions and devastates great areas of coral. Crinoids are brought up in trawls from the deep sea several thousand at a time. If it is improbable that any further major developments will come from this stock, it is also unlikely, on the evidence of the last six hundred million years, that the group will disappear as long as life remains possible at all in the seas of the world.

Worms with segmented bodies

The third category of creatures on the reef contains those with segmented bodies. In this instance, we do have fossil evidence of even earlier forms than the trilobites found in the Moroccan hills. The Ediacaran deposits in Australia which contain the remains of jellyfish and sea pens also preserve impressions of segmented worms. One species has a crescent-shaped head and up to forty segments, fringed on either side by leg-like

Perfect fossils of soft-bodied creatures

The conditions for fossilisation in the Burgess Shales of Canada were so perfect that soft-bodied creatures of great age have been preserved in detail. The multiplicity of creatures in the shales — so much greater than in any other rocks of a similar age — shows not only how varied life was in the oceans of 560 million years ago, but how incomplete a picture of past faunas is given by rocks that retain only the hard parts of animals.

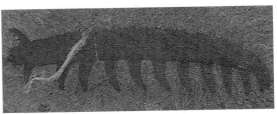

A PROBABLE ANCESTOR OF MILLIPEDES AND INSECTS

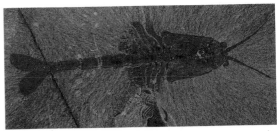

A SHRIMP–LIKE TRILOBITE (ABOVE)   A CONE-SHAPED MOLLUSC (BELOW)

The burning fire-worm

Bristle worms usually have only a few stiff hairs to each segment, but one, the fire-worm, about 20 centimetres long, has luxuriant clumps on each side. If touched, whether by a human finger or a fish's mouth, they break off in the skin and cause a severe burning pain. The worm's brilliant colours warn of its defence.

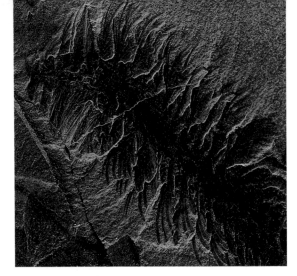

A SPINY BRISTLE WORM

A PROBABLE MOLLUSC WITH SCALES AND SPINES

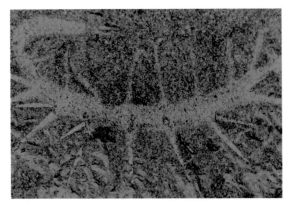

HALLUCIGENIA, WITH SEVEN PAIRS OF STILT LEGS

projections. It looks extraordinarily like the bristle worms that abound on the reef. The grooves encircling the bodies of these living creatures correspond to walls that divide the interior into separate compartments. Each of these is equipped with its own set of organs – on either side, leg-like projections sometimes equipped with bristles and another pair of feathery appendages through which oxygen is absorbed; and within the body wall, a pair of tubes opening to the exterior from which waste is secreted. A gut, a large blood vessel and a nerve cord run from front to end through all the segments, linking and coordinating them.

Even the exceptionally ancient remains of Ediacara offer no clue about the connection between the segmented worms and the other early groups. However, there is one further category of evidence to be looked at – the larvae. The segmented worms have spherical larvae with a belt of cilia round their middles and a long tuft on top. These are almost identical to those of some molluscs, a strong indication that the two groups sprang from common stock. The echinoderms, on the other hand, have a larva that is quite different, with a twist to its structure and winding bands of cilia around it. This group must have separated from the ancestral flatworms at a very early stage indeed, long before the split between the molluscs and the segmented worms.

Segmentation may have developed as a way of enabling worms to increase their efficiency as burrowers in mud. A line of separate limbs down each side is clearly a very effective structure for this purpose and it could have been acquired by repeating the simple body unit to form a chain. The change must have taken place long before Ediacaran times for when those rocks were deposited the fundamental invertebrate divisions were already established. The Ediacaran fossils, however, provide only a brief isolated glimpse of the progress of the invertebrates. Thereafter their history remains virtually invisible for 100 million years. Only after this vast span do we reach the period, 600 million years ago, represented by the Moroccan deposits and others throughout the world. By that time many organisms had, as we have seen, developed shells.

The most perfect fossils in the world
One exceptional fossil site close to this age exists which provides far more detailed information about the bodies of animals than can come from mere shells. In the Rocky Mountains of British Columbia, the Burgess Pass crosses a ridge between two high snowy peaks. Close to its crest lies an outcrop of particularly fine shales and in these some of the most perfectly preserved fossils in the world have been discovered. The shales were laid down about 550 million years ago in a basin of the sea floor at a depth of about 150 metres. It must have been sheltered by a submarine ridge, for there were no currents to disturb the fine sediments on the floor or to bring in oxygenated water from nearer the surface. Few animals lived in these dark stagnant waters. There are no signs of tracks or burrows. Once in a while, however, mud from the ridge above slipped down in a turbid cloud, carrying with it all kinds of small creatures and dumped them there. Since there was neither oxygen to fuel the processes of decay nor any scavenging animals to feed on the bodies and destroy them, the tiny carcasses remained complete as

the settling mud particles slowly entombed them. Eventually the entire deposit became consolidated into shale. Earth movements elevated and folded great areas of these marine deposits during the building of the Rocky Mountains. Many parts of them were distorted and crushed until most traces of life in them were obliterated. But miraculously, this one small patch survived virtually undamaged.

The range of creatures it contains is far wider than that found in rocks of a similar age at any other site. There are the jellyfish that Ediacara would lead us to expect. There are echinoderms, brachiopods, primitive molluscs, and half a dozen species of segmented worms – further representatives of the lineage that stretches from the beaches of Ediacara to the Barrier Reef of today. There are also several creatures which, while they seem to be related to the segmented worms, are rather more complex in structure and quite unlike any other animals that we know, living or fossil.

One had fifteen segments, a trunk in front of its mouth and five eyes, including one pointing upwards. Another, named rather despairingly by the scientist who first examined it Hallucigenia, had seven pairs of limbs beneath and seven tentacles waving above, each of which ended, apparently, with a mouth. They seem to be experiments in animal design that did not work efficiently enough to survive in the competition that became more and more intense as time passed and animal life proliferated.

The great variety of creatures in the Burgess Shales is a reminder of how incomplete our knowledge is of all fossil faunas. The ancient seas had many more kinds of animals in them than we can ever know. In this one site, conditions allowed a uniquely large proportion to be preserved, but even this is only a hint of what must have existed.

The Burgess Shales also contain superbly preserved examples of trilobites like those in the Moroccan limestones. The body armour of these creatures was constructed partly of lime and partly of a horny substance called chitin. But it was not expandable and as the creature grew, it had to shed its shell regularly. Many of the trilobite fossils found commonly elsewhere in the world are these empty suits of armour. Sometimes they occur in great drifts, sorted by sea currents, as shells often are on beaches today. The underwater avalanches in the Burgess Shales Basin, however, swept down living trilobites and buried them. Mud particles filtered into the animal's bodies and preserved the finest details of their anatomy. Here we can see the paired jointed legs that are attached to each body segment, the feathery gill on a stalk alongside each leg, two feelers at the front of the head, the gut running the entire length of the body, even the muscle fibres along the back which enabled the animal to roll itself up into a ball.

The arrival of the high-definition eye
Trilobites were the first creatures on earth to develop high-definition eyes. They are mosaics, a cluster of separate components, each with its own lens of crystalline calcite orientated in the precise position in which it transmits light most efficiently. One eye may contain 15,000 elements, providing images that together constitute an almost hemispherical field of view. Late in the dynasty, some species developed an even more sophisticated kind of eye and one that has never been paralleled by any other animal.

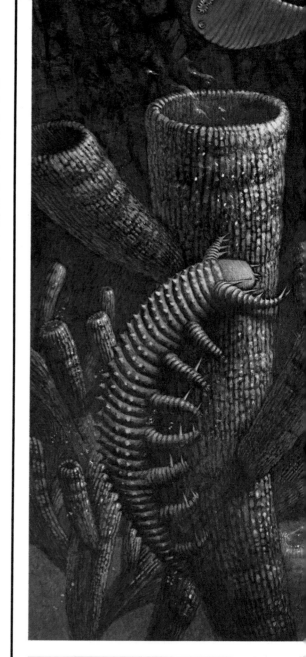

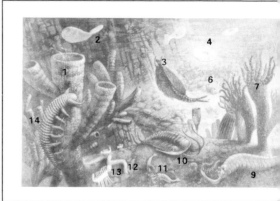

KEY TO THE ILLUSTRATION

1 Vauxia (sponge)
2 Odontogriphus omalus
3 Perspicaris dictynna
4 Peytoia nathorsti
5 Wiwaxia (mollusc)
6 Eiffelia (sponge)
7 Echmatocrinus (crinoid)
8 Marella splendens (trilobite)
9 Opabinia regalis
10 Olenoides serratus (trilobite)
11 Yohoia tenuis
12 Louisella pedunculata
13 Hallucigenia sparsa
14 Aysheaia pedunculata

MARINE ANIMALS OF 530 MILLION YEARS AGO

These ancient animals, fossilised in exquisite detail by fine ocean sediment, provide a rare view of life in the primeval seas. The sea-bed where they lived is now part of the Canadian Rockies.

This scene of the submarine world of 530 million years ago has been reconstructed on the evidence of fossils found in the Burgess Shales of British Columbia. It is one of the few sites where exceptional conditions have made possible the fossilisation of animals with no hard parts in their bodies. Among the creatures are some of the earliest sponges, crinoids and trilobites. There are also a spiny-backed mollusc, Wiwaxia, burrowing worms such as Louisella, a wide variety of primitive arthropods like Perspicaris and

Yohoia, and a relative of the jellyfish shaped like a pineapple-ring, Peytoia. Bizarre creatures which cannot be placed in any living group of invertebrates include the aptly named Hallucigenia, which walked along the sea floor on seven pairs of sharply pointed spines. Opabinia, about 7 centimetres long, had five eyes and a long, grasping organ on its head. One of the most interesting animals is the arthropod, Aysheaia, which could have been an ancestor of such living arthropods as the insects.

Building bodies

A swimming trilobite

Deiphon had eyes on the front edge of its head-shield, and would have been frequently blinded if it had lived on the ocean floor. Its deeply dissected body gave it a very low weight in proportion to its surface area. Both of these features suggest that it swam in the upper waters of the sea.

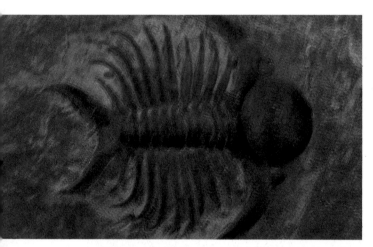

Here the components are fewer but larger. Their lenses are much thicker and it is thought that these species lived where there was little light and needed thick lenses to collect and concentrate what light there was. However, the optical properties of a simple calcite lens in contact with water are such that it transmits light in a diffused way and cannot bring it to a sharply focused point. To do this, a two-part lens is needed which has a waved surface at the junction between its two elements. And this is exactly what these trilobites have developed. The lower element of the double lens was formed by chitin and the surface between the two conforms to a mathematical principle that man discovered only three hundred years ago when trying to correct the spherical

An armoured bottom-dweller

Mitaspis had a protective armour of spines, each segment carrying two pairs, one long and slender, the other shorter and fringed with barbs. Its eyes were placed at the end of two shelled stalks that project from either side of the head. It almost certainly spent its life crawling over the sea floor.

Curling for defence

Most trilobites were able to protect their vulnerable undersides by rolling up. The earliest ones could only do so incompletely, but later species like Phacops (above) had front shields and tail pieces that met in a neat fit. Rolled-up specimens of trilobites are quite common, and between them give a complete picture of the process (below).

The first mosaic eye

The earliest trilobites so far discovered had well developed and very efficient eyes (below, magnified 22 times). They contained a multitude of tightly packed elements, numbering in some cases as many as 15,000. All were covered by a single transparent membrane, the cornea, and each produced a spot of light which together produced the eye's single picture. This kind of eye is possessed today by crustaceans and insects.

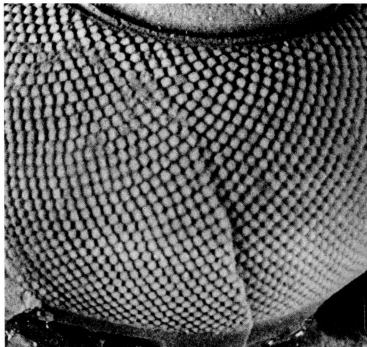

A unique eye

Late in their dynasty, some trilobites developed an eye adapted for use in low-light conditions (left, magnified 16 times). The eye is shaped like a turret. It has many fewer components, but each is separately enclosed and has its own individual cornea with, beneath it, a double-component lens of calcite capable of concentrating the dim light. No other creature since has evolved an eye like it.

63

aberration of lenses in his telescopes.

As the trilobites spread through the seas of the world, they diversified into a great number of species. Most seem to have lived on the sea floor, champing their way through mud. Some colonised the deep seas where there was little light and lost their eyes altogether. Others, to judge from the shape of their limbs, may well have paddled about, legs uppermost, scanning the sea floor below with their large eyes.

The horseshoe crab – last of a dynasty

In due course, as creatures of many kinds and varying ancestries came to live on the bottom of the seas, the trilobites lost their supremacy. Two hundred and fifty million years ago, their dynasty came to an end. One relation alone survives, the horseshoe crab. Measuring 30 centimetres or so across, it is many times bigger than the largest known trilobite and its armour no longer shows any signs of segmentation. Instead, it forms a huge domed shield on the front of which are two bean-shaped compound eyes. A roughly rectangular plate, hinged to the back of the shield, carries a sharp spike of a tail. But beneath its shell, the segmented character of the horseshoe crab is clear. It has several pairs of jointed legs with pincers on the end and behind these, plate-like gills, large and flat like the leaves of a book.

Horseshoe crabs are seldom seen, for they live at considerable depths, some in Southeast Asian waters, others in the seas along the North Atlantic coast of America. Every spring, they migrate towards the coast. Then on three successive nights, when the moon is full and the tides are high, hundreds of thousands emerge from the sea.

The females, their huge shells glinting in the moonlight, drag smaller males behind them. Sometimes, in their anxiety to reach a female, four or five males cling to one another and form a chain. As she reaches the edge of the water, the female half-buries herself in the sand. There she sheds her eggs and the males release sperm. For mile after mile along the dark beaches, the living tide of horseshoe crabs is so thick that they form a continuous strip, like a causeway of giant cobbles. The breakers sometimes overturn them and they lie in the sand, with their legs waving, their stiff tails slowly swivelling, in an effort to lever themselves back. Many fail and are abandoned by the receding tide to die as thousands more swim in the shallows, pressing forward to take their turn.

This scene must have been enacted every spring for several hundred million years. When it began, the land was without life of any kind and on such beaches the eggs were safe from sea-dwelling marauders. Perhaps this is why the horseshoe crabs developed the habit. Today beaches are not quite so safe, for hordes of gulls and small wading birds congregate to share the prodigal feast. But many of the fertilised eggs remain buried deep among the sand grains where they will stay for a month until, once more, high water reaches this part of the beach, stirring the sand, releasing the larvae to swim freely in the sea. And at this stage, the relationship of the horseshoe crab with the trilobites becomes evident, for in these little immature creatures which have not yet developed the all-enclosing armour of the adults, the segments are clearly visible even from the top. Indeed, they are often referred to as 'trilobite larvae'.

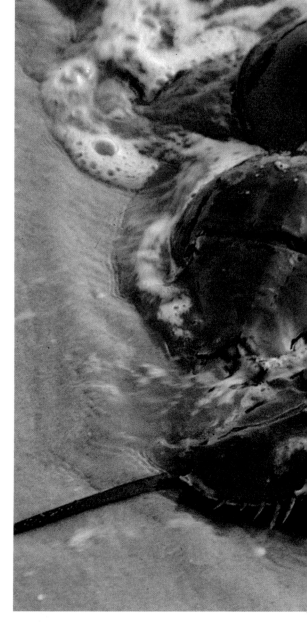

The spawning of the horseshoe crabs
Horseshoe crabs feed on worms, soft-shelled clams and other small creatures, digging for them in the sediments of the sea floor with shovelling movements of their rounded carapaces. When they come up to the beaches to spawn, the females use the same techniques to excavate a shallow nest for their thousand or so eggs. The male clings to the back of the female's shell, ready to release his sperm as soon as the eggs appear.

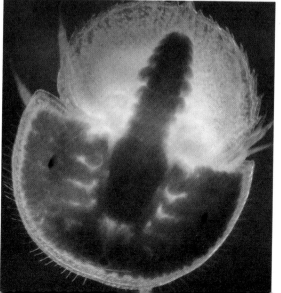

A larval hint of ancestry

Only 2 centimetres across, the newly hatched horseshoe crab (left) shows the segmentation that links it with its ancestors, the trilobites.

Replaceable eyes

Like the trilobites, the horseshoe crab has a pair of mosaic eyes (right). Their surface is part of the shell, so when the crab moults, it also sheds the honey-combed top-part of the eyes, which has to be regrown.

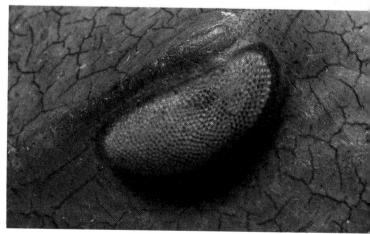

Colourful shrimps that live unseen

There are about 2000 different kinds of shrimps. They live in all parts of the sea, from the ocean depths to the shallows, as well as in fresh water. Many are brilliantly coloured, even the prawn below which lives in very deep water where there is no light and no way of seeing its colours.

Crustaceans take over, and produce 35,000 species

Although the trilobites were so successful, they were by no means the only armoured creatures to develop from the segmented worms. Another group, the crustaceans, appeared at just about the same time. They differed in the seemingly trivial but nonetheless diagnostic character of having not one but two pairs of antennae on their heads. They survived the millions of years of trilobite dominance and eventually, when the trilobite dynasty came to an end, it was they who took over. Today there are about 35,000 species of crustacean – four times as many as there are of birds. Most prowl among the rocks and reefs – crabs, shrimps, prawns and lobsters. Some take up a static life – the barnacles; others swim in vast shoals – the krill which forms the food of

A brilliant camouflage

The painted shrimp (below) looks conspicuous in isolation, but the blotches on its body break up its outline so effectively that, among seaweed and coral, it can be almost invisible. It feeds on the flesh of starfish.

Advertising a nasty taste

The coral reef prawn (left) also has a striking pattern in brilliant colours, but it seems that in this instance the elaborate design serves not to conceal the animal but to make it more obvious. This species has an extremely unpleasant taste, and fish will spit it out. Even so, that might be the death of the prawn, so individuals cluster together to form a patch of colour so vivid that no fish will eat one by mistake.

The tools of a scavenger

Despite the ferocious look of their pincers, lobsters (left) are not great hunters, but scavengers that pick the flesh from the bodies of dead creatures.

The food of whales

Euphausids (below) form immense shoals containing as many as 100 million individuals. These vast assemblages feed on microscopic organisms floating in the sea, and are themselves the basic food for a great number of bigger creatures, from sardines to whales.

Barnacle legs

Barnacles (right) are almost unrecognisable as crustaceans. Their identity is only apparent from the form of their larvae, which are unmistakably crustacean. By tracing the way they change, when they settle down on a rock to take up their sedentary adult life, it becomes clear that the waving tentacles, projecting from the shell, are their greatly modified legs.

whales. The external skeleton is highly versatile; it serves the tiny water flea as well as it does the giant Japanese spider crab that measures over three metres from claw to claw.

Each species modifies the shape of its many paired legs for particular purposes. Those at the front may become pincers or claws; those in the middle, paddles, walking legs or tweezers. Some have feathery branches, gills through which oxygen is absorbed from the water. Others develop attachments so that they can carry eggs. The limbs, which are tubular and jointed, are operated by internal muscles. These extend from the end of one section, along its length, to a prong from the next section which projects across the joint. When the muscle contracts between these two attachment points, the limb hinges. Such joints can only move in one plane, but crustaceans deal with that limitation by grouping two or three on a limb, sometimes close together, each working in a different plane so that the end of the limb can move in a complete circle.

The external shell gives the crustaceans the problem it gave the trilobites. It will not expand and since it completely encloses their bodies, the only way they can grow is to shed it periodically. As the time for the moult approaches, the animal absorbs much of the calcium carbonate from its shell into its blood. It secretes a new, soft wrinkled skin beneath the shell. The outgrown armour splits and the animal pulls itself out, leaving it more or less complete, like a translucent ghost of its former self. Now its skin is soft and it must hide, but it grows fast and swells its body by absorbing water and stretching out the wrinkles of its new carapace. Gradually this hardens and the animal can again venture into a hostile world. The hermit crab partly avoids this complicated and hazardous process by having a shell-less hinder part and protecting it with a discarded mollusc shell, switching into a new one in a minute or so whenever it has the need.

The external skeleton has one incidental quality which has had momentous results. Mechanically, it works almost as well on land as it does in water, so that providing a creature can find a way of breathing, there is little to prevent it walking straight out of the sea and up the beach. Many crustaceans, indeed, have done so – sand shrimps and beach hoppers stay quite close to the sea; pill bugs and penny sows have colonised moist ground throughout the land. The most spectacular of all these land-living crustaceans is the robber crab. It is so big that it can embrace the trunk of a palm tree between its outstretched legs. It climbs the palm with ease and once in the crest, cuts down with its gigantic pincers the young coconuts on which it feeds. At the back of its main carapace, at the junction with the first segment of its abdomen, there is an opening to an air chamber, lined with moist puckered skin, through which the crab absorbs oxygen. It returns to the sea to lay its eggs, but otherwise it is entirely at home on land.

Other descendants of the marine invertebrates have also left the water. Among the molluscs, there are the snails and shell-less slugs, but these emerged fairly recently in the group's history. The first to make the move to land were descendants of the segmented worms. Some 400 million years ago, they found ways of surviving out of water and made such a success of life in their new surroundings that they ultimately gave rise to the most numerous and diverse group of all land animals, the insects.

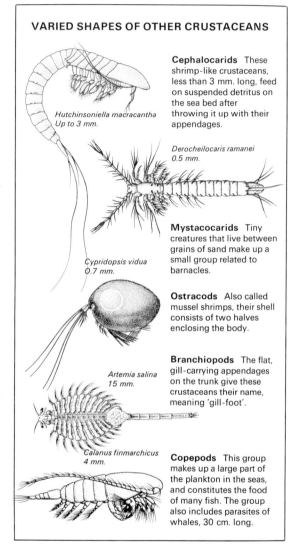

VARIED SHAPES OF OTHER CRUSTACEANS

Hutchinsoniella macracantha
Up to 3 mm.

Cephalocarids These shrimp-like crustaceans, less than 3 mm. long, feed on suspended detritus on the sea bed after throwing it up with their appendages.

Derocheilocaris ramanei
0.5 mm.

Mystacocarids Tiny creatures that live between grains of sand make up a small group related to barnacles.

Cypridopsis vidua
0.7 mm.

Ostracods Also called mussel shrimps, their shell consists of two halves enclosing the body.

Artemia salina
15 mm.

Branchiopods The flat, gill-carrying appendages on the trunk give these crustaceans their name, meaning 'gill-foot'.

Calanus finmarchicus
4 mm.

Copepods This group makes up a large part of the plankton in the seas, and constitutes the food of many fish. The group also includes parasites of whales, 30 cm. long.

The biggest crustacean of all
The Japanese spider crab (right) may measure over 3 metres across. Its great limbs, without the support of water, are too heavy for its muscles to operate, so when hauled out by fishermen's nets, it is virtually helpless.

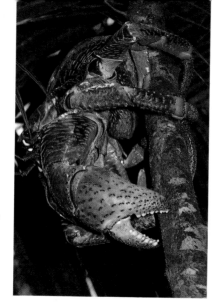

The largest of land crabs

The robber crab (right) starts life as a hermit in a borrowed shell, but eventually it outgrows the largest of shells, curls up its soft abdomen beneath its body and takes up life on land. The adult is so large that it can embrace a palm trunk with its legs. It climbs to the top and there chews off the coconuts on which it feeds.

New tenants for old homes

Hermit crabs use empty mollusc shells as homes, shifting swiftly into bigger ones as they grow. Their claws are so shaped that, when a crab withdraws into its shell, they fit together to form a neat and near-impregnable armoured door.

3. THE FIRST FORESTS

Plants eventually colonised the land. The segmented animals developed ways of breathing and breeding out of water; they crawled up out of the sea to browse on the new plants and to prey on one another

There are few more barren places on earth than the plains surrounding a volcano in the aftermath of its eruption. Black tides of lava lie spilt over its flanks like slag from a furnace. Their momentum has gone but they still creak and boulders still tumble as the flow settles. Steam hisses between the blocks of lava, caking the mouths of the vents with yellow sulphur. Pools of liquid mud, grey, yellow or blue, boiled by the subsiding heat from far below, bubble creamily. Otherwise all is still. No bush grows to give shelter from the scouring wind; no speck of green relieves the black surface of the empty ash plains.

This desolate landscape has been that of much of the earth for the greater part of its history. The first volcanoes to appear on the surface of the cooling planet erupted on a far greater scale than any that we know today, building entire mountain ranges of lava and ash. Over the millennia, the wind and rain destroyed them. Their rocks weathered and turned to clay and mud. Streams transported the debris, particle by particle, and strewed it over the sea floor beyond the margins of the land. As the deposits accumulated, they compacted into shales and sandstone. The continents were not stationary, but drifted slowly over the earth's surface, driven by the convection currents moving deep in the earth's mantle. When they collided, the sedimentary deposits around them were squeezed and rucked up to form new mountain ranges. As the geological cycles repeated themselves for some three thousand million years, as the volcanoes exploded

---

A frond from a 250-million-year-old forest

Seams of coal were once beds of rotting leaves and stems, accumulating beneath trees that stood in immense swamps. The processes of decay and the weight of the sediments deposited above these peat beds destroyed much of the structure of the plant remains. Occasionally, however, a frond was carried away by a stream, stranded on a sand bank and buried in isolation. When the bank turned to sandstone, an impression of the leaf survived that is full of detail. Superb fossils, such as this one of an ancient fern, have made it possible to reconstruct the anatomy of the gigantic ferns and horsetails that were the first tall trees to appear on earth.

A vision of a sterile land

*For 3000 million years, life was restricted to water,
and the land remained bare. Such desolation is hard to
parallel today, but in Iceland there is a hint of what it
might have been like. Ash, thrown out by volcanoes, is
deposited by rivers on immense flats and these are as
bleak and lifeless as any place on earth today.*

and spent themselves, life in the sea burgeoned into many forms; but the land still
remained barren.

Some marine algae, no doubt, managed to live on the edges of the seas, but they could
not have spread far beyond the splash zone, for they would have dried out and died.
Then about 420 million years ago, some forms developed a waxy covering, which
warded off desiccation. Even this, however, did not totally emancipate them from
water. They could not leave it because their reproductive processes depended on it.

Algae reproduce themselves in two ways – by straightforward asexual division and
by the sexual method, of such importance to the progress of evolution, in which the sex
cells will only develop if they meet each other and fuse in pairs. To make these journeys
and achieve these meetings, they need water.

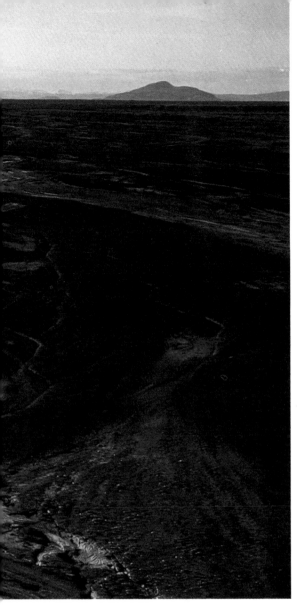

The first plants begin life on land

This problem still besets the most primitive land plants living today – the moist skins known as liverworts, and the filaments covered with green scales, the mosses. They practise these two methods of reproduction, sexual and asexual, in alternate generations. The familiar green moss is the generation which produces the sex cells. Each large egg remains attached to the stem at the top, while the smaller microscopic sperms are released into water and wriggle their way to fertilise it. The egg then germinates while still attached to the parent plant and produces the next asexual generation – a thin stem with, at its tip, a hollow capsule. In this, great numbers of grain-like spores are produced. When the atmosphere becomes dry, the capsule wall expands until it suddenly snaps apart, throwing the spores into the air to be distributed by the wind. Those that land on a suitably moist site then develop into new plants.

Moss filaments have no rigidity. Some kinds achieve a modest height by packing closely together in cushions and so giving one another support, but their soft, perme-

Two generations: two functions

A pad of moss contains sufficient moisture to enable the plant's sperm cells to swim to the egg cells at the top of the filaments. After this sexual fertilisation, the egg sprouts a stalk bearing a capsule within which great numbers of spores develop asexually. They will be blown far and wide to start new moss colonies elsewhere.

The first forests

able, water-filled cells do not provide enough strength to enable individual stems to stand upright. Plants like these are very likely to have been among the earliest forms to colonise the moist margins of the land, but so far no fossil relics of undoubted mosses have been discovered from this early period. The first land plants we know, dating from over 400 million years ago, are simple leafless branching strands which occur as filaments of carbon in the rocks of central Wales and in some cherts in Scotland. Like moss, they had no roots, but when their stems are carefully prepared and examined under the microscope, they are seen to contain structures that no moss possesses – long, thick-walled cells for conducting water up the stem. These structures gave them strength and enabled them to stand several centimetres tall. That may not sound very imposing, but it represented a major advance.

Pioneer animals colonise the miniature forests

Such plants, together with primitive mosses and liverworts, formed green tangled carpets, miniature forests that spread inland from the edges of estuaries and rivers, and into these the first animal colonists crept from the sea. They were segmented creatures, ancestors of today's millipedes, pre-adapted by their chitinous armour to movement on land. At first they doubtless kept close to the edge of the water, but wherever there was moss there was both moisture and vegetable debris and spores to eat. With the land to themselves, these pioneering creatures flourished. Their name millipede, 'thousand legs', is something of an over-statement. No species alive today has many more than two hundred legs and some have as few as eight. Nevertheless, the first ones grew to magnificent dimensions. One of them was two metres long and must have had a devastating effect on the plants as it browsed its way through the wet green bogs. It was, after all, as long as a cow.

Rulers of the ancient seas

Sea-scorpions first appeared some 500 million years ago. They were distantly related to trilobites, for like them they had a segmented body and many legs, but some were over 2 metres long and dominated the seas, being hunters, armed with formidable pincers. As time passed, they invaded rivers and lakes. Some may even have crawled on to land, for they had partially enclosed gills that may have enabled them to breathe in air. The whole group finally disappeared some 400 million years ago.

PLANTS AND ANIMALS THAT PIONEERED THE LAND

This artist's impression of life on land 380 million years ago includes some of the first animals to inhabit the continents, living in a miniature forest only a metre or two high.

The first forms of life that spread over the barren continents of the world were primitive moss-like plants that formed miniature green forests about 5 centimetres high. Into this new habitat crept tiny creatures that lived on the plants, and then came flesh-eating creatures to prey on the plant-eaters. The greatly magnified scene above has been reconstructed from fossils found throughout the world, dating back to 380 million years ago when the land had only recently been colonised. The first moss-like plants had been followed by others that developed thick-walled cells for conducting water up their stems – plants such as Cooksonia, Hedeia, Taeniocrada, and Rebuchia. These gave rise to more advanced plants such as Psilophyton and the club-moss-like Drepanophycus. None of the plants was more than a metre or two in height. The herbivorous animals that lived on them included millipedes and primitive wingless insects such as the 3 millimetre long Rhyniella. The carnivores included early spider-like creatures, primitive centipedes and scorpions.

The problems of breathing and reproducing out of water

The external skeleton inherited from their water-living forebears, needed few modifications for life on land, but the millipedes did have to acquire a different method of breathing. The feathery gill attached to a stalk alongside the leg that had served their aquatic relatives, the crustaceans, would not work in air. In its place, the millipedes developed a system of breathing tubes, the tracheae. Each tube begins at an opening on the flank of the shell and then branches internally into a fine network that leads ultimately to all the organs and tissues of the body, the tips even entering individual cells and delivering gaseous oxygen to them.

Reproduction out of water posed problems for the millipedes. Their marine ancestors had relied, like the algae, on water to enable their sperm to reach their eggs. On land the solution was an obvious one – male and female, being well able to move about, must meet and transfer the sperm directly from one to the other. This is exactly what millipedes do. Both sexes produce their reproductive cells in glands close to the base of

A pick-a-back nursery
Scorpion eggs hatch within the mother's reproductive pouch and the young are born alive. They immediately clamber up on to her back (right) and will remain there until their first moult about a week later.

The confident embrace of the millipede
Since millipedes eat only plants, a mate does not risk being mistaken for a meal. The male (on the right of the picture) has removed a bundle of sperm from his reproductive pouch with specially modified legs and has brought it alongside the female's second segment so she can take it in.

PRIMITIVE TECHNIQUES OF MATING

The male pseudo-scorpion, like many other primitive land animals, deposits his sperm in a little sack – the spermatophore – which a female takes up. Many species of pseudo-scorpions have developed complex mating dances to help the female find the sack.

A courting dance
When the male Lasiochernus pilosus meets a female he pulls her close.

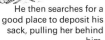

He then searches for a good place to deposit his sack, pulling her behind him.

He again grasps her by both 'hands' and vibrates the feelers on his head. The pair then step forward and backward in a slow dance.

Finally, he deposits his spermatophore. She approaches closer and he suddenly pulls her over it.

A silken path The male Serianus carolinensis deposits a spermatophore after meeting a female. He then spins two rows of silken threads to form a path down which the female will walk. The path is wide at the beginning and narrows to the spot where the spermatophore stands.

the second pair of legs. When the male meets the female in the mating season, the two intertwine. The male reaches forward with his seventh leg, collects a bundle of sperm from his sex gland and then clambers alongside the female until it is alongside her sexual pouch and she is able to take it in. The process looks rather laborious but at least it is not dangerous. Millipedes are entirely vegetarian. Fiercer invertebrates which came to the moss jungles to prey on this grazing population, could not indulge in such trusting relationships.

The predators arrive – centipedes, scorpions, spiders

Three groups of these predatory creatures still survive today – centipedes, scorpions and spiders. Like their prey, they are members of the segmented group of animals, though the degree to which they have retained divisions in their bodies varies considerably. The centipedes are as clearly and extensively segmented as the millipedes. The scorpions show divisions only in their long tails; and most spiders have completely lost all signs of segmentation, only a few South-east Asian species having clearly recognisable relics of their segmented past.

The scorpions resemble creatures, now long extinct, called sea-scorpions that at this period terrorised the oceans. Some grew to a length of two metres and were armed with immense pincers with which they seized smaller creatures. The land scorpions were not direct descendants, but belonged to the same broad group and certainly shared the same savage habits.

77

The scorpions that live today have not only fearsome-looking claws but a large poison gland with a sharp curving sting drooping from the end of a thin tail. Their copulations cannot be the somewhat hit-and-miss gropings practised by the millipedes. Approaching such an aggressive and powerful creature is a dangerous enterprise even if the move is made by another individual of the same species and its intentions are purely sexual. There is a real risk of it being regarded not as a mate but a meal. So scorpion mating demands, for the first time among the animals that have appeared so far in this history, the ritualised safeguards and placations of courtship.

The male scorpion approaches the female with great wariness. Suddenly he grabs her pincers with his. Thus linked, with her weapons neutralised, the pair begin to dance. Backwards and forwards they move with their tails held upright, sometimes even intertwined. After some time, their shuffling steps have cleared the dancing ground of much of its debris. The male then extrudes a packet of sperm from the genital opening beneath his thorax and deposits it on the ground. Still grasping the female by the claws, he jerks and heaves her forward until her sexual opening, also on her underside, is brought directly above the sperm packet. She takes it up, the partners disengage and go their separate ways. The eggs eventually hatch inside the mother's pouch, the young crawl out and clamber up on to her back. There they stay for about a fortnight until they have completed their first moult and can fend for themselves.

A centipede grows

The skin of a centipede, like that of trilobites, will not stretch, so if the animal is to grow it has to moult. The skin splits around the head and the centipede eventually wriggles out, leaving the old skin, like a crumpled jersey, behind it.

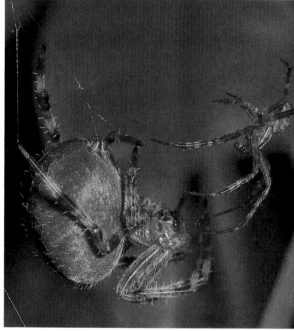

The courting spider that dallied too long

The female diadem spider is very much larger than the male and he only ventures on to her web with the greatest of caution. If she threatens him, he will jump off and swing down on a thread that he has prudently anchored some way behind him.

SHE SUBMITS AND HE DRAWS NEAR *At last the female spider drops down in an attitude of submission. Only in this position is mating possible, and the male draws nearer.*

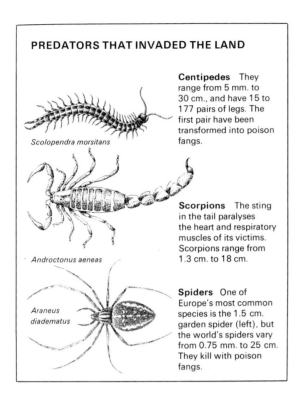
The hazardous mating of spiders

Spiders, too, must be extremely cautious in their courtship. Matters are made even more hazardous for the male because he is nearly always smaller than the female. And he prepares for his encounter with his mate long before he meets her. He spins a tiny triangle of silk a few millimetres in length and deposits a drop of sperm onto it from the gland that lies underneath his body. He then sucks it into the hollow first joint of a special limb, the pedipalp, rather in the same way as one fills a fountain pen. Now he is ready.

The courtships of spiders are beguilingly various and ingenious. Jumping spiders and wolf spiders hunt primarily by sight and have excellent eyes. The courting male, consequently, relies on visual signals to make the female aware of his presence and his purpose. His pedipalps are brightly coloured and patterned and as soon as he sights a female, he begins to signal with them in a kind of manic semaphore. Nocturnal spiders, on the other hand, depend largely on an extremely delicate sense of touch to find their prey. When they meet one another, they gingerly caress each other's long legs and only after a great deal of hesitation do they come to closer quarters. Web-making spiders are sensitive to the vibrations on their silken threads that tell them when a victim has blundered into the web. So when the male of such a species approaches a female hanging, large and menacing, on her web, or lurking hidden beside it, he signals to her

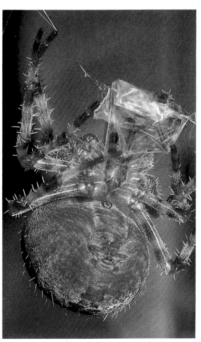

A WARNING THAT GOES UNHEEDED *The male now thrusts his pedipalp, loaded with sperm, into her genital opening. The female draws herself up, a warning that he should now retire. But in this instance he dallies.*

A MATE BECOMES A MEAL *The female bites the male while he lingers and neatly wraps him in silk, twirling him between her fore-legs like a bobbin.*

THE FINAL, FATAL BITE *When he is neatly trussed and packaged, like any other insect that might have blundered into her web, she bites him again. Then she carries his corpse to the side of the web and eats him.*

A GIFT FROM A COURTING SPIDER

Pisaura, like other spiders, has no sense of smell. The male "tastes" the presence of a nearby female through his sense organs when he crosses her track in the mating season.

Wrapping the gift He then catches a fly and wraps it in threads from his abdomen.

A hopeful pose When he finds the female, he poses with two legs over his head.

Acceptance If she wishes to mate she advances and he leans further and further back.

Mating As she reaches for the fly he swivels and fertilises her with his pedipalps.

by twanging the threads at one side in a special and meaningful way which he trusts the female will recognise. Other species put their faith in bribery. The male catches an insect and carefully parcels it up in silk. Holding this in front of him, he cautiously approaches the female and presents it to her. While she is occupied in examining the gift, he quickly scuttles over her and ties her to the ground with bonds of silk before he risks an embrace.

All these techniques lead to the same conclusion. The male, having survived every danger, thrusts his pedipalp into the female's genital opening, squirts out the sperm and then hastily retreats. It has to be recorded that in spite of all his precautions he sometimes fails to make his getaway in time and the female eats him after all. But in terms of the success of the species as a whole, that individual disaster is of limited consequence: he lost his life after, not before, he had completed his purpose.

A meeting in the heather

Crab spiders do not build webs but lurk in ambush on plants. This species favours heather with flowers the same colour as its body. A courting male, only a third the length of the female, crawls delicately up to his mate. Though he has good eyes, he examines her primarily by smell and taste. Having established her identity, he crawls over her, vibrating his legs reassuringly, until he finds her genital opening and can take up his mating position.

The eight-eyed jumper
The jumping spider (right) has four small eyes on the top of its head with which it can detect the approach of a flying insect. If the prey settles, the spider uses the two eyes on either side of the head, which have wide fields, to gauge how far away it is. Then it begins its stalk, watching its prey with its two huge central eyes, which give the clearest image of all.

Courtship by semaphore
The male wolf spider (above) relies on the excellent eyesight of his kind for the success of his courtship. His palps are brightly coloured or patterned, according to his species. He waves them at the female in a special manner, vibrating them and sometimes his whole body, until at last she signals acknowledgment of his message by vibrating her own front legs.

The first forests

Competition for light produces the first forests

While the early segmented animals were perfecting their adaptations for living on land and away from moisture, the plants were also changing. Neither the mosses nor the other early forms had true roots. Their upright stems sprang from a horizontal one of a similar character lying along the ground or just below it. This construction served well enough in moist surroundings, but in many parts of the world the only permanent water supply lies below the ground. To tap that requires roots that probe deep between the particles of the soil and can absorb the film of water that clings to them in all except the most arid environments. Three groups of plants appeared that possessed such structures and all three have descendants that have survived without much change – club-mosses which resemble mosses but have stiffer stems; horsetails which grow in waste patches and ditches and have stems encircled at intervals with rings of needle-like leaves; and ferns. All three have within their stems strong woody vessels to transport the water absorbed by their roots. The rigidity thus provided enables them to grow to considerable heights and this introduced a new kind of competition between plants.

All green plants depend on light to power the chemical processes by which they synthesise their body substances from simple elements. Height is therefore of the greatest value. If a plant does not grow tall, it risks being overshadowed by its neighbours and condemned to shade where, starved of light, it may die. So these early groups used the newly-acquired strength of their stems to grow very tall and become trees. The club-mosses and horsetails were still, for the most part, swamp-dwellers and there they stood in dense ranks, 30 metres tall, some with woody trunks two metres in diameter. The compacted remains of their stems and leaves today form coal. The great thicknesses of the seams are impressive evidence of the abundance and persistence of the early forests. Other species of both these groups also grew farther inland and there mingled with ferns. These had developed true leaves, large spreading structures with which to collect as much light as possible. They grew tall with curving trunks, like the tree ferns that still thrive in tropical rain forests.

The height of these first forests must have caused considerable problems for the animal inhabitants. Once, there had been a superabundance of leaves and spores close to the ground. Now the soaring trunks had raised this source of food high in the sky, creating a dense canopy that cut out much of the light. The floor of these forests was, at best, only sparsely vegetated and great areas may have been entirely without any living leaves. Some of the multi-legged vegetarians found their fodder by clambering up the trunks.

There may have been another factor that induced these creatures to leave the ground. About this time, animals of a completely new kind joined the invertebrates on the land. They had backbones and four legs and wet skins. They were the first amphibians and they too were carnivorous. A description of their origins and fate will have to wait until we have followed the development of the invertebrates to its climax, but their presence at this stage must be mentioned if the scene in these first jungles is not to be misrepresented.

The first insects climb trees

Some of the new-style invertebrate families still survive – the bristletails and springtails. Although they are little known and infrequently seen, they are enormously abundant. There is hardly a spadeful of soil anywhere in the world that does not contain some of them. Most are only a few millimetres long. Only one is commonly noticed, the silverfish that glides smoothly across cellar floors or is occasionally discovered making a meal of the dried glue in the bindings of books. Its body is clearly segmented but it has very many fewer divisions than the millipede. It has a well-defined head with compound eyes and antennae; a thorax bearing three pairs of legs, the result of fusing together three segments; and a segmented abdomen which, while it no longer has limbs on each segment, retains little stumps as signs that it once possessed them. Three thin filaments trail from its tail. It breathes like the millipedes by means of tracheae and it reproduces in a manner reminiscent of those early land invertebrates, the scorpions. The male silverfish deposits a bundle of sperm on the ground and then, one way or another, he entices the female to walk over it. When that happens, she is stimulated to take it up into her own sexual pouch.

There are several thousand different species within this group. They all have six legs and tripartite bodies and these characters clearly make them members of that great and varied group of land invertebrates, the insects. But they vary considerably in their anatomy and, as is often the case when considering the simpler members of a group, it is sometimes difficult to decide whether a characteristic represents a truly primitive survival or is secondarily reduced to suit a particular way of life. The silverfish, for example, has compound eyes but others in the group are blind. All lack wings. Some even lack tracheae and breathe through their chitinous skeleton which is particularly thin and permeable. Is this because they never had them or because they have lost

---

Survivors from the first forests

Tree ferns still grow in the moist jungles of the tropics. Like their ancestors, they do not increase their girth and strength with layer after layer of wood, but grow only at the crown. Their slender trunks are fibrous throughout, reinforced, in some cases, by an external mesh of aerial roots. A few living species of tree ferns still rival their ancestors in size, reaching heights of 20 metres or so in today's forests.

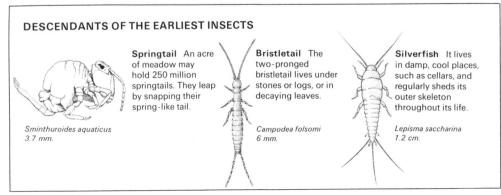

DESCENDANTS OF THE EARLIEST INSECTS

Springtail An acre of meadow may hold 250 million springtails. They leap by snapping their spring-like tail.

Sminthuroides aquaticus 3.7 mm.

Bristletail The two-pronged bristletail lives under stones or logs, or in decaying leaves.

Campodea folsomi 6 mm.

Silverfish It lives in damp, cool places, such as cellars, and regularly sheds its outer skeleton throughout its life.

Lepisma saccharina 1.2 cm.

A monster transformed
The larva of the dragonfly lives in fresh water, devouring other aquatic creatures with its grotesque protrusible jaws. When fully grown, it climbs up a reed, its skin splits and out climbs the beautiful adult, leaving behind its larval skin, like a ghost of its former self.

them? Many such debatable questions raised by the anatomy of these creatures still await universally agreed answers.

The primitive insects must have found some of their food by climbing the trunks of the early tree ferns and horsetails. The ascent was doubtless relatively easy. The climb down, involving long detours over the upward pointing leaf-bases, may have been very much more laborious and time-consuming. Whether or not the prevalence of such obstacles had anything to do with the next developments, we cannot be sure. It is certain, however, that some of these primitive insects did develop a much swifter and less laborious method of getting down. They flew.

We have no direct evidence of how they achieved flight but the living silverfish provides a clue. On the back of its thorax it has two flap-like sideways extensions of the chitinous shell that look as though they might be the rudiments of wings. The early wings may not have served initially for flight. Insects, like all animals, are greatly affected by body temperature. The warmer they are, the quicker the energy-producing chemical reactions of their body can proceed and the more active they can be. If their blood were to be circulated through thin flaps extending laterally from the back they could certainly warm themselves very effectively and quickly in the sunshine. If, furthermore, these flaps had muscles at their base they could be tilted to face squarely to the sun's rays. Insect wings do originate as flaps on the back and they do, initially, have blood flowing in their veins, so such a theory seems very plausible.

Winged insects whirr and buzz through the forests
However this may be, insects with wings appeared some three hundred million years ago. The earliest so far discovered are dragonflies. There were several species; most were about the size of those living today but with the dragonflies, as with millipedes and other groups that have pioneered a new environment, the absence of competition allowed some early forms to develop to an enormous size, and dragonflies eventually appeared with a wingspan of 70 centimetres, the largest insects ever to exist. When the air became more thickly populated, such extravagant forms disappeared.

Dragonflies have two pairs of wings which have simple joints to them: they can only move up and down and cannot be folded back. Even so, they are highly accomplished flyers, shooting over the surface of a pond in a blur of gauzy wings at up to 30 kph. At such speeds, they need accurate sense organs if they are to avoid damaging collisions. A tuft of hair on the front of the body helps them to check that their motion through the air is straight, but their primary navigational guidance comes from huge mosaic eyes on either side of the head, which provide superbly accurate and detailed vision.

Because of this dependence on sight, the dragonflies cannot be active at night. They are daytime hunters, flying with their six legs crooked in front of them to form a tiny basket in which they catch smaller insects. That fact alone makes it clear that they must have been preceded into the air by other vegetarian forms which, judging from the primitive nature of their anatomy, were probably cockroaches, grasshoppers, locusts and crickets.

The earliest-known aeronaut

Co-ordinating two independent pairs of rapidly beating wings requires complex nervous controls, and the dragonfly has them. Only occasionally, when it banks steeply or hovers, do fore and hind wings brush against one another and then they make an audible rustle.

A near-perfect design

The dragonfly is such an efficient aerial hunter that its anatomy has remained virtually unchanged for a vast period. This fossilised one, from the Solnhofen limestones of Bavaria, is very similar to some living forms, yet it flew around dinosaurs and pterodactyls.

The alternating generations of a fern
The thallus of a fern is only a few centimetres across. It produces male cells from its underside which swim through the water film of the moist ground beneath to fertilise the egg cells. Then a tiny shoot sprouts from it, and this will grow into a new feathery-leaved fern. In its turn, the fern distributes asexual spores which grow into new thalli.

Plants take advantage of the insects' messenger service

The presence of these large populations of insects, whirring and buzzing through the air of the ancient forests, was eventually to play an extremely important part in a revolution that was taking place among the plants.

The early trees, like their predecessors, the mosses, existed in two alternating forms, a sexual generation and an asexual one. Their greater height posed no problem for spore dispersal: if anything, it was a help since up in the tree tops, spores were more easily caught by the wind and carried away. The distribution of sex cells, however, was a different matter. Hitherto, it had been achieved by the male cells swimming through water, a process which demanded that the sexual generation be small and close to the ground. That of ferns, club mosses and horsetails still is. The spores of these plants develop into a thin filmy plant called the thallus which looks not unlike a liverwort and releases its sex cells from its underside where there is permanent moisture. After its eggs have been fertilised, they grow into a tall plant like the previous spore-producing generation.

On the ground, the thallus is clearly vulnerable. It is easily cropped by animals; if it dries out it dies; and the very success of the asexual generation with their arching fronds cuts it off from life-giving light. Many advantages would follow if it too could grow tall, but this would require a new technique for getting the male cell to the female.

There were two mechanisms available – the ancient, rather hazardous and capricious method that distributed spores, the wind; and the newly-arrived messenger service, the flying insects, which were now regularly moving from tree to tree, feeding on the leaves and the spores. Plants took advantage of both mechanisms. About 350 million years ago, some appeared in which the sexual generation no longer grew flat on the ground, but up in the crowns of the trees. One group among these plants, the cycads, survives today and shows the development at a particularly dramatic stage.

Cycads look superficially like ferns, with long coarse feathery fronds. Some individuals produce tiny spores of the ancient type that can be distributed by the wind. Others develop much larger ones. These are not blown away but remain attached to the parent. There they develop the equivalent of the thallus, a special kind of conical structure within which there eventually appear eggs. When a wind-blown spore – which now can be called pollen – lands on an egg-bearing cone, it germinates, not into a filmy thallus for which there is now no need, but into a long tube which burrows its way down into the female cone. The process takes several months but eventually, when the tube is complete, a sperm cell is produced from the remains of the pollen grain. It is a majestic ciliated sphere, the largest known sperm of any organism, plant or animal, so big that a single one is visible to the naked eye. Slowly it makes its way down the tube. When it reaches the bottom, it enters a small drop of water that has been secreted by the surrounding tissues of the cone. There it swims, slowly spinning, driven by its cilia, as it re-enacts in miniature the journeys made through the primordial seas by the sperm cells of its algal ancestors. Only after several days does it fuse with the egg and so complete the long process of fertilisation.

FROM MOSS TO MAGNOLIAS: HOW PLANTS EVOLVED THROUGH 400 MILLION YEARS

Miniature forests of plants like moss and liverworts first carpeted the land. Then plants sent down roots and grew higher. Their new size demanded new methods of reproduction, leading first to the development of cones and, eventually, to flowers.

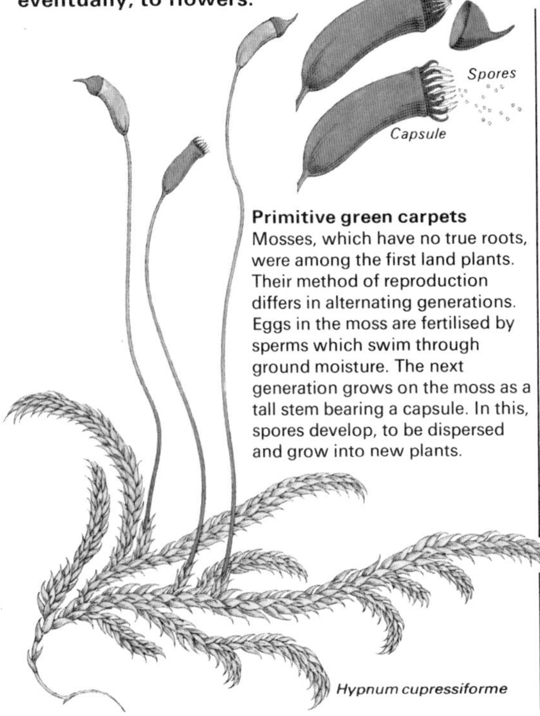

Spores

Capsule

Cone

Spore-bearing leaf from cone

Spore clusters

Primitive green carpets

Mosses, which have no true roots, were among the first land plants. Their method of reproduction differs in alternating generations. Eggs in the moss are fertilised by sperms which swim through ground moisture. The next generation grows on the moss as a tall stem bearing a capsule. In this, spores develop, to be dispersed and grow into new plants.

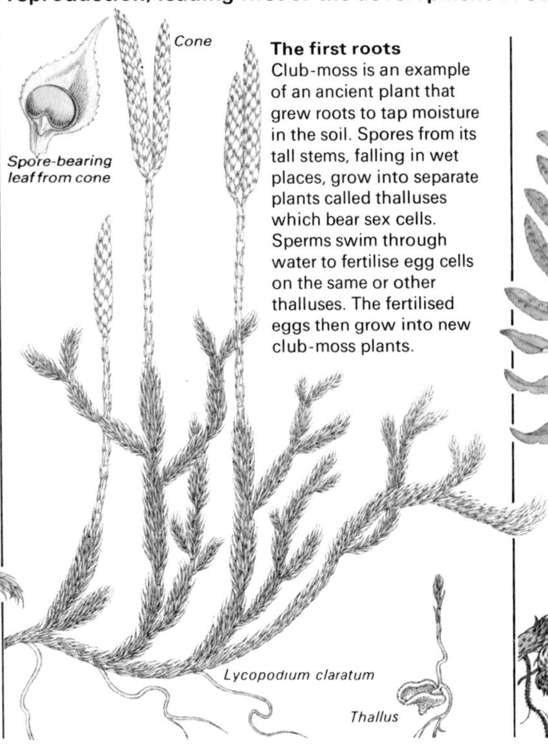

The first roots

Club-moss is an example of an ancient plant that grew roots to tap moisture in the soil. Spores from its tall stems, falling in wet places, grow into separate plants called thalluses which bear sex cells. Sperms swim through water to fertilise egg cells on the same or other thalluses. The fertilised eggs then grow into new club-moss plants.

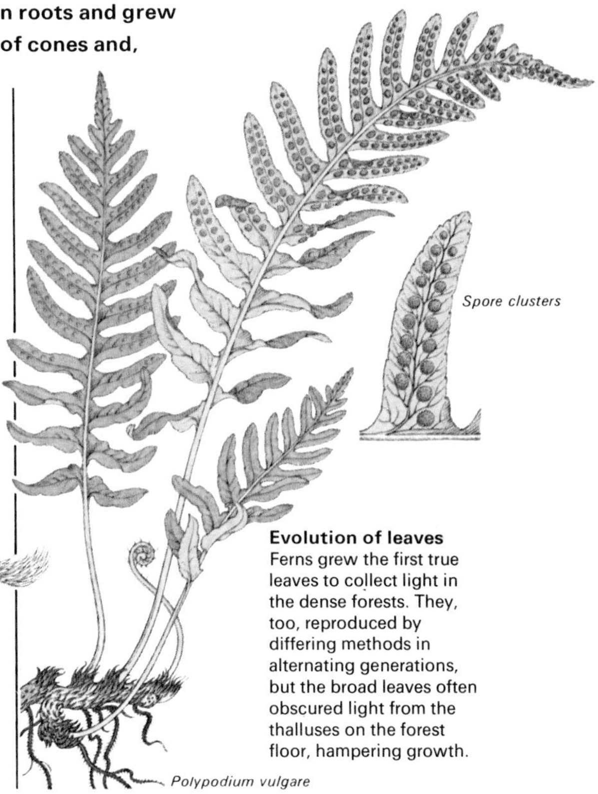

Evolution of leaves

Ferns grew the first true leaves to collect light in the dense forests. They, too, reproduced by differing methods in alternating generations, but the broad leaves often obscured light from the thalluses on the forest floor, hampering growth.

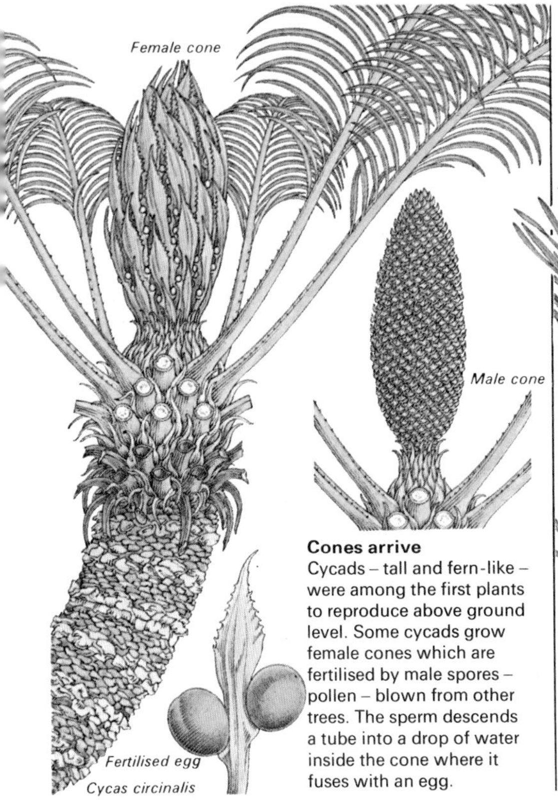

Hypnum cupressiforme

Lycopodium claratum

Thallus

Polypodium vulgare

Female cone

Male cone

New male cone

New female cone

Stigmas

Bee pollinating flower (petals removed)

Stamens

Cones arrive

Cycads – tall and fern-like – were among the first plants to reproduce above ground level. Some cycads grow female cones which are fertilised by male spores – pollen – blown from other trees. The sperm descends a tube into a drop of water inside the cone where it fuses with an egg.

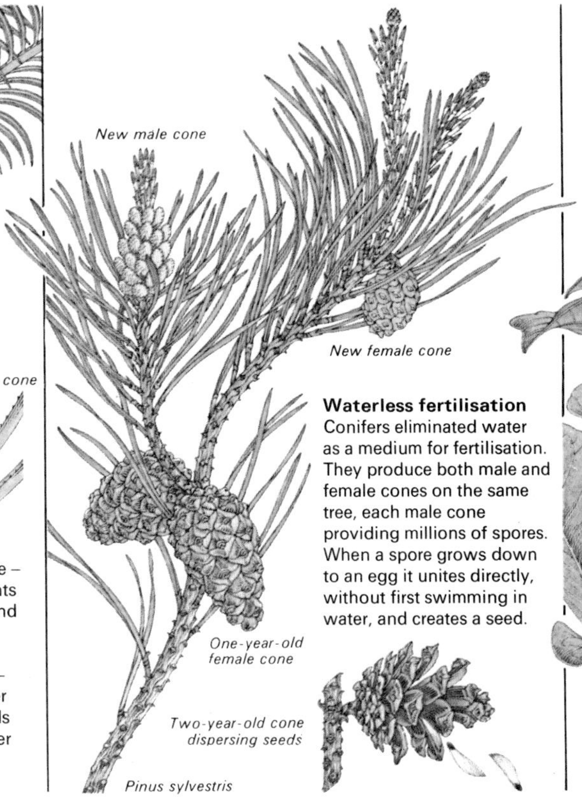

Waterless fertilisation

Conifers eliminated water as a medium for fertilisation. They produce both male and female cones on the same tree, each male cone providing millions of spores. When a spore grows down to an egg it unites directly, without first swimming in water, and creates a seed.

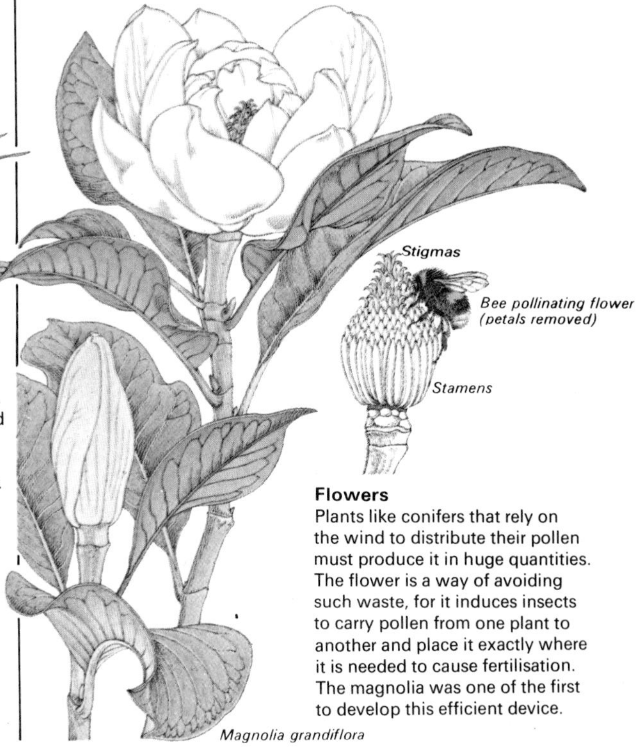

Flowers

Plants like conifers that rely on the wind to distribute their pollen must produce it in huge quantities. The flower is a way of avoiding such waste, for it induces insects to carry pollen from one plant to another and place it exactly where it is needed to cause fertilisation. The magnolia was one of the first to develop this efficient device.

Fertilised egg

Cycas circinalis

One-year-old female cone

Two-year-old cone dispersing seeds

Pinus sylvestris

Magnolia grandiflora

The first forests

Another group of plants adopting a similar strategy as the cycads arose at about the same time. These were the conifers – pines, larches, cedars, firs and their relations. They too rely on the wind to distribute their pollen. Unlike the cycads, they produce both pollen and egg-bearing cones on the same tree. The process of fertilisation in a pine takes even longer. The pollen tube requires a whole year to grow down and reach the egg, but once there, it contacts the egg cell directly and the male cell does not tarry in a drop of water but fuses directly with the egg. The conifers have at last eliminated water as a transport medium for their sexual processes.

They have also developed one further refinement. The fertilised egg remains in the cone for one more year. Rich food supplies are laid down within its cells and waterproof coats are wrapped round it. Eventually more than two years after fertilisation started, the cone dries and becomes woody. Its segments open, and out drop the fertilised fully-provisioned eggs – seeds – which if necessary can wait for years before moisture penetrates them and stimulates them to spring to life.

By any standards, the conifers are a great success. Today, they constitute about a third of the forests of the world. The biggest living organism of any kind is a conifer, the giant redwood of California, which grows to 100 metres in height. Another conifer, the bristle-cone pine which grows in the dry mountains of the south-western United States, has one of the longest life-spans of any individual organism. The age of trees can easily be calculated if they grow in an environment where there are distinct seasons. In summer, when there is plenty of sunshine and moisture, they grow quickly and produce large wood cells; in winter when growth is slow, the wood is much more dense. This produces annual rings in the trunk. Counting those in the bristle-cone pine establishes that some of these gnarled and twisted trees germinated over five thousand years ago at a time when man in the Middle East was just beginning to invent writing, and have remained alive throughout the entire duration of civilisation.

Conifers protect their trunks from mechanical damage and insect attack with a special gummy substance, resin. When it first flows from a wound it is runny but the more liquid part of it, turpentine, quickly evaporates leaving a sticky lump which seals the wound very effectively. It also, incidentally, acts as a trap. Any insect touching it becomes inextricably stuck and very often buried within it as more resin flows around it. Such lumps have proved to be the most perfect fossilising medium of all. They survive as pieces of amber which contain in their translucent golden depths the ancient insects. When the amber is carefully sectioned, it is possible, through the microscope, to see mouthparts, scales and hairs with as much clarity as if the insect had become entangled in the resin only the day before. Scientists have even been able to distinguish tiny parasitic mites, clinging to the legs of the bigger ones.

The oldest pieces of amber we have date from a hundred million years ago, a very long time after the conifers and the flying insects first appeared, but they contain a huge range of creatures, including representatives of all the major insect groups that we know today. Each has already developed its own characteristic way of exploiting that major insect invention, flight.

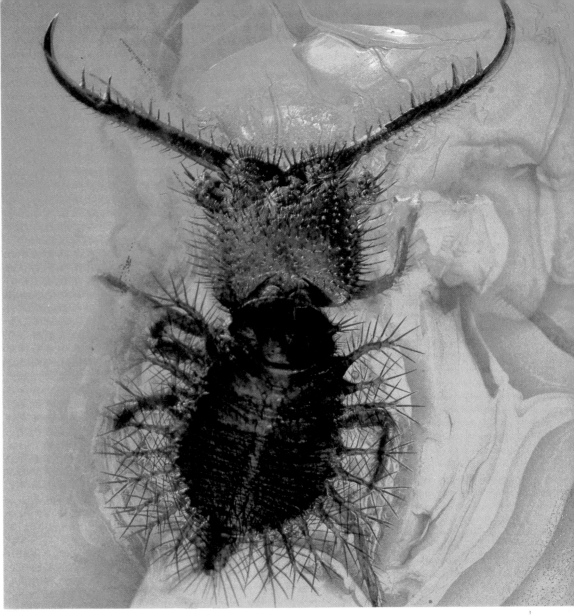

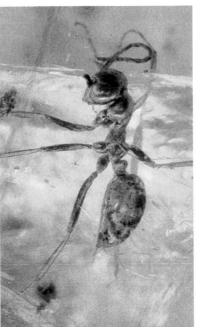

Insects trapped by ancient trees

Sometimes, tree trunks, buried in sediments, become impregnated with silica. This preserves them so well that it is possible to count their annual rings and discover their age. The log on the far left belonged to a redwood, a kind of conifer, that grew 35 million years ago in Colorado and lived for about 500 years. Resin, exuding from such trunks, survives as amber and often contains insects. The ant (left) was trapped in New Jersey 100 million years ago; the ant-lion larva (above) was entombed beside the Baltic 50 million years ago. Their external skeletons have been preserved, but the resin did not permeate their bodies and their internal organs turned to dust. So if the surrounding amber is dissolved away, the insect vanishes.

Insects develop astonishing flying skills

The dragonflies beat their two wings synchronously, but this makes for very considerable physiological complexities. Their wings do not normally come into contact, but even so there are problems when the dragonfly executes sharp turns. Then the fore and hind wings, bending under the additional stress of the turn, beat against one another making an audible rattle that you can easily hear as you sit watching them make their circuits over a pond.

The later insect groups seem to have found that flight was more efficiently achieved with just one pair of flapping membranes. Bees and wasps hitch their fore and hind wings together with hooks to make, in effect, a single surface. Butterfly wings overlap. Hawkmoths, which are among the swiftest insect flyers capable of speeds of 50 kph, have reduced their hind wings very considerably in size and latched them on to the long narrow fore-wings with a curved bristle. Beetles use their fore-wings for a different purpose altogether. These creatures are the heavy armoured tanks of the insect world and they spend a great deal of their time on the ground, barging their way through the vegetable litter, scrabbling in the soil or gnawing into wood. Such activities could easily damage delicate wings. The beetles protect theirs by turning the front pair into stiff thick covers which fit neatly over the top of the abdomen. The wings are stowed neatly beneath, carefully and ingeniously folded. The wing veins have sprung joints in them. When the wing covers are lifted, the joints unlock and the wings spring open. As the beetle lumbers into the air, the stiff wing covers are usually held out to the side, a posture that inevitably hampers efficient flight. Flower beetles, however, have managed to deal with this problem. They have notches at the sides of the wing-covers near the hinges so that the covers can be replaced over the abdomen leaving the wings extended and beating.

The most accomplished aeronauts of all are the flies. They use only their fore-wings for flight. The hind wings are reduced to tiny knobs. All flies possess these little structures but they are particularly noticeable in the crane flies, the daddy-long-legs, in which the knobs are placed on the ends of stalks so that they look like the heads of drumsticks. When the fly is in the air, these organs which are jointed to the thorax in the same way as wings, oscillate up and down a hundred or more times a second. They act partly as stabilisers, like gyroscopes, and partly as sense organs presumably telling the fly of the attitude of its body in the air and the direction in which it is moving. Information about its speed comes from its antennae which vibrate as the air flows over them.

Flies are capable of beating their wings at speeds up to an astonishing 1000 beats a second. Some flies no longer use muscles directly attached to the bases of the wings. Instead they vibrate the whole thorax, a cylinder constructed of strong pliable chitin, making it click in and out like a bulging metal tin. The thorax is coupled to the wings by an ingenious structure at the wing base, and its contractions causes them to beat up and down.

The insects were the first creatures to colonise the air and for a hundred million years

Two wings: two stabilisers

The crane fly appears to have only one pair of wings, but vestiges of the rear pair still exist. They have become tiny sticks that during flight whirl around and act as gyroscopic stabilisers.

Four wings, two aerofoils

Butterflies and moths have four separate wings, but in flight fore and hind wings combine to form a single surface. A few species are able to beat these broad aerofoils very fast, but most, like this yellow underwing moth, only manage to beat them about ten times a second and consequently they have a somewhat fluttering flight.

INSECT WINGS: VARIETY IN FLIGHT

Honey bees The two pairs of wings are joined by a row of tiny hooks on the hind wing, which grip a fold along the edge of the fore-wing. Honey bees beat their wings 225 times a second.

Honey bee
Apis mellifera

Butterflies The fore-wing, which overlaps the hind wing, provides most of the power for the down-stroke, and drives both wings simultaneously – beating 8 to 12 times a second.

Nymphalis io
Peacock butterfly

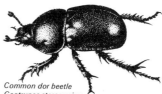

Common dor beetle
Geotrupes stercorarius

Beetles The fore-wings have developed as horny shields to protect the hind wings – the sole organs of flight. Winged beetles beat their wings about 50 times a second.

Houseflies Flies have fore-wings only. The hind wings have become a pair of stalks which vibrate in flight and help keep the fly stable. The fore-wings beat 200 times a second.

Housefly
Musca domestica

it was theirs alone. But their lives were not without hazards. Their ancient adversaries, the spiders, never developed wings, but they did not allow their insect prey to escape totally. They set traps of silk across the flyways between the branches and so continued to take toll of the insect population.

The first flower

Plants now began to turn the flying skills of the insects to their own advantage. Their reliance on the wind for the distribution of their reproductive cells was always haphazard and expensive in biological terms. Spores do not require fertilisation and they will develop wherever they fall, provided the ground is sufficiently moist and fertile. Even so, the vast majority of them, from such a plant as a fern, fail to find the right conditions and die. The chances of survival of a wind-blown pollen grain are very much smaller still for their requirements are even more precise and restricted. They can only develop and become effective if they happen to land on a female cone. So the pine tree has to produce pollen in gigantic quantities. A single small male cone produces several million grains and if you tap one in spring, they fall out in such numbers that they form a golden cloud. A whole pine forest produces so much pollen that ponds become covered with curds of it – and all of it wasted.

Insects represented a much more efficient transport system. If properly encouraged, they could carry the small amount of pollen necessary for fertilisation and place it on the exact spot in the female flower where it was required. This courier service could be most economically operated if both pollen and egg were placed close together on the plant. The insects would then be able to make both deliveries and collections in the same call. And so developed the flower.

The earliest and simplest of these marvellous devices so far discovered were those produced by the magnolias. They appeared about a hundred million years ago. The eggs are clustered in the centre, each protected by a green coat with a receptive spike on the top called a stigma, on which the pollen must be placed if the eggs are to be fertilised. Grouped around the eggs are many stamens producing pollen. In order to bring these organs to the notice of the insects, the whole structure is surrounded by brightly coloured modified leaves, the petals.

Beetles had fed on the pollen of cycads and they were among the first to transfer their attentions to the early flowers like those of magnolias and waterlilies. As they moved from one to another, they collected meals of pollen and paid for them by becoming covered in excess pollen which they involuntarily delivered to the next flower they visited.

One danger of having both eggs and pollen in the same structure is that the plant may pollinate itself and so anticipate and prevent cross-fertilisation, the very purpose of all these complexities. This possibility is avoided in the magnolia, as in many plants, by having eggs and pollen that develop at different times. Magnolia stigmas will accept pollen as soon as the flower opens. Its own stamens, however, do not produce their pollen until later when its eggs will have been cross-fertilised by exploring insects.

The shape of pollen
Pollen grains of insect-pollinated plants like the daisy (below, × 1900) are rough, and cling to an insect's legs. Wind-pollinated plants like timothy grass (left, × 800) also have sculptured pollen surfaces. So characteristic are these shapes that it is possible to tell the species of a grain by looking at it under the microscope.

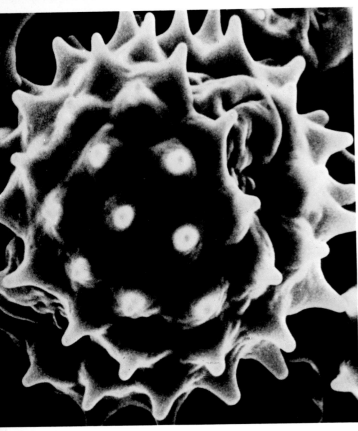

The appearance of the flowers transformed the face of the world. The green forest now flared with colour as the plants advertised the delights and rewards they had on offer. The first flowers were open to all that cared to alight on them. No specialised organs were required in order to reach the centre of the magnolia flower or the water-lily, no particular skill was needed to gather the pollen from the loaded stamens. Such blooms attracted several kinds of insects – bees as well as beetles. But a variety of visitors is not an unmitigated advantage for they themselves are also likely to call upon several kinds of unspecialised flowers. Pollen of one species deposited in flowers of another is pollen wasted. So throughout the evolution of the flowering plant, there has been a tendency for particular flowers and particular insects to develop together, each catering specifically for the other's requirements and tastes.

Right from the times of the giant horsetails and ferns, insects had been accustomed to visiting the tops of trees to gather spores as food. Pollen was an almost identical diet and it still remains a most important prize. Bees collect it in great baskets on their thighs and take it back to their hives for immediate consumption or for turning into pollen bread which is an essential food for their developing young. Some plants, among them species of myrtle, produce two kinds of pollen, one that fertilises their flowers, and another of a particularly tasty kind that is designed only to be eaten.

Other flowers developed a completely new bribe, nectar. The only purpose of this sweet liquid is to please insects so greatly that they become addicted to it and devote all possible time during the flowering season to collecting it. With this they recruited a whole new regiment of messengers, particularly bees, flies and butterflies.

These prizes of pollen and nectar have to be advertised. The bright colours of flowers

A honey-baited messenger service
A bee approaches a flower of meadow sage. As it enters, its head pushes against a plate hinged to the stamens, which swing down and stamp pollen on its abdomen. The stigma, projecting from the upper lobe, lengthens with age, so if the bee next enters an older flower, it will brush against the stigma and so deliver the pollen. This prevents a flower being fertilised by its own pollen and ensures, as far as possible, cross-fertilisation.

make them conspicuous from considerable distances. As the insect approaches, it is provided with markings on the petals which indicate the exact placing of the rewards they seek. Some flowers intensify their colours towards the centre or introduce another shade altogether – forget-me-nots, hollyhocks, bindweed. Others are marked with lines and spots like an airfield to show the insect where to land and in which direction to taxi – foxgloves, violets, rhododendrons. There are more of these signals than we may realise. Many insects can perceive colours of the spectrum that are invisible to us. If we photograph what seem to be plain flowers with film that is sensitive to ultra-violet light, we can see many more such markings on the petals.

Scent is also a major lure. In most cases, the perfumes that insects find attractive, such as lavender, roses, and honeysuckle, please us as well. But this is not always the case. Flies feast on rotting flesh. Flowers that enlist them as pollinators must cater for their tastes and produce a similar smell and often do so with an accuracy and pungency far beyond the endurance of the human nose. The maggot-bearing stapelia from southern Africa not only reeks dreadfully of carrion but reinforces its appeal to flies by producing flowers with wrinkled brown petals covered with hairs that look like the decaying skin of a dead animal. To complete the illusion, the plant generates heat to mimic the warmth produced by corruption. The whole effect is so convincing that flies not only visit flower after flower, transporting the stapelia's pollen, but even complete the activity for which they visit real carrion – laying their eggs on the flower just as they do in a carcass. When these hatch, the maggots find that they are not provided with a meal of rotting meat but only an inedible petal. They die from starvation, but the stapelia has been fertilised.

Perhaps the most bizarre imitations of all are those of some orchids that attract insects by sexual impersonation. One produces a flower that closely resembles the form of a female wasp complete with eyes, antennae and wings and even gives off the odour of a female wasp in mating condition. Male wasps, deceived, attempt to copulate with it. As they do so, they deposit a load of pollen within the orchid flower and immediately afterwards receive a fresh batch to carry to the next false female.

Sometimes insects are disinclined to collect pollen, preferring nectar, or will pack it away in places from which it is not easily dislodged. Then the flowers have to have devices to force their pollen on the insect. Some blooms have become obstacle courses during which their visitors are pummelled by stamens and bombarded with pollen before they are able to leave. Broom flowers are so constructed that as the insect lands, the stamens, packed under tension inside a sealed capsule of petals, shoot out and strike the underside of the bee, covering its furry abdomen with pollen. The bucket orchid from Central America drugs its visitors. Bees clamber into its throat and sip a nectar so intoxicating that after they have taken only a little they begin to stagger about. The surface of the flower is particularly slippery. The bees lose their foothold and are shot into a small bucket of liquid. The only way out of this is up a spout. As the inebriated insect totters up, it has to wriggle beneath an overhanging rod which showers it with pollen.

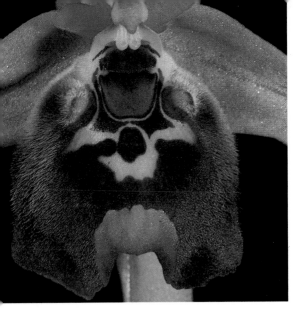

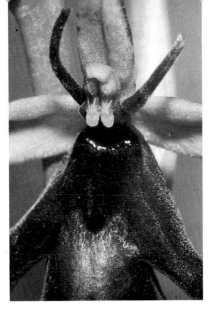

The orchids that pretend to be wasps

The flowers of the bee orchid, the spider orchid and the fly orchid (left) mimic female wasps, developing false antennae, eyes, wings and even a similar perfume. Each species attracts a particular species of wasp. A male settles on the flower and moves its body as if in copulation, collecting pollen in the process. An Australian orchid, Cryptostylis (below), attracts male ichneumon wasps by a similar technique. The wasp has to position himself very precisely on the flower in order to 'mate' with it. This is the one position in which the pollen will fasten on his abdomen.

Sometimes plant and insect become totally dependent one upon the other. The yucca grows in Central America. It has a rosette of spear-shaped leaves from the centre of which rises a mast bearing cream-coloured flowers. These attract a small moth with a specially curved proboscis that enables it to gather pollen from the yucca stamens. It moulds the pollen into a ball and then carries it off to another yucca flower. First it goes to the bottom of the flower, pierces the base of the ovary with its ovipositor and lays several eggs on some of the ovules that lie within. Then it climbs back up to the top of the stigma rising from the ovary and rams the pollen ball into the top. The plant has now been fertilised and in due course, all the ovules in the chamber at the base will swell into seeds. Those that carry the moth's eggs will grow particularly large and be eaten by the young caterpillars. The rest will propagate the yucca. If the moth were to become extinct, the yuccas would never set seed. If the yuccas disappeared, the moth's caterpillars could not develop. Each is inextricably in the debt of the other.

One further debt is clear. Flowers, exquisitely perfumed and graced with a multitude of colours and shapes, bloomed long before man appeared on the earth. They evolved in order to appeal not to him but to insects. Had butterflies been colour-blind and bees without a delicate sense of smell, man would have been denied some of the greatest delights that the natural world has to offer.

The hazards of interdependence

A female yucca moth has gathered a ball of pollen from a yucca flower and now kneads it into the stigma of another. Only she has the correctly shaped mouthparts to extract pollen from yucca stamens and she visits no other kind of flower, so yucca pollen is not wasted. The moth claims a price. She has already pierced the ovary below the stigma and laid an egg on one of the ovules within. When her caterpillar hatches, it will have food immediately available. But this efficient system has its dangers. Should either partner disappear, the other will be unable to reproduce.

A modern-style leaf, 50 millions years old

The first tall trees appeared 350 million years ago. They reproduced asexually with spores and had a separate sexual generation living on the ground. During the next 200 million years coniferous trees arrived, bearing seeds that eliminated the two-generation method of reproduction. Then suddenly flowers appeared for the first time, and a great number of new species of plants developed, exploiting this new technique. This leaf (right), though it drifted down to the bottom of an inland lake in Utah about 50 million years ago, is almost indistinguishable from those of the living flowering tree, the sycamore.

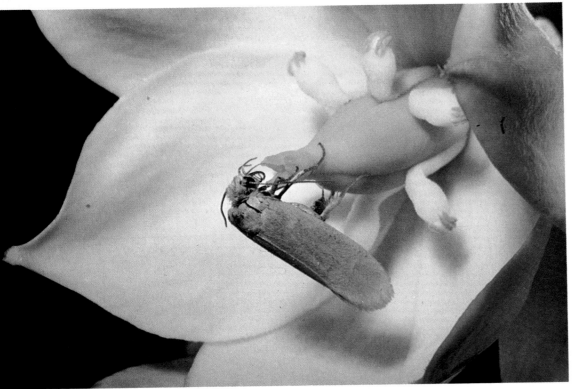

4. THE SWARMING HORDES

The insect body works best on a small scale, but some kinds assemble in millions and become super-organisms

By any standards, the insect body must be reckoned the most successful of all the solutions to the problems of living on the surface of the earth. Insects swarm in deserts as well as forests; they swim below water and crawl in deep caves in perpetual darkness. They fly over the high peaks of the Himalayas and exist in surprising numbers on the permanent ice caps of the Poles. One fly makes its home in pools of crude oil welling up from the ground; another lives in steaming hot volcanic springs. Some deliberately seek high concentrations of brine and others regularly withstand being frozen solid. They excavate homes for themselves in the skins of animals and burrow long winding tunnels within the thickness of a leaf. The number of individual insects in the world seems beyond any computation, but someone has made the attempt and concluded that at any one time, there must be something of the order of one thousand million thousand million. Put another way, for every human being alive, there are about a million insects – and together these insects would weigh about twelve times as much as he does.

There are thought to be about three times as many species of insect as of all other kinds of animal put together. So far, man has described and named about 700,000 of them and there are certainly three or four times as many still unnamed, awaiting the attentions of anyone who has the time, patience and knowledge to sit down and make a systematic review of them.

The doomed legions
The number of eggs laid by a female insect varies enormously. Some beetles lay only a dozen or so. Most, however, produce them in vast numbers. A fruit fly lays as many as 3000 and a moth 500 or 600. Moths whose caterpillars eat only one kind of leaf carefully place their eggs on the appropriate food plant, which they themselves as adults have never tasted. Since many females often lay on a single plant, the result can be a plague of many thousand caterpillars, like these swarming over the branch of a tree in Mexico. Nearly all will die long before they reach maturity, but if only four or five caterpillars out of every thousand survive, the population level of the species will be maintained.

The swarming hordes

Insect portraits

The scanning electron microscope reveals in extraordinary detail the structures that insects use to find their way about. All insect eyes contain many elements that combine to form a single picture. Sight is particularly important to those that fly, and a bee's eyes (below left, magnified 26 times) each contain over 6000 elements. Hairs, which pick up pollen, sprout all over them. The gall gnat (below right, magnified 295 times) is only 1.5 millimetres long. Its tiny eyes have fused in front of its head to give it a view of its surroundings that is poorly detailed, but takes in a complete panorama.

A three-part body encased in chitin

Yet all these different forms are variations of one basic anatomical pattern: a body divided into three distinct parts – a head bearing the mouth and most of the sense organs; a thorax filled almost entirely with muscles to operate the three pairs of legs beneath and, usually, one or two pairs of wings above; and an abdomen carrying the organs needed for digestion and reproduction. All three sections are enclosed within an external skeleton made, primarily, of chitin. This brown fibrous material was first developed over 550 million years ago by the early segmented creatures, the trilobites and crustaceans. Chemically, it is similar to cellulose and in its pure form it is flexible and permeable. The insects, however, cover it with a protein called sclerotin that makes it become very hard. This produces the heavy inflexible armour of the beetles, and mouthparts sharp and tough enough to gnaw through timber and even cut metals like copper and silver.

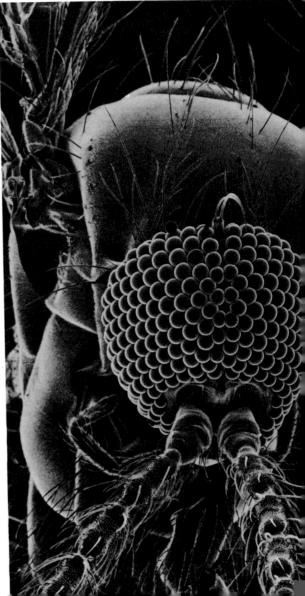

A brown ant from Argentina

The eye of the Argentinian brown ant (right, magnified 65 times) is bigger than a gnat's, but is not as acute as that of the honey bee, for it has far fewer elements. This species crawls over the ground and relies less on sight and more on the sensations of touch and smell provided by its waving antennae. Ant eyes vary greatly in size. Those species living underground are often totally blind, whereas tree ants may have eyes that rival those of a bee.

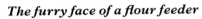

The furry face of a flour feeder

This small moth (left, magnified 150 times) swarms over sacks of flour in warehouses. Its white fluffy body is covered with scales which even extend over the top part of its proboscis, coiled beneath its head.

How the flour moth sucks up its food

The proboscis of the flour moth (above) is formed from its two mandibles enormously elongated. In action, these two halves are zipped together by lines of hooks forming a tube up which the moth can suck its food.

101

The swarming hordes

Escape from an unexpandable prison

The chitinous external skeleton seems to be particularly responsive to the demands of evolution. Its surface can be sculpted without affecting the anatomy beneath. Its proportions can be varied to take on new shapes. Thus the chewing mouthparts possessed by the early cockroach-like insects have been turned by their descendants into siphons and stilettos, saws, chisels, and probes that when unreeled are as long as the whole body. Legs have become elongated into catapults that can propel an insect two hundred times its own body length, broad oars to row it through water or thin hair-tipped stilts with a wide stride that enables their owners to walk on the surface of pools. Many limbs carry special tools moulded from the chitin – pouches for holding pollen, combs for cleaning a compound eye, spikes to act as grappling irons and notches with which to fiddle a song.

An external skeleton, however, is also an unexpandable prison. The trilobites in the ancient seas escaped its restrictions by moulting. That is still the insects' solution. The process may sound wasteful, but they conduct it with great economy. A new chitinous shell, much folded and compressed, forms beneath the old one. A layer of liquid separates the two and this absorbs the chitin from the old skeleton, leaving the hard sclerotised parts connected by the thinnest of tissues. The chitin-rich liquid is then absorbed through the still permeable new skeleton back into the insect's body. The old plates split apart, usually along a line running down the back, and the insect hauls itself out. As it does so, its liberated body begins to swell, filling out the folds in the new skin. In a short time, the chitin hardens and becomes strengthened by new deposits of sclerotin.

Primitive insects like the bristletails and the springtails do not change their shape very much as they grow. They merely moult as they increase in size. Even after they have begun to breed they may continue to moult. The ancient winged insects – cockroaches, cicadas, crickets and dragonflies – also grow in a similar way, their early forms closely resembling the adults except that they lack wings. These will only appear after the final moult, except in damsel flies which take two moults, one very soon after the other, to bring their wings to perfection. Even when these insects adopt a very different existence for the first part of their lives, they do not change their form very radically. The larvae of the cicadas that sit shrilling on trees spend their lives below ground sucking sap from roots. Larval dragonflies hunt on the bottom of ponds, grabbing worms and other small creatures with long protrusible mouth-parts. Yet in both the image of the adult is discernible.

More advanced insects, however, undergo such wholesale changes that there is no possible way of linking the larva to the adult except by watching the creature make the change. Maggots turn into flies, grubs into beetles, and caterpillars into butterflies.

The job of a grub, a maggot or a caterpillar is simply to eat. Its body is dedicated to this one purpose. Since it will not breed in this form, it has no sexual equipment; since it has no cause to attract a mate, it needs no mechanisms to send out call-signals whether by sight, smell or sound, nor any sense organs to receive such messages; and as its

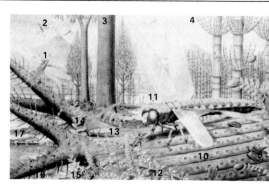

LIFE IN THE COAL FORESTS OF 300 MILLION YEARS AGO

Today's coal consists of the petrified remains of luxuriant vegetation which grew in freshwater swamps over much of the Northern Hemisphere.

The coal measures of Europe, in particular those of Commentry in France, have yielded the fossils which enabled scientists and an artist to reconstruct this scene of 300 million years ago. The dominant trees were giant club-mosses 30 metres or more high. There were thickets of horsetail trees, up to 15 metres high, with whorls of leaves on their hollow stems. Smaller horsetails grew in the undergrowth, with early ferns which bore nut-like seeds on their fronds. There was a great variety of winged insects in the coal forests. The giant dragonfly-like Meganeura with a wingspan of 70 centimetres is the largest insect known. The omnivorous cockroaches of the forest floor, such as Dictyomylacris, differed little from some modern species, but the related Stenoneura was a high-flying predator. Oedischia and Cnemidolestes are relatives of grasshoppers, but the six-winged Stenodictya and Mischoptera belong to groups with no living descendants. Lurking in the water were amphibians such as Phlegethontia and Gephyrostegus.

parents have gone to considerable trouble to ensure that when it hatches it is surrounded by the great quantities of the particular food it requires, it needs no wings. Its one essential tool is a pair of efficient jaws. Behind these it requires little more than a bag. In order that this may swell easily to accommodate its rapidly accumulating tissues, this simple body is not burdened with a heavy sclerotised skeleton but enclosed in a thin and to some degree stretchable cuticle. When this can expand no further, it splits and is rolled off, like a nylon stocking from a leg.

With no shell and thus no firm base on which to attach a muscle and nothing rigid to serve as a lever, these larvae are indifferent movers. They cannot hop, skip or jump. Indeed, they can barely manage even to run, for they have only soft ballooning tubes to serve as stumpy legs. These however are quite efficient enough to move the eating machines that are their owners from one mouthful to another.

A vivid warning

Many grasshoppers are relished by birds, but this one has an acrid taste. With such a defence, it is important to give advance warning. Otherwise a bird may deliver a lethal peck before it discovers its mistake.

Mimicry by teamwork

Insects without poison sometimes mimic those that have it. These newly hatched plant bugs (below) cluster in a formation that resembles a type of slug moth caterpillar related to the one at the bottom of the page.

A stinging defence

The caterpillar of the spiny oak slug moth (left) bristles with barbed filaments which can give a painful sting. To proclaim their effectiveness, the caterpillar is vividly coloured so no one will touch it accidentally.

A back-to-front defence
Some butterflies, like this one from Malaysia (above), have developed a false head on the rear wings, complete with eye-spots and antenna-like filaments. It baffles an attacking bird by apparently taking off backwards.

The colours of caterpillars
The lack of shell leaves the larvae unprotected. This is of little consequence to grubs and maggots, for they hold their interminable feasts out of sight of the rest of the world, gobbling their way around the heart of an apple or gnawing tunnels in wood, shielded by what they are eating. But caterpillars, most of which banquet out in the open, must look to their defences.

They are unexcelled as camouflage artists. Those of geometer moths are coloured and patterned to look like twigs and when they hold themselves with one end in the air at exactly the same angle to a stem as other twigs springing from it, they are virtually impossible to detect. A swallowtail caterpillar, sitting on a leaf, is certainly conspicuous, being green with irregular flecks of white, but it is seldom noticed for it looks like a bird dropping. If disguises are penetrated, many caterpillars have a second line of defence.

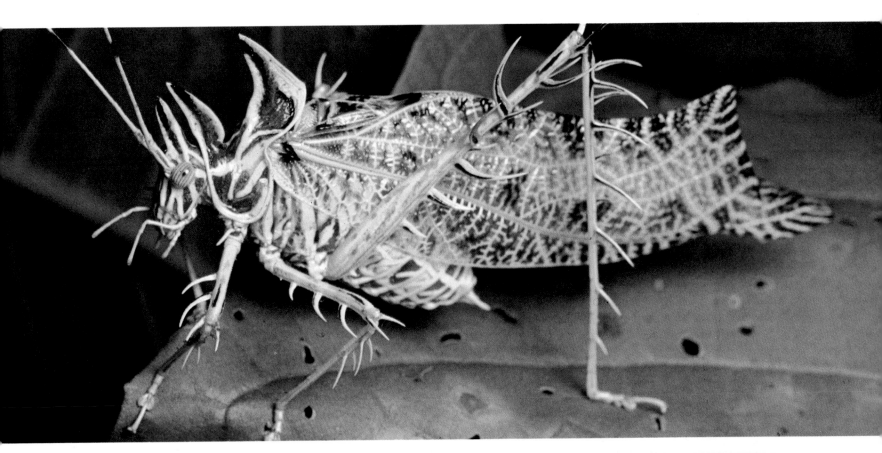

Opposite ways of achieving the same end
The outline of a body can be dangerously revealing. The katydid grasshopper (above) sprouts filaments over its legs, and so becomes invisible in vegetation. The orchard butterfly caterpillar (right) remains obvious, but is ignored because it looks like a bird dropping.

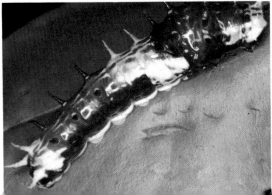

The swarming hordes

A gallery of vegetable disguises

Many insects are restricted to only one species of plant because that is the only one which can supply them with the particular kind of food that they need. Some of them, however, may also be confined there by the very perfection of their disguises. They mimic the colour and the shape of the twigs, leaves, thorns and flowers of their chosen plant with such accuracy that if they strayed on to any other kind, they would immediately become so conspicuous that they would be eaten.

The pussmoth caterpillar browses head-down on leaves. Its body colour is exactly that of its food plant, but if an intruder shakes the branch and alarms it, the caterpillar suddenly lifts its head from its meal, exposing a scarlet face. Simultaneously it protrudes a pair of blood-red filaments from its tail and squirts formic acid. Another moth caterpillar in South America can be even more alarming. It has a large round mark on either side of its head and when agitated, weaves its front end from side to side, making itself look unnervingly like a wide-eyed snake.

Some caterpillars have made themselves unpleasant to eat. They are covered with poisonous hairs or have within their bodies a particularly acrid-tasting substance. It pays these creatures to be very conspicuous indeed. The hairy ones are mustachioed and bewhiskered in the most flamboyant way, the unpleasant-tasting ones have skins brilliantly coloured in reds, yellows, blacks and purples – all warnings to potential

BUFF TIP MOTH, EUROPE

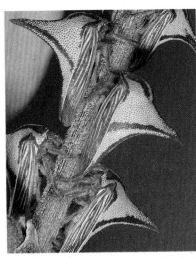

THORN BUG, THE AMERICAS

TREE HOPPER, MEXICO

JUNGLE GRASSHOPPER, BORNEO

MOTH CATERPILLAR, AUSTRALIA

LEAF MANTIS, COSTA RICA

Ambushed by a pink mantis

Disguises not only conceal the timid but also allow the aggressive to lurk undetected. All members of the mantis family are hunters and many have developed elaborate disguises. Some are shaped like leaves. The species above, from Africa, is found on both green and pink flowers, but each individual manufactures pigments in its skin to match its chosen background. So when an insect, in this case a bee-fly, visits the flower, lured by the pollen and nectar, it ends in the arms of the unseen mantis.

hunters that these morsels, for one reason or another, are not worth eating. There are also some that are actually innocuous but are seldom eaten for they have taken a rather complicated gamble by copying the colours of poisonous caterpillars to delude aggressors into giving them as wide a berth as the creatures they mimic.

Many insects spend nearly all their lives as such larvae, growing bigger and building up their stores of food. Beetle grubs may spend seven years boring through wood and extracting nutriment from that most indigestible of materials, cellulose. Caterpillars munch for months, packing away their favourite leaves before the season finishes. But sooner or later, they all reach their full size and the end of the allotted span of their larval lives.

The amazing change inside the pupa

Now comes the first of two highly dramatic transformations. It is a change some make in private. Only the larvae of insects have silk glands. They have used them already to build communal tents, to extrude life-lines guiding them over plants, or ropes to let themselves down from one twig to another. Now, however, many spin silk to conceal themselves from the world. The silk moth caterpillar surrounds itself with a fuzzy bundle of threads, the moon moth constructs a cocoon with a silvery metallic sheen, the ermine moth builds an elegant casket of lacy net. Many butterfly larvae produce no covering at all. They simply spin a silken sling to attach themselves to a twig.

As soon as they are settled, they discard their caterpillar costumes. Their skin splits and rolls down revealing a smooth, brown hard-shelled object, the pupa. The only movement it makes is an occasional twitch of its pointed tip. It has spiracles along its side through which it can breathe, but it neither feeds nor excretes. Its life seems to have been suspended. Internally, however, the most profound changes are taking place. The entire body of the larva is being dismembered and reassembled.

When the larva first began to develop from the egg, its cells were segregated into two groups. Some stopped dividing after a few hours and remained generalised in form and in dense clusters. The rest continued to build the body of the caterpillar. After it hatched and had begun to feed, its body cells divided no more. Instead they simply enlarged until, by the time that the caterpillar was full grown, they were vastly distended and many thousand times bigger than their original size. All this time, the other cell clusters remained tiny and inactive. But now, inside the pupa, their moment has come.

The giant cells of the caterpillar's body die and the dormant cell clusters suddenly begin to divide rapidly, nourishing themselves on the soup of the disintegrated caterpillar body. The insect, in effect, is eating itself. Slowly it builds a new body of a completely different form. Its shadowy features can be seen on the outside of the brown pupa, like the anatomy of a mummy, vague beneath its wrappings. Indeed, the name 'pupa' derives from a Latin word meaning a doll, for at this stage the insect within seems to be wrapped in swaddling clothes.

A defended retreat
This caterpillar of an Australian moth is protected throughout its larval life by poisonous bristles (left). Nor does it lose their help during the long time that it hangs as a pupa, for when it begins to spin (above) it weaves around the bristles of its discarded skin so that they project through its translucent silken shroud ready to give a painful prick to those that interfere with it.

The actual emergence usually takes place under cover of darkness. A butterfly pupa, hanging from a twig, begins to shake. A head with two huge eyes and antennae pressed over its back pushes through the pupa at one end. Legs come free and begin clawing frantically in the air. Slowly and laboriously, with frequent pauses to gather strength, the insect hauls itself out. The thorax emerges and there on its back are two flat crumpled objects, its wings, wrinkled like the kernel of a walnut. The insect jerks itself free and hangs on the empty pupa case, its body trembling. With convulsive

Transformation

The heliconius caterpillar eats the leaves of the passion flower. When fully grown, it pupates. Months later, the pupa splits and a crumple-winged creature crawls out. Its wings expand and the butterfly is ready for flight.

THE CATERPILLAR

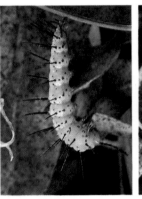

THE PUPA

THE WINGS SPREAD

THE BUTTERFLY BEGINS TO EMERGE

The swarming hordes

shudders, it begins to pump blood into a network of veins within the baggy wings. Slowly they expand. The blurred pattern on the outside of the wings enlarges and becomes focused. Blotches swell into miraculously detailed eye-spots. Within half an hour the wings are fully distended so that the two sides of the bag meet flat against one another enclosing the veins between them. The veins themselves are still soft. If the tip of one of them were damaged now, it would drip blood. But gradually the blood is drawn back into the body and the veins harden into rigid struts that will give the wing its strength. All this time, the wings have been held together like the leaves of a book. Now, as they dry and become rigid, the insect slowly moves them apart to show the world for the first time the unblemished perfection of its shimmering colours and awaits the dawn of its first day.

ELINA ICARUS (ABOVE)

MORPHO (BELOW)

RED ADMIRAL

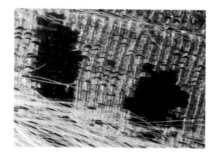

CHRYSIRIDIA

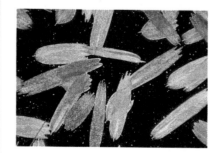

MEADOW BROWN

SWALLOWTAIL (RIGHT)

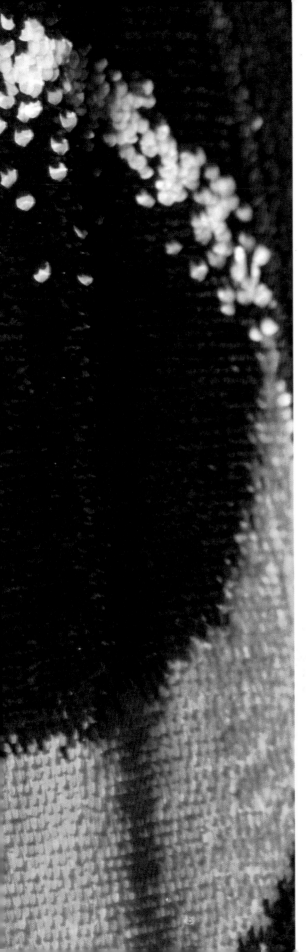

The race to find a mate

The insect can now spend the calories that it so assiduously collected and stored when it was a larva. For the adult, feeding is of secondary importance. Mayflies and some moths do not even have mouthparts. Others sip nectar during their brief lives to renew their energies and to provide sustenance for egg production, but none need to feed in order to build their bodies; their growth has come to an end. The urgency of their lives now is to find a mate.

Butterflies do so by displaying their wings, the marvellous intricate patterns of which are statements of identity so that individuals may recognise those with whom mating can be fertile. Unlike their larvae, butterflies have excellent compound eyes – the male usually has even bigger ones than the female, for it is he that does the searching. Since their eyesight is sensitive to parts of the spectrum that are invisible to us, butterflies' wings, like flowers, have even more complex patterns than our ultra-violet-blind eyes can see. Colours and designs created by tiny scales, overlapping like tiles on a roof, come from pigments, or the effects of microscopic structures which split the light falling on them and reflect back only a part of it. Drop a spot of highly volatile liquid on such a wing and the colours disappear as the liquid occludes the physical structure, only to reappear as it evaporates and the light is splintered once more.

These dazzling wings, iridescent and downy, trailing pennants and variegated with transparent windows, veined, fringed and spotted with the loveliest of colours, are the most elaborate visual summons in the whole insect world. Other insects use other media and produce equally complex and powerful signals. The cicadas, crickets and grasshoppers rely on sound. Most insects are deaf, so these groups have had to develop not only voices but ears. Cicadas have circular eardrums on either side of the thorax. Grasshoppers listen with their legs. They have two slits on the first pair of thighs which lead to deep pockets. The common wall between these forms a membrane which is the equivalent of an eardrum. The angle at which sound strikes the slits greatly affects the strength in which it reaches the drum, so the grasshopper, by waving its legs in the air, can discover the direction from which a call is coming.

Some grasshoppers produce their whirring trills by sawing the notched edge of their hind legs against a prominent strengthened vein of the wing. Cicadas, the loudest of insect singers, have a much more complicated apparatus. Their abdomen contains two chambers, one on each side. The inner wall of each chamber is stiff and when it is moved in or out, it makes a click, as the lid of a tin may do. In the abdomen behind there is a muscle which can pull the wall back and forth up to 600 times a second. The noise this produces is greatly amplified for most of the abdomen behind the vibrating plate is also hollow and two large rectangular sections of the abdominal wall are stiffened to form resonators. These are covered by flaps projecting from the lower edge of the thorax that can be opened or closed so as to increase or dampen the sound like shutters

The overlapping tiles of a butterfly's wings
The wings of a large butterfly may hold a million and a half scales. Some are grooved and structured internally so they split light and produce a shining iridescence. Others contain pigments. Transparent ones overlapping coloured ones produce the effect of soft velvet or burnished metal, and some wings have patches with no scales at all that form windows.

on an organ. Each species produces its own characteristic call. Some sound like a mechanical saw hitting a nail, some like a knife being ground on a wheel or fat dropping on an overheated plate. So loud are these calls that a single insect can be heard half a kilometre away and a chorus of them can set a whole forest ringing and echoing.

There is much more detail in these penetrating songs than our ears can detect. We cannot hear a break between sounds of less than one tenth of a second. Cicadas are able to distinguish intervals of one hundredth of a second. When they sing, they vary the frequency of individual clicks from, for example, two hundred a second to five hundred a second and do so in a regular rhythmic way. By such changes and rhythms, which are totally inaudible to us, an individual can identify the call of its own species; a male can avoid the territory of another singing male and a female fly towards it.

Mosquitoes also use sound as a mating call, but they produce and receive it in a way that is all their own. The female, beating her wings as fast as 500 times a second creates the high-pitched hum that is so unsettling as you lie in camp trying to go to sleep without a mosquito net. The male is able to detect this sound with an ear-drum at the base of his antennae, which vibrate in sympathy with this one frequency, and so fly towards her.

Other insects attract their mates by exploiting the third of the senses, smell. The females of some moths produce an odour that the males can detect with large feathery antennae. So sensitive are these organs and so characteristic and powerful is the scent, that a female has been known to summon a male from eleven kilometres away. At such a distance there must be as little as one molecule of scent in a cubic yard of air, yet it is sufficient to cause the male to fly in pursuit of its source. He needs both antennae to do this. With only one, he cannot establish direction, but with two he can judge on which side the scent is stronger and so fly steadily towards it. A female emperor moth, in a cage in a wood, transmitting a perfume undetectable to our nostrils, has attracted over a hundred huge males from the surrounding countryside within three hours.

So, by sight, sound and smell, the adult insects attract their mates. Male grasps female sometimes only briefly, sometimes for several hours. The couple may even fly through the air awkwardly, in tandem. Then the female lays her fertilised eggs and provisions them. Butterflies seek out the one plant whose leaves provide the only food their caterpillars will eat; beetles bury pellets of dung and lay their eggs within them; flies feverishly deposit their eggs within carrion; and solitary wasps catch spiders, paralyse them with a sting and stack them around their eggs so that the young larvae will have fresh meat awaiting them. The female ichneumon wasp has an ovipositor like a dagger with which she drills a hole in wood at the exact point where she has detected a beetle grub lying beneath. She pierces it and deposits an egg in its soft body. Her larva when it hatches will eat the grub alive. And so the whole process of egg-larva-pupa-adult begins once more.

The insect body has produced an almost infinite variety of forms. In one characteristic only does there seem to be a limitation – size. The largest living insects today are not longer than about 30 centimetres – the wingspan of exceptional specimens of the atlas

The voice of a grasshopper
The long, hind legs of a grasshopper enable it not only to jump, but also to sing. They each carry a row of pegs, here magnified 1700 times. The grasshopper rubs these energetically against its wing covers, making them vibrate and produce its shrilling call.

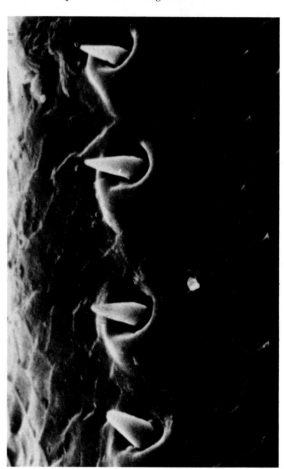

The ear of a mosquito
The movable antennae on either side of the male mosquito's head, magnified 120 times, act as stereo aerials. Each hair on them can resonate to the female's whine and is connected by a separate nerve to a sense organ in the base of the antenna.

moth, and the length of the largest of the stick insects. The biggest of beetles, the hercules, reaches the same sort of size and weighs as much as 100 grams. But that is only the size of a mouse. Why are there not beetles as big as badgers and moths as large as hawks? The restricting factor is their breathing technique. Like their close relatives, the early millipedes, the insects rely on tracheae, the system of tubes opening to the outside by a line of spiracles along the flank and running to every part of the body. They work by gaseous diffusion. Oxygen in the air that fills the tracheae is absorbed through the wall at the extremities. Similarly carbon dioxide is expelled from the tissues and diffuses away. The system works excellently over short distances but as the length of the tube increases, so it becomes more and more inefficient. Some insects are able to improve the circulation of air by inflating and deflating their abdomens with a muscular pumping action. The tiny tracheae, which are strengthened with rings in their walls, do not flatten but shorten and expand like concertinas. A few insects have tracheae that swell into thin-walled balloons which are depressed and expanded as the abdomen pumps up and down. But even with all these refinements the system becomes ineffective above a certain size; the gigantic cockroaches and murderous man-hunting wasps of nightmares are physiological impossibilities.

A fly's wedding gift

Dance-flies, only about 1 centimetre long, feed by sucking the bodies of other insects dry with their stiletto-like proboscises. At breeding time, thousands assemble in dancing swarms, rising and sinking in the air. To these ceremonials, the male fly brings an insect that he has captured and killed, and presents it to a female. While she feeds from it, he copulates with her.

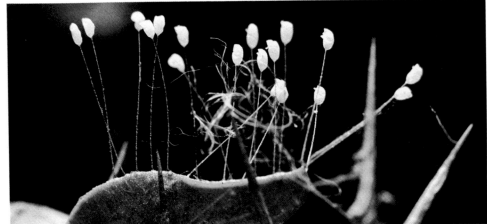

A false fungus

The female lacewing attaches each of her eggs to leaves and twigs with a long hair-like stalk (above). They look so like the fruiting bodies of a fungus that for some time scientists classified them as such.

Floating eggs

Midges assemble over fresh water in immense mating swarms, millions strong. The females lay their eggs in floating rafts (left). The coating on each egg swells in the water to form a slippery transparent mucilage which provides excellent protection. When the eggs hatch, the larvae bury themselves in the mud at the bottom.

The nose of a moth

The atlas moth of Asia is one of the largest of all flying insects, big specimens having a wing span of 26 centimetres. It is also one of the moths that signal to their mates by smell. This one is the male, who carries huge feathery antennae to detect perfumes in the air over great distances, where there may be only one molecule of scent in a cubic yard of air. The female, who produces the scent, has antennae that are small and unbranched.

The swarming hordes

A super-organism

But the insects have, in another way, transcended even the limitation of scale. All over the tropics stand termite hills. In some parts they are grouped in swarms hundreds strong, as thick as herds of grazing antelope. The comparison is not entirely fanciful. A single hill contains a colony of several million insects. They are not just creatures that have elected to live together in one communal dwelling, like human beings in some gigantic tower block. For one thing they are all one family, the offspring of a single pair of adults. For another, all of them are incomplete creatures, incapable of independent life. The workers, scurrying along the tracks through the undergrowth, are blind and sterile. The soldiers that stand guard beside the entrances to the colonies and rush to defend any breach in the walls, are armed with jaws so huge that they can no longer gather food for themselves and have to be fed by the workers. At the centre of the colony lies the queen. She is imprisoned within massive earthen walls from which she can never escape for her body is far too big to get through the passages that lead to it. Her abdomen is swollen into a white heaving sausage, 12 centimetres long, from which she produces eggs at the almost unbelievable rate of 30,000 a day. She too would die if she were unattended. Teams of workers deliver food to her at one end and collect eggs from the other. The only sexually active male, the wasp-sized king, stays alongside her and he too is fed by the workers.

The link that binds all these individuals together into one coordinated super-organism is a highly effective system of communication. Soldier termites sound an alarm by beating their large hard heads on passage walls. Workers, having a new source of food, leave a scent trail which their blind fellows can easily follow. But the most pervasive and important mechanism is based on chemical substances called phero-mones. This circulates instructions throughout the colony with great speed. All the members of the colony continually exchange food and saliva with one another. Workers pass it from mouth to mouth or gather one another's excrement in order to reprocess the partially digested food and extract the last particle of nutriment from it. They in turn

An animated egg factory
All the members of a termite colony are the offspring of the queen except for her mate. Throughout her life, she lays thousands of eggs a day. She may live for 50 years and produce more eggs than any other creature.

BEETLES THAT LIVE ON A MOUSE

Sexton beetles are rare examples of insects that remain in pairs to care for their young. They can quickly bury a small mammal or bird to provide food for the whole family while the larvae grow.

Burial begins A dead mouse may be found within an hour by a beetle. A potential mate soon arrives, and together they begin its burial.

The tomb When the mouse is buried the pair mate. Unlike most male insects which leave after mating, the male sexton helps to rear the young.

The eggs The beetles remove the mouse's skin, and the female lays her eggs above. A pool of liquid food is made from part-digested mouse flesh.

Feeding The larvae move to the food pool where they are fed by their parents. When the larvae pupate, the adults burrow out and fly away.

EAST AFRICAN SAVANNAH

WEST AFRICAN FOREST

SOUTHERN AFRICAN SAVANNAH

Building for the weather
The shape of termite mounds
varies according to climate. In
hot dry areas, they have tall
towers with ventilating flues. In
wet areas, they are given a new
mushroom roof each season.

feed both the larvae and the soldiers. They also attend the queen lying in her chamber, constantly licking her rippling flanks and collecting drops of liquid from her anus. In the course of this they gather the pheromones that she produces and circulate them quickly throughout the colony. The young larvae hatching from the queen's eggs are potentially of both sexes, but the queen's pheromones with which they are fed by the workers inhibit their development and they remain sterile, wingless and blind. The soldiers too produce a pheromone, contributing to the mix of chemical messages circulating in the colony and in a similar way preventing the development of any of the larvae into soldiers.

But pheromones only remain effective for a short period. If the number of soldiers in the colony falls, then so does the amount of soldier-pheromone in circulation. The queen not only produces pheromones but is fed them, so she receives all this information. Whether she responds to it by producing special kinds of eggs destined to be soldiers or whether the workers treat the existing larvae in a special way is not certain. It probably varies in any case from species to species, but in such a situation, more soldiers are certainly reared until the correct proportion is restored. The queen will also, on occasion, change the nature of her pheromone excretion so that the development of the larvae is no longer suppressed and they become sexually mature. Then the dark corridors of the colony are filled with rustling hordes of young winged adults. In some species, the workers open special slits in the sides of the mound and build take-off ramps in front of them. These exits are guarded by the soldiers. Then, just after the beginning of the rains, the soldiers stand aside and flying termites pour out of the clefts and swirl into the sky like smoke.

The occasion is a bonanza for the animals of the bush. Frogs and reptiles gather beside the exits snapping at the insects as they flock out on to the ramps. As the exodus proceeds, the sky becomes filled with birds wheeling back and forth. The termites seldom go far. They come down on to the ground and immediately their wings break off close to the thorax. They have served their function. Now male chases female across the ground in determined processionary dances. Those few that escape being eaten form pairs and go off together to find a nest site in a crevice in the ground or a crack in a tree. There they construct a small royal cell. Within it, they copulate and lay eggs. The first larvae to hatch have to be fed by their parents, but once they are big enough to forage for food and build walls of mud, the royal couple devote themselves entirely to the production of eggs and the colony is founded.

Termites are closely related to those ancient insects, the cockroaches. Like them, their bodies do not have a waist and the young larvae are markedly similar to the adult winged form. They grow by a series of moults but never pass through a pupal stage or undergo transformation. Like cockroaches too, the termites feed almost entirely on vegetable matter. There are some two thousand different species of them. Twigs, leaves and grass are standard fare. Some specialise in eating timber, boring away inside posts and logs until they become hollow shells that collapse at the touch of a finger.

Termites construct some of the greatest of all insect buildings. A termite fortress,

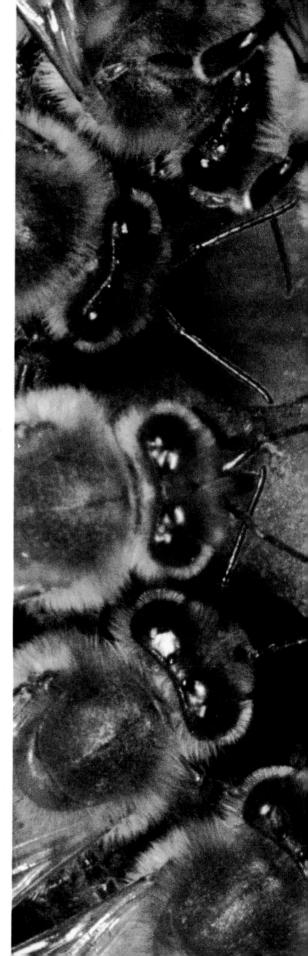

walled, buttressed and castellated, may contain ten tons of mud and stand three or four times as tall as a man. Several million inhabitants, busily running their errands within, can cause overheating and produce a foul oxygen-poor atmosphere so ventilation is of the greatest importance. Around the margins of the hill, the termites construct tall, thin-walled chimneys which stand out from the sides like ribs. No insects live inside these huge smooth-walled ducts. Their only function is ventilation. As the sun warms their walls, the air inside becomes hotter than that in the centre of the nest. It rises, drawing exhausted air from the central galleries and the deeper parts of the hill, creating a circulation. The thin, external walls of the chimneys are porous and so oxygen from the outside atmosphere diffuses in. The air, thus refreshed, rises to the top of the nest and then circulates back down other passageways. In very hot weather, the workers descend tunnels that go deep into the ground to the water table. Each returns carrying a crop full of water with which it wets the walls of the main part of the nest. The heat evaporates the water and this also lowers the temperature. By such devices, the worker termites manage to keep a very even temperature inside the nest.

In Australia, the compass termites build castles in the shape of huge flat chisel blades, always with their long axis pointing north and south. Such a shape exposes the minimum possible area to the ferocious midday sun but catches the maximum of the feebler rays in the early morning and evening when, especially in the cold season, the termites are grateful for warmth. In West Africa and other areas where there is heavy rain, the colonies build nests like mushrooms with flat roofs which shed the water. Termitologists have made great advances in working out how the pheromone communication system controls and coordinates a colony's activities, but no one has yet explained how the millions of blind workers, each carrying a tiny pellet of mud, manage to construct between them such ingeniously designed, efficient and large-scale buildings.

The dance of the worker bee

One other group of insects has taken to the colonial life on a scale that is comparable to the termites: those with narrow waists, two pairs of transparent wings and powerful stings, the wasps, bees and ants. Wasps still show the stages by which colonialism may have developed. Some hunting wasps live entirely solitary lives. The female, after mating, builds her own mud cells, lays an egg in each, provides it with a collection of paralysed spiders for food and then abandons it. In other species, she stays beside the nest and when the young hatch, brings food to them day after day. In yet others, the females build their individual nests close to one another but, after a few weeks, some abandon their own constructions and join others in building theirs. Eventually, one female becomes dominant and lays all the eggs while the others concentrate on building cells and collecting food for her.

The dancing courtiers around a queen

A queen bee, wherever she moves in the hive, is surrounded by an ever-changing entourage of workers tending her, exchanging liquid food with her and, with it, chemical messages. These messages keep all the inhabitants of the hive informed about the state of the hive's population levels and of the absence or presence of the queen.

The swarming hordes

Work in the nursery

Some cells in the bees' combs are used to store supplies of food – honey and pollen. In others, the queen lays eggs that develop into female workers or male drones, whose function is to fertilise the queen's eggs. Specially large cells are built for rearing queens.

WORKERS ON THE COMB. THE LIGHT-COLOURED CELLS CONTAIN POLLEN

LEFT: AN EGG AT THE BOTTOM OF A CELL

ABOVE: PUPAE OF WORKERS IN THEIR CELLS

The honeybees have taken this basic arrangement and elaborated it to an extreme degree so that they live in colonies of many thousands. The single queen stays on the comb, laying eggs in the cells that have been built by the workers to receive them. Once again, the community, like that of the termites, is bound together by a system of chemical messages, the pheromones, perpetually circulating within the hive, which inform all the inhabitants of the state of the population and of the absence or presence of the queen. But bees have other ways of communicating between one another. Flying through the air to find food, they cannot leave scent trails behind them for other members of the colony as earth-bound termites do. Instead, they dance.

When a worker bee arrives back in the hive after visiting a newly opened honey-laden flower, it performs a special dance on the landing platform in front of the entrance to the colony. First it scurries round in a circle, then it bisects it, emphasising the importance of this last movement by waggling its abdomen and making a particularly excited kind of buzzing. Its track points directly to the source of food. Workers observing it and about to leave on their own foraging, immediately fly off in the direction indicated. Then the dancer goes into the hive to dance again. The farther it goes from the entrance before it dances, the farther away is the flower that it has discovered. The combs of the nest, in both wild and domestic colonies, are vertical so now the waggle-steps cannot point directly to the food source. Instead they refer to the sun. If the bee crosses the circle vertically, then the target is in line with the sun. If it is, say, 20° to the right, then the dance will be 20° to the right of the vertical. The workers surrounding the dancer watch it closely, remember the message and fly away to find the flower. When they return with the honey, they too will perform a dance so that, in a very short time, most of the worker force in the hive is actively gathering honey from the new source.

The most complex and highly evolved forms of colonialism in the insect world are those created by the relations of the wasps and bees, the ants. Some live within plants, stimulating the tissues of their hosts to provide them with custom-built homes by growing special galls, hollow stems or thorns with swollen bases. The leaf-cutting ants of South America build vast underground nests and set off from them, day and night, in long columns to demolish trees, removing every shoot, leaf and stem, section by tiny section and transporting them all back to their underground chambers. They do not eat this material but chew it up to form a compost on which they cultivate a fungus. The tiny white fruiting bodies of this provide them with their food. Tree ants in Southeast Asia construct nests by sewing leaves together. A party of workers haul two leaf edges together, gripping one with their jaws and the other with their feet. Other workers on the inside begin the work of sewing them together. No adult insect can produce silk, so these ants bring young larvae to the site, holding them between their jaws and giving them little squeezes so that the larvae will produce their silk. The builders then move these living tubes of glue back and forth across the leaf junction until the two edges are joined by a silken fabric. In Australia, the honeypot ants collect nectar and force-feed it to workers of a special caste until their abdomens are distended to the size of peas and their skins stretched so thin that they are quite transparent. The workers then hang them up by their forelegs in underground galleries, like living storage jars.

Most ants, however, are carnivorous. Many prey upon termites, raiding the great mounds and doing battle with the soldiers. If they win, they devour the defenceless workers and larvae. Others, in one of the most astounding forms of social behaviour, make slaves of a different kind of ant. They raid the nest, collect the pupae and carry them back to their own colony. When these hatch, the young ants serve their captors, collecting food and feeding it to them, for the slave-makers have such large jaws that they cannot feed themselves.

The most terrifying ants of all are those that make no nest but wander through the countryside seeking prey. In South America they are known as army ants, in Africa as drivers. They march in columns so long they may take several hours to pass one spot.

Co-ordinated construction teams

The green tree ant of Southeast Asia builds its nest from the growing leaves of trees. Teams of workers, standing on one leaf, grip the margin of a neighbouring one with their jaws and then, gripping with the tiny hooks on their feet, walk backwards, so hauling the two leaves together. Meanwhile, other teams carrying silk-producing larvae work from inside the nest, making the junction permanent with a fabric of silk.

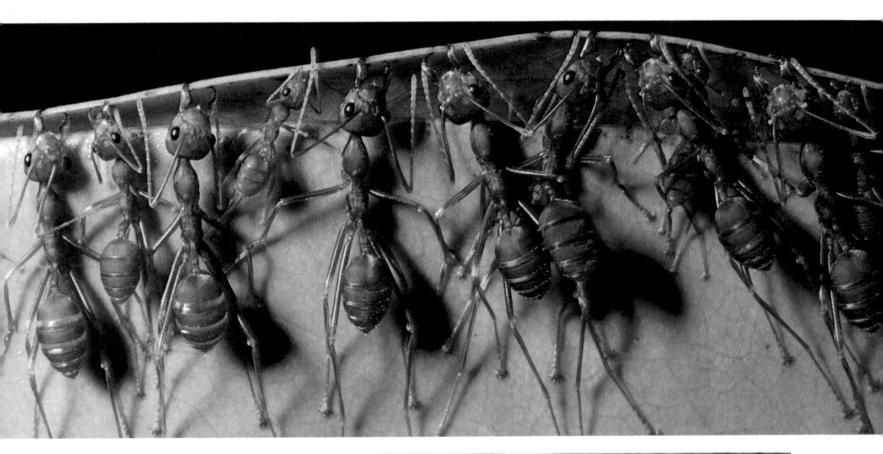

Compost for the garden

The leaf-cutting ants of South America cut leaves into fragments and carry them along well-worn paths, sometimes for dozens of metres, to their nests. But they do not eat the leaves. Instead they chew them into compost on which they cultivate tiny mushrooms to be harvested later as food.

The blind warriors

Army ants avoid bright sunlight. If they have to cross a patch, they build themselves walls to provide shade, and sightless soldiers mount guard on top, their huge jaws apart ready to slice anything that interferes.

The marching queen

The queen of the army ants cannot grow to the gigantic size of a queen termite for she has to be able to march day after day. But when her army bivouacs, her ovaries suddenly begin to develop. After a week, she begins to lay, producing as many as 300,000 eggs within a few days. A week later, they all hatch and the army resumes its march.

At the head, the soldiers fan out to forage. Behind comes a column of workers, scurrying along a dozen or so abreast, many of them carrying larvae. Where the column crosses an exposed area its flanks are guarded by soldiers, armed with huge jaws and totally blind. They stand in rows, stiffly craning themselves upwards, jaws apart, ready to bite anything that interferes with them. When the hunters at the head of the column discover prey, they swarm all over it, cutting it apart. Grasshoppers, scorpions, lizards, young birds in their nests, anything that cannot get out of the way is attacked. Anyone in West Africa who takes it upon himself to tether an animal or restrict its movement, must pay regard to the possibility of an attack by one of these armies. I once made a large collection of snakes there. We had Gaboon vipers, puff adders, spitting cobras as well as harmless species like tree snakes and pythons. We kept them in a mud-walled hut and posted a guard to keep watch, armed with a can of paraffin. Only that, poured on the ground and set alight, will deflect a raid by the ants. In spite of all precautions, one afternoon a column got into the hut through a hole in the wall at the back. By the time we had discovered what had happened, the ants were attacking the entire collection, swarming over the snakes within their gauze-covered boxes. Infuriated by the painful bites, the snakes were striking dementedly and uselessly at their tiny attackers. Every one had to be taken out and held down while we picked off the ants that were sinking their jaws between the scales. In spite of all we could do, several snakes died as a result of the ant bites.

Army ants march and forage for weeks, day after day. The larvae produce pheromones and these, circulating within the army, stimulate it to keep on the move. Eventually, the larvae begin to pupate and no longer exude their chemical messages. Then the army bivouacs. There may be as many as 150,000 individuals and they cluster in a vast ball between the roots of a tree or beneath an overhanging stone. Clinging to one another, they make a living nest from their bodies, complete with passageways along which the queen moves and chambers where the pupae are deposited. The queen's ovaries now begin to develop and she swells greatly. After about a week, she begins to lay. During the next few days, she may produce 300,000 eggs. They hatch very quickly and at the same time a new generation of workers and soldiers emerge from the stored pupae. These now begin to secrete their characteristic pheromone and once more the army, with its ranks swollen by these new recruits, is stimulated to march off to war.

If the super-organism created by a colony of termites can be compared to an antelope, then the disciplined aggressive columns of the army ants must be reckoned to be the insect equivalent of a beast of prey. Hungry for food, relentless in pursuit of it and capable of killing most creatures that cannot run from them, they terrorise the bush. The small size of their individual members is of no consequence. Thousands can be lost without seriously affecting the vigour and power of the army. In these columns, the insects have created a super-organism that is among the most powerful, feared and long-lived of all the animals in the forest.

The insects colonised the land before the vertebrates and they still exploit every organism on it. There is no known species of plant that is not attacked in one way or another by them. In some parts of Africa, they regularly claim three-quarters of all the crops grown by man. Even in the United States where farmers have the most sophisticated means of protecting their crops, insects claim over ten per cent of them. The boll weevil infests cotton fields and millionaires go bankrupt. The Colorado beetle spreads over a potato crop and a human population starves. Not only do insects rob man of his food, but they suck his blood, bury themselves in his skin and infect him with all kinds of serious diseases. He, in retaliation, has launched against them the most concentrated onslaughts that he has been able to devise. He attacks them with flame-throwers. He bombards male insects with radioactive particles to sterilise them and then releases them in huge numbers, so condemning generations of females to infertility. He synthesises new chemical poisons of the most lethal kind and sprays the countryside wholesale. And yet, in spite of all his efforts and ingenuity, of huge expenditures of labour and money, he has so far failed to exterminate a single insect species.

An army raid

When marching, the ant army fans out over a broad front, swarming over the ground and through the trees. Here a detachment of soldiers has discovered the nest of a solitary wasp built beneath the leaf of a palm tree. The adult wasp has flown off and escaped, but her grubs are immobile and defenceless. The soldiers have entered the cells and plundered them. Those at the top of the picture are carrying away the last of the grubs.

5. THE CONQUEST OF THE WATERS

Sea-living creatures developed a backbone, then jaws and eventually an air bladder, and so became superb swimmers

Among the sea anemones sticking limply to the rocks exposed at low tide, there are, almost everywhere in the world, rather different lumps of jelly. Anemones tend to dribble a little water from their centres if you press them. Tread on one of these others and a jet of water squirts up your leg. These shapeless lumps are called, in consequence and not unreasonably, sea squirts. Underwater, the difference between them and the anemones is easy to see. The anemone has a flower-like cluster of tentacles around a single central opening; the sea squirt has no tentacles and two openings connected to each other by a U-shaped tube. The whole structure is surrounded by a thick coat of jelly. Underwater and dilated, this dull bag becomes beautiful. One European species is nearly transparent, with trembling circlets of hazy blue around each opening and thin rings of muscle strengthening the inner tube so that the creature looks like the most delicate bubble of Venetian glass. The jacket of jelly of other species is opaque and coloured pink or gold. Some grow in clusters like grapes; some are larger, more elongated and solitary.

They are all filter-feeders, drawing water in through one opening, passing it through a bag with slits in its wall, and then discharging it back into the sea through the other tube. Food particles, sticking to the wall of the bag, are swept down to its bottom by cilia and into a little gut which leads out of the bottom of the bag and curves round to join the exhalant tube.

It is a simple structure and an unobtrusive life. But these creatures have the most sophisticated relatives. Their most ancient forebears were connections of the echinoderms, but their cousins, much more unexpectedly, became the ancestors of the first

---

A superb swimming machine
A shark is propelled by powerful sideways beats of the back half of its body and its tail. The horizontal paired fins at the front are fixed and prevent it from nose-diving. This magnificent design for swimming was first perfected about 350 million years ago. About 240 species of shark are alive today, including the great white shark that grows to over 6 metres.

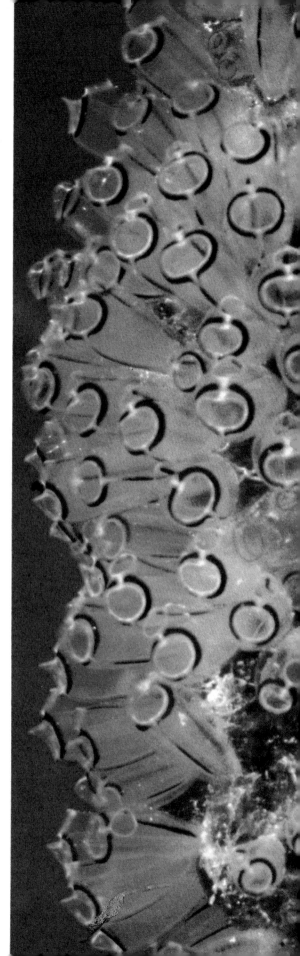

of the backboned animals, the vertebrates. The evidence for this conclusion is hard indeed to discover in the adult sea squirt, but more visible in its larva. This looks like a tiny tadpole. The globular front part contains the U-shaped tube and the beginnings of the gut. It swims by wriggling its tail which is stiffened by a thin rod, running from the tip to the middle of the body. This, at least, is some suggestion of a backbone, but the larva does not keep it for very long. After a few days, the little creature glues its nose on a rock, loses its tail and settles down to a life of sedentary filtration.

The sea squirt larva is not the only filter-feeder with such a significant rod in its back. Another somewhat larger sliver of flesh, the lancelet, also has one. This creature, shaped like a slim leaf about 6 centimetres long, lives half-buried in the sand of the sea floor. Its front end projects above the surface and carries a little coronet of tentacles around the opening through which it sucks in water. It, too, has a very simple body. There is nothing that could reasonably be called a head; merely a small light-sensitive spot; no heart, only a number of pulsating arteries; no fins or limbs, only a slight dilation at the hind end like the flight feathers of an arrow. Even so, in this simple organism you can see the first hint of a fish. The flexible rod in its back which runs the entire length of its body carries transverse bands of muscles. When the creature contracts them rhythmically, a series of waves runs down its body. These push water backwards and in consequence the lancelet moves forward. It swims.

When assessing family connections, the anatomy of a larva is obviously as valid a piece of evidence as that of the adult. Indeed, it is usually even more significant, for animals have the remarkable tendency to repeat during their individual development the stages through which their ancestors passed during evolutionary history. Larval termites look like those most primitive of insects, the bristletails; larval horseshoe crabs are visibly segmented and so reveal a similarity with the trilobites difficult to perceive in the adult; the free-swimming molluscan larva looks very like that of the segmented worms and thus suggests a link between the two groups. So it is not unreasonable to regard the similarity between the lancelet and the larval sea squirt as evidence of a relationship. But which form was ancestral? Was it a creature like a sea squirt which gave rise to the more mobile lancelet-like form by producing descendants that abandoned the stationary condition and reproduced during the hitherto larval stage? Or was the lancelet-shape the more ancient pattern from which animals like sea squirts developed by sticking their heads to rocks, losing their muscles and retreating into as undemanding a life-style as the seas can provide?

For many years, the first proposition was believed to be the case. Today comparative studies of the whole sea squirt group, which is large and varied, have led to the belief that the second possibility is the correct one. And now, very recently indeed, confirmation has come from that remarkable treasury of early fossils, the Burgess Shales in the Canadian Rockies. There, lying among trilobites, brachiopods and bristle-worms,

---

A colony of sea squirts

There are some 2000 species of sea squirts in the world. Some grow singly and large – over 10 centimetres long. Others, like these from the Caribbean, are smaller and live in groups. An individual, after it has settled down, sends out a bud from its base which develops into another which in turn buds again until a whole interconnected colony is formed.

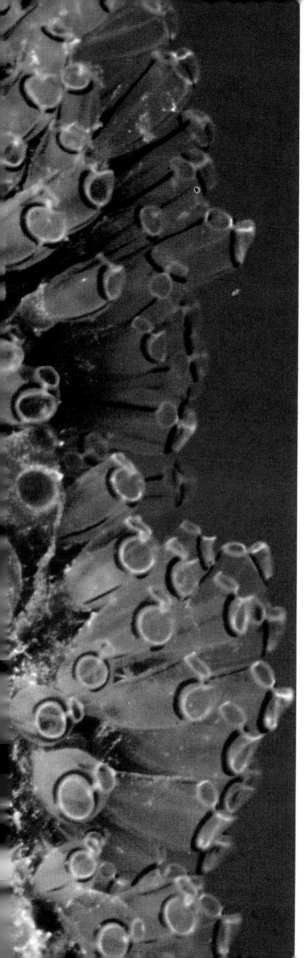

in the mud of the seas of 550 million years ago that had yet to see a finned or backboned swimmer, has been found the impression of a creature very similar indeed to the living lancelet.

Jawless proto-fish evolve

Another larva provides evidence for the next step in vertebrate history. The rivers of Europe and America contain animals that look like the lancelet, though they are somewhat larger, up to 20 centimetres long. They, too, live in holes in the mud and filter-feed. They are jawless, blind and without fins except for a fringe around the tail. For many years they were thought to be adult creatures, given a special name, ammocoete, and classified as obvious relatives of the lancelet. Then it was discovered that they are only the larvae of a very well-known animal. They eventually leave their holes, develop true eyes and long rippling fins along the back, grow to the size of an eel and turn into lampreys.

You might be excused for thinking, at first sight, that the lamprey is a true fish. But it is not. It has a kind of backbone, in the form of the flexible rod, but it does not have jaws. Its head ends in a large circular disc in the centre of which is a tongue covered with sharp spines. There are two small eyes with a single nostril between them leading to a

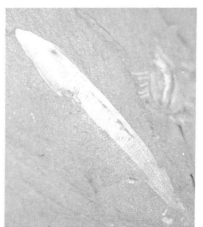

An ancestor of the fish?

The lancelet (above) is a simple filter-feeder, but it has a flexible rod in its back which, together with several other features, suggests that it might be the kind of creature from which fish and all backboned creatures developed. This is a view strengthened by the discovery of a fossil very like it (left) in the Burgess Shales in Canada, which contain fossils of creatures that lived in the seas before the arrival of fish with backbones.

The rasping sucker of a lamprey

Even though lampreys lack jaws, they are very effective eaters of flesh. The sucker-like mouth is studded with short, sharp teeth and once the lamprey gets a grip on a fish, it is extremely difficult to dislodge. Glands in its mouth produce a saliva containing an anti-coagulant so that the wound made by the sucker remains open and the blood which forms much of the lamprey's diet continues to flow.

blind sac, and on either side of the neck a row of gill slits. With the disc, the lamprey clamps itself on the flank of a fish, and with the tongue it rasps off the flesh, eating the fish alive. Lampreys and their wholly sea-living relatives, hag-fish, are still common. Sometimes their population in American rivers reaches plague proportions. The swarming lampreys consume not only dead or sickly fish but set upon otherwise healthy ones. Their tiny eyes, rubbery sucking mouths and writhing bodies scarcely make them attractive from a human point of view. Nonetheless they deserve notice and respect, for their forebears were once the most advanced and revolutionary creatures in the seas. Their remains have now been found in rocks that are about 540 million years old, very nearly as ancient as the Burgess Shales. These newly discovered pieces of evidence are only fragments of scales, but they can be identified because they match those from complete skeletons that have been found in later rocks.

A simple swimmer

The lamprey may, at first sight, look like an eel (above), but it is very much simpler in structure than any true fish. Not only has it no jaws, but also no limbs, no skull, no scales and no true bones. Its gills have no covers, and water taken in at the mouth passes through muscular pulsing pouches and is expelled through a line of seven holes down each flank. Lampreys are capable swimmers, moving with snake-like undulations, but for much of their lives they are transported by the fish on which they are feeding (left).

These jawless proto-fish were mostly quite small, the size of large minnows, and they were heavily armoured. In some forms, the whole of the head and body was encased in a cuirass of bony plates. In front there were two eyes and a single central nostril, like that of a lamprey. From the back of the armoured box projected a muscular tail fringed by a fin. By beating this they could drive themselves through the water but their heavy fore-parts must have kept their heads low and close to the bottom. Although one or two species had simple flaps of skin in the shoulder region, most had no fins at all, apart from their tail, to help them navigate or give precision to their movements. So few were able, initially, to swim consistently above the sea floor. Those waters remained the domain of the jellyfish and other floating invertebrates. Without jaws, the proto-fish could not prey upon shelled molluscs. Their lot was to nuzzle their way across the sea bottom, sucking up mud and refuse through their simple circular mouths, filtering out the edible particles and expelling the rest through the slits on either side of their throats.

The little proto-fish, however, survived and increased in numbers and variety. Their heavy armour-plating may have originated as a way of disposing of the salts derived from their food which accumulated in their bodies. It also must have given them much-needed protection, for the seas at this time were tyrannised by the huge, 2-metre-long sea scorpions armed with massive claws which fed on the smaller creatures of the sea floor.

The heavy deposits of bone in the head regions of some of these proto-fish make possible the most detailed investigation of their anatomy. By taking a whole series of slices through the fossilised skull, the shape of the cavities that contained the nerves and blood vessels can be charted. Such research has shown that one group of these creatures had a brain very like that of the living lamprey. It also had a balancing mechanism contrived from two arching tubes at right angles to one another in a vertical plane. The liquid within them, moving over their sensitive inside surface, enabled the proto-fish to be aware of its posture in the water. Living lampreys have a very similar mechanism.

Some of these creatures now grew to a considerable size, 60 centimetres or so. Many were quite mobile, with suits of scales, and were probably able to make sallies into the waters well above the sea floor. None of them, however, could be described as skilled swimmers. The single median fins down the mid-line of their backs or undersides prevented them from spinning in the water and gave them a degree of stability, but none had paired lateral fins.

The first vertebrate hunters prowl the seas

So the situation remained for a hundred million years. During this immensity of time, the corals arrived and began to build reefs, and the segmented animals developed into forms that soon would leave the sea and establish a bridgehead on land. Important changes also took place among the proto-fish. The slits in the sides of their throats,

Almost a fish – from the sandstones of Scotland

This creature, 15 centimetres long, comes from the 420-million-year-old red sandstones of Scotland. It pushed itself over the sea floor by beating the flexible rear half of its body. On top of its bony head-shield, it had a pair of eyes and a single central nostril, and beneath it simple gill openings like a lamprey.

which had originated as filtering mechanisms, were walled with thin blood vessels so that they also served as gills. Now the pillars of flesh between them were stiffened with bony rods and the first pair of these bones, slowly over the millennia, gradually hinged forward. Muscles developed around them so that the front ends of the rods could be moved up and down. The creatures had acquired jaws. The bony scales in the skin which covered them grew larger and sharper and became teeth. No longer were the backboned creatures of the sea lowly sifters of mud and strainers of water. Now they could bite. Flaps of skin grew out of either side of the lower part of the body, helping to guide them through the water. These eventually became fins. Now they could swim. And so, for the first time, vertebrate hunters began to propel themselves with skill and accuracy through the waters of the sea.

It is possible to walk across the sea bed of that time, 350 million years ago. In the flat desert land of a cattle station in Northwestern Australia, close to a place called Gogo by the aborigines, rises a line of strange steep-sided rocky bluffs, 300 metres high. Geologists, mapping the site, found it difficult to understand how they could have been shaped by the normal forces of erosion. When they came to examine their gully-riven fronts in detail, they discovered that the rocks were full of the remains of coral. Once sea had covered this area and these cliffs were reefs, bordering deep fish-filled lagoons. Rivers from the land behind had flowed through them, their muddy waters, in which coral cannot grow, maintaining gaps in the reefs. Slowly the lagoons filled with accumulated sediments and the sea retreated. Eventually the level of the whole Australian continent rose. Rain and rivers eroded the soft sandstones that had filled the lagoon basin, scouring them away so that today the reefs are exposed once more, high and dry, facing not the sea but desert covered with clumps of spinifex grass and stunted mulga trees. At their foot, on what was once the sea floor, lie nodules. From the ends of some of them project groups of thin blade-like bones. The dead bodies of lagoon fish had occasionally acted as a focus for the processes of petrification. The surrounding sand and mud became particularly hard, staying solid while the rest of the deposit crumbled. The geologists took the nodules back to the laboratory and soaked them for months in acetic acid. Gradually the rock fell away and exposed, in astonishing perfection, the first complete and undistorted skeletons of the world's earliest true fish.

There were many different species. Most, like their predecessors, were armoured in some way, with heavy scales attached to bony plates in the skin, and they had fearsome teeth in their jaws. They were also acquiring an internal bony skeleton including the beginnings of a vertebral column running longitudinally through the body and surrounding the primitive flexible rod. All of them had well-developed lateral fins, usually in two pairs, the pectorals just behind the throat, and the pelvics near the anus. There were, however, many variations. One form had a whole line of lateral fins; the pectoral fins of another were encased in tube-like bones and looked like probes or props. Some were bottom-living, some free-swimming, and one or two were gigantic, reaching two metres in length. In the face of this competition, nearly all the jawless proto-fish died out.

KEY TO THE ILLUSTRATION

1 Moythomasia (ray-finned fish)
2 Mimia (ray-finned fish)
3 Griphognathus (lungfish)
4 Ctenurella
5 Chirodipterus (lungfish)
6 Montecaris (crustacean)
7 Eastmanosteus
8 Bothriolepis

THE EARLIEST REAL FISH OF 350 MILLION YEARS AGO

An artist's reconstruction of some of the earliest true fish has been drawn from the superbly preserved remains found in the rocks of the Gogo Formation, Western Australia.

The remains of more than 20 species of fish have been found at Gogo, together with crustaceans, molluscs and corals. Most of the fish lived on the sea-bed, although the predatory Eastmanosteus which measured between 0.5 and 1.3 metres probably ventured into mid-water. The heavily armoured Bothriolepis poled its way along the bottom with stilt-like pectoral fins, and fed by passing a continuous stream of mud through its digestive tract. Ctenurella also lived near the bottom but was more choosy in its eating habits. The lungfish were at the height of their evolution. They lived both in the sea and in fresh water, and many species breathed primarily through their gills. Present in smaller numbers are ray-finned fish such as the 15 centimetre long Moythomasia and the similar-sized Mimia, illustrated here as a shoal of young. More numerous than any of the fish were crustaceans called phyllocarids. A specimen of Montecaris, which grew up to 70 centimetres, has been illustrated.

The fish that developed skeletons of cartilage

At about this time, a pronounced split appeared in the fish dynasty. One group developed which lost nearly all the bone in their skeletons but developed instead, cartilage, a softer, more elastic and lighter material. The descendants of this group are the sharks and rays. The reduction of bone in their bodies doubtless made them considerably lighter, size for size, than their ancestors. Even so, flesh and cartilage is heavier than water and to remain above the sea floor, the sharks have to keep swimming. They drive themselves through the water in the same way as their ancestors, by the sinuous motion of the rear half of their bodies and the powerful thrash of their tails. But with the thrust coming from the back the body is nose-heavy and liable to dive downwards. To correct this, the shark has two pectoral fins spread horizontally like the vanes of a submarine or the wings of a rear-engined aircraft. They are, however, relatively inflexible. The shark cannot suddenly twist them to a vertical position to act as brakes. Indeed, a charging shark cannot stop, it can only swerve away to one side. Nor can it swim in reverse. Furthermore, if it stops beating its tail it sinks. Some species, indeed, take rests at night and slumber on the sea floor.

A skin covered with tiny 'teeth'

A shark's skin feels prickly because it contains numberless small scales, each with a bony base and a sharp tip of dentine covered with enamel, which project through the surface. The huge teeth of the jaw have just the same structure and originate in the same way. Sharks breathe by taking water in through the mouth, passing it over gills and expelling it through open gill slits on either side of the head, just in front of the fins. Some species may do this with such force that breathing helps to propel them through the water.

One branch of the cartilaginous fish has adopted this position more or less permanently, abandoning the energy-consuming labour of perpetually beating their tail to maintain themselves in mid-water. These are the rays and skates. Their bodies have become greatly flattened, their pectoral fins enlarged into undulating lateral triangles that have taken over the function of locomotion. The tail, therefore, need no longer beat. It has lost nearly all its muscles and become thin and whip-like, sometimes with a poisonous spine at the end. The method works very well but it does not provide the

The soaring elegance of the manta ray

Rays (right) differ from sharks in having their gill slits on the underside of their bodies, beneath their greatly enlarged wing-like pectoral fins. The gill slits can be clearly seen on this manta ray as it soars close to the surface of the water, filter-feeding. A sucker fish is clinging to its head.

speed possessed by the free-swimming sharks. But the rays do not need that. They are not active hunters and live largely on molluscs and crustaceans which they grub up from the sea floor and crush in their mouths which open on the underside. This position of the mouth is convenient for feeding but causes considerable complications in breathing. Sharks take in water through the mouth, pass it over the gills and out through slits. Were the rays to collect their water in the same way, it would be full of mud and sand. So instead they have two openings on the upper surface of the head that take in water and lead it straight to the gills. It is then expelled on the underside through the gill slits.

One kind of ray, the manta, has reverted to swimming in the surface waters. The lateral extensions of its body enable it to remain aloft with only a small expenditure of energy using the water for support as gliders use air. But undulating side-wings are not such powerful propellants as a thrashing tail, so the manta cannot swim as fast as its shark cousins or rival them as hunters. Instead it sails slowly through the water on flapping wings, sometimes as much as 7 metres across, its immense slot-like mouth wide open, gathering by filtration the floating shoals of crustaceans and small fish.

A fossil descendant of the sharks
The first fossil sharks appear in rocks laid down about 400 million years ago, but skates and rays, like this one from the Green River formation of Wyoming, do not begin to develop until 200 million years later.

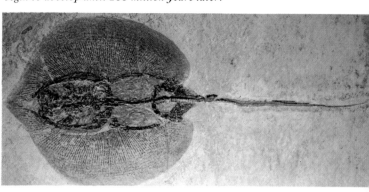

The conquest of the waters

Bladders of air help fish to control their depth of swimming

The second great group of fish retained bone in their skeleton and it is their descendants that today dominate the waters of the world. They arrived, in a round-about way, at a very effective solution to the problem of weight. During the early period when most fish had heavy bone-based scales in their skins, several families spread from the open seas into coastal waters and eventually into shallow lagoons and swamps. Breathing for a fish is difficult in such places. The warmer water becomes, the less oxygen it can hold in solution. The open seas never become hot, but shallow waters do and in consequence become oxygen-poor. So when fish came to live there, they had to develop additional ways of getting oxygen. The bichir, a heavy-scaled fish of ancient ancestry which lives in the rivers and swamps of Africa, still demonstrates the method they adopted. It regularly rises to the surface of the water and takes a gulp of air. This goes down its throat and into a pouch that opens from the top wall of its gut. This has walls thick with blood capillaries which absorb gaseous oxygen. The bichir, in fact, not only has gills like any other fish, but a lung as well.

But an air-filled pouch brings other incidental advantages. It provides buoyancy and this, for the bulk of the descendants of these air-breathing pioneers, became a more important faculty. With a bag of air inside them, they could float in the water without perpetually labouring their tails. Eventually bony fish with swim bladders appeared in the sea. Many different species with such structures swam in the lagoons beside the Gogo reefs, together with other more antiquated kinds.

Soon species appeared which could fill their air-bags by diffusing gas into them from the blood rather than by rising to the surface and swallowing air. In some cases the tube connecting the bag to the gut became no more than a solid thread. So the fish acquired a swim-bladder.

The techniques of swimming were now revolutionised. By diffusing gas in or out of the bladder or expelling it directly through the connecting tube, a fish could accurately control its level in the water. Its pectoral fins, freed from the job of providing lift, could be used to give great refinement to the fish's control of movement, and swimming skills reached near-perfection.

Water is eight hundred times as dense as air, and the slightest bump or protuberance on the body can cause drag, more even than it would on a bird or an aeroplane. So the high-speed ocean-going fish – tuna, bonito, marlin, mackerel – have most marvellously streamlined bodies, sharply pointed in the front, swelling quickly to maximum diameter and then tapering elegantly to the two-bladed symmetrical tail fin. The whole of the rear half of the fish is in effect the engine for this propeller. Banks of muscles are attached to the backbone so that the tail can be beaten from side to side with unflagging strength throughout the fish's life. The scales, so heavy and rough in the early forms, have now become thin and smoothly fitting or been lost altogether. The surface is

The mysteries of schooling

Many fish swim in vast shoals like these shad. This may be for safety, for a multitude of darting shapes tends to baffle a predator. The members of a shoal co-ordinate their movements, swerving and turning as one. How this is achieved is still not properly understood, though the lateral line which enables a fish to 'feel at a distance' plays a part.

lubricated by mucus. The plate covering the gills fits closely to the body and the eyes barely bulge above the smooth contours. The pectoral and pelvic fins and the dorsal along the crest of the back play no part in propulsion. They serve only as rudders, stabilisers or brakes. When the fish is moving at speed and they are not required they are clamped to the fish's side, fitting exactly into depressions and grooves on the surface. And along the top and bottom edge of the body, on either side of the tail, are tiny triangular blades that serve as spoilers to prevent turbulence.

The perfection of this design is attested by the fact that species belonging to quite different families of fish have adopted it and thus bear a strong resemblance to one another. Once a species moves into the open ocean, and relies on great speed, either to eat or to avoid being eaten, the ruthless selections of evolution refine the fish's shape towards this, the most efficient, the most mathematically perfect form for the purpose.

Some species of surface-living fish, in danger of being out-paced by the hunters, have turned their pectoral fins to a special purpose. When pursued, they shoot out of the water and spread greatly elongated, broad pectorals which until now have been held close to the body. As the air catches the membranes, the fish is lifted above the waves and it glides for hundreds of metres leaving its pursuers baffled. Sometimes as they fly, they tilt their bodies so that their tails dip into the water, and beat a further few strokes, renewing their impetus and extending their flight.

When a fish takes to the air

Fleeing from a predator, a flying fish takes off from the water at about 30 kph. Flying fish may glide hundreds of metres to lose their pursuers, but some predators continue the chase and seize their prey at the end of its flight. Sea birds also attack flying fish in mid-air.

The conquest of the waters

Finned ferocity

The pike (right) hangs in the water with such stillness that it is easily ignored. If a small fish swims carelessly close, one beat of the pike's tail and a gape of its jaws will bring death. The dragonfish (below) also eats other fish. The splendour of its fins seems to conceal its character and acts as an ambush. The fins also protect it from interference by bigger creatures for each sharp ray is loaded with poison. If an intruder comes too close, the dragonfish warns it off by quivering its fins.

Inflating for defence

The puffer fish (below) is one of a whole group that have developed an extremely unusual form of defence. It is able to gulp water into its stomach extremely rapidly and so swell out its spiny body to many times its normal girth. As a consequence, an attacker may find a reasonably sized morsel suddenly transformed into a globe it cannot get into its jaws. Once inflated, the puffer cannot move. It will be several minutes before it can expel the water, return to its normal size and swim away.

Not all fish have adopted a life of speed. Those living in mid-water or along the shores have different problems and requirements, but for them too, the acquisition of a swim-bladder has had a potent effect on structure, for it has freed their body fins for all kinds of purposes. Those of a pike have become elegant filmy sculls, rotating slowly back and forth from a joint within the body, so that the fish can compensate for the tiniest variation of current and hang above a rock as though it were suspended from an invisible wire. Gouramis have turned their pelvic fins into long thread-like feelers with which they explore the water ahead of them and, at breeding times, caress their mates. The dragonfish has expanded them into spectacular defensive weapons, each ray barbed with poison.

Several species, since body weight is no longer such a problem, have once again taken to armour. The box-fish, in the highly populated and potentially dangerous world of the reef, sails over the coral packaged in a crate of bone, its pectorals whirling, its tail fin

flickering. The sea horse is also armoured and stiff-bodied. Its tail has no fin on it but is used as a hook with which the fish anchors itself to weed or coral. Its body is held upright and what was the dorsal fin has become an undulating rear engine, which with the help of whirling pectorals on either side, enables it to move erect and stately through the corals and weed forests. The trigger fish feeds on coral, crunching the stony branches and extracting the little polyps. It has concentrated its finnage on its rear half, with a large flapping dorsal next to the tail and an equivalent one on the underside. This keeps its head free so that it can thrust it deep between the branches of the coral and select a particularly toothsome piece. The trigger, which gives the fish its name, is the leading ray of its dorsal fin which has become bony. The two rays behind have been turned into a locking device on the joint of its base. When waves crash over the reef, the fish swims into a crevice, sticks up its bony trigger and locks itself in place so firmly that neither ocean currents, hungry predators nor inquisitive skin divers can extract it.

Some bony fish have emulated the cartilaginous skates and rays and taken to the bottom-living life, abandoning the swim-bladder that, ancestrally, was the source of their success. Their pectoral fins have been turned to yet more purposes. The gurnard has dispensed with the membrane on the front part so that the rays are free and can be moved independently rather like the legs of a spider. It uses them to turn over stones when it is looking for food. The flounder has become adapted to bottom-living to a quite extraordinary degree. It illustrates again the tendency of creatures to rehearse their past history during their own individual development, for when it hatches, it swims above the sea floor just as its ancestors undoubtedly did. After a few months, it undergoes a transformation. It loses the swim-bladder it has had until now. Its head becomes twisted and the mouth moves sideways. One eye shifts right round the body so that it takes up a position alongside the other. Then the fish descends to the bottom and lies on its side. The pectoral fins are now of little use, though the fish still retains them. It swims by undulating the much enlarged dorsals and anals that fringe its sides.

So, driven by their beating tails, sculled by their pectorals, planing on lateral fringes, the fish swim with speed and accuracy through all the varied habitats of the sea, from the rococo constructions of the reef to the mountains and plains of the sea bed, from the swaying forests of kelp to the blue sunlit waters of the open ocean. But mobility demands sensitivity: if you travel, one way or another you must be aware of where you are going.

How a fish finds its way

All fish have one sense for which we have no parallel. Down their flanks and branching over the head, runs a line with a slightly different texture from the rest of the body. It consists of a number of pores, connected by a canal running just below the surface. This lateral line system enables the fish to detect differences of pressure in the water. As it swims, a fish creates a pressure wave that travels ahead of it. When this meets some other object, the fish by means of its lateral line can detect the change. It is also made aware, by this ability to feel at a distance, of the movements of other fish

The hidden flounder

The upper side of the flounder's body contains pigment cells which, by contracting or expanding, can make the overall colour closely match that of the sand. The fish further conceals itself by throwing up sand with beats of its fins, leaving little more than its eyes unburied. Some species of flatfish always settle on their right side, and some on their left. Oddly, young flounders may settle on either side, though two-thirds do so on their left.

THE FISH WITH A ROVING EYE

Flat-fish, such as plaice and sole, have adapted to life on the sea-bed, eating worms and shell-fish. At birth, flat-fish have eyes on both sides of the head, like other fish, and swim near the surface. But after a few weeks one eye moves across the top of the head to the other side, and the fish swims to the bottom of the sea to rest on its 'blind' side.

Life begins The young flat-fish has eyes normally placed, as in a young herring.

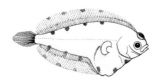

The change Soon, one eye moves to the top of the head, and the dorsal fin grows forward.

Adulthood The eye settles on the other side, where it focuses independently of the second.

swimming alongside it, an important ability for those species that form shoals.

The fish's sense of smell is most acute. The nostrils open into cups which can detect the most minute changes in the chemical composition of water. Sharks, when the current is in their favour, can smell blood issuing from a body at a distance of nearly half a kilometre. They rely greatly on smell to guide them to food which may be an explanation for the shape of that most grotesque of sharks, the hammerhead. Its nostrils are placed at the ends of two extremities that grow out from the side of its head. If it scents its prey, it swings its head from side to side to determine the direction from which the smell is coming. When it is equally strong in both nostrils, then the hammerhead swims straight ahead – and is often one of the first predators to reach the scene.

Fish are likely to have been able to detect sound from a very early period. The capsule containing the two arching semicircular canals that are found in either side of the skull of the proto-fish and the lamprey has been improved considerably by the jawed fish. They have a third canal in a horizontal plane and beneath it a large sac. All three canals and the sac have very sensitive linings and contain small limy particles which move and vibrate. Sound travels better in water than in air, and as the fish's body contains a high proportion of water within it, the sound waves penetrate the skull and reach the semicircular canals without the aid of the special passage needed by vertebrates that live in air. So fish are aware of the popply, slapping noises that other fish make as they travel at speed through the water, of the clicks made by crustaceans

---

A TYPICAL BONY FISH

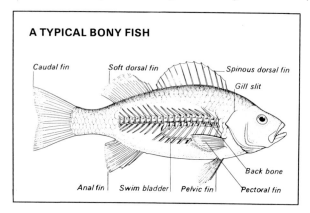

Caudal fin   Soft dorsal fin   Spinous dorsal fin

Gill slit

Anal fin | Swim bladder | Pelvic fin   Pectoral fin

Back bone

The murderous hammer

The enormous side extremities of the hammerhead shark carry not only its nostrils but also large glaring eyes. There are several different species with such heads. The largest grows to a length of 5 metres and is regarded as one of the most aggressive of all sharks.

A CLEANING SERVICE FOR INFESTED CLIENTS

Some small fish remove parasites from larger fish. The cleaners could easily be eaten by the big fish, but a regular cleaning service is a greater advantage than a quick meal. A hazard for the clients lies in other small fish which mimic the cleaners to get in close, and then eat pieces of the clients' fins.

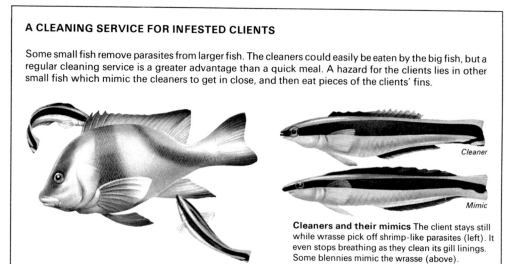

Cleaner

Mimic

Cleaners and their mimics The client stays still while wrasse pick off shrimp-like parasites (left). It even stops breathing as they clean its gill linings. Some blennies mimic the wrasse (above).

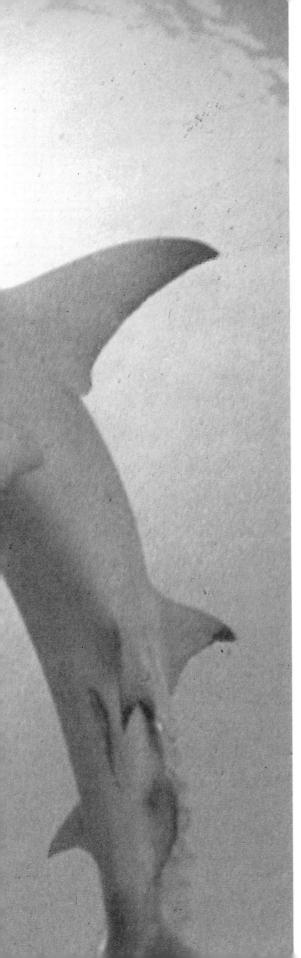

snapping their hard shells and the scrapings made by fish grazing over the coral.

The acquisition of a swim-bladder brought the possibility of further improvements in both receiving and transmitting sound. Several thousand species of fish have developed bony connections of some kind to link their swim-bladders to the inner ear capsules, so that the vibrations picked up and amplified by the sympathetic resonance of the swim-bladder are transmitted to the semicircular canals. Some have also developed special muscles so that they can vibrate the swim-bladder and produce a loud drumming noise. Catfish of several species do so and appear to be calling to one another as they move in murky water.

The brilliance of pattern and colour that aids recognition

Sight was also an ability acquired very early. The lancelet's eye-spot makes it aware of the difference between light and dark. The jawless fish, even though their heads were heavily plated with bone, had chinks in their armour to accommodate eyes. Since the laws that govern the behaviour of light are universal, it is not surprising that the number of basic designs for an efficient eye are small. The trilobites produced the mosaic eye which has been retained by the insects. Otherwise, image-producing eyes, no matter which organism develops them, have a similar fundamental structure – a closed chamber with a transparent window and a lens in front and a photosensitive lining at the back. This is the pattern of the squid and octopus eye as well as of the artificial mechanical one built by man, the camera. It is also the basis of the eye developed by the fish and bequeathed by them to all land-living vertebrates. The lining may contain two kinds of differently shaped cells, the rods and the cones. The first distinguish between light and dark, the second are sensitive to colour.

The eyes of almost all sharks and rays lack cone cells, so they cannot perceive colour. Not surprisingly, therefore, they are themselves drab creatures dressed in browns and greys, olive green and steel blue. When they are patterned, their designs tend to be simple spots and dapples. Bony fish, on the other hand, are strikingly different. Their eyes have both rods and cones, their colour vision is, for the most part, excellent and their body colours are accordingly vivid and various. Sulphur fins are attached to sapphire bodies, orange spots are scattered on a sage-green flank, chocolate-brown scales are individually rimmed with peacock blue, tails are patterned like archery targets with a golden centre surrounded by outers of scarlet, black and white. There seems to be no pattern, no shade in the spectrum, that the bony fish have not deployed to decorate their bodies.

The most brilliantly patterned of all are those fish that live in clear sunlit waters where their designs are easily seen – in tropical lakes and rivers and, particularly and most lavishly, around coral reefs. Here because of the abundance of all forms of life and the richness of food, there is a huge and crowded population. In such circumstances, species identification becomes very important and the fish have adopted the most vivid liveries to assist in it.

One group of fish, called because of the beauty of their coloration, butterfly fish,

FISH THAT USE COLOUR IN BATTLE

When one cichlid fish attempts to invade the territory of another, the territory holder intercepts it and tries to drive it out. Usually the intruder retreats, but sometimes a long border encounter takes place. Both fish display their size and strength, using their fins to beat water against each other. Eventually they may fight. As the aggressiveness of each fish increases, its colour darkens.

Interception The territory holder (right) intercepts the intruder. Both fish are their normal pale colour.

Display The two fish circle each other with erect fins, making exaggerated body movements to display their size and power. Dark patches appear on their bodies.

Combat Now dark in colour, the fish fight, biting the opponent's fins and body, and occasionally locking jaws.

Retreat Realising it has lost, one fish loses its dark colour, contracts its fins and flees.

show how diverse such patterning can be within one small family. They are all about the same size – only a few centimetres long – with roughly the same shape, slim, approximately rectangular, with high foreheads and small pouting mouths. Each species has its own particular place on the reef, with its own favoured depth and preferred source of food. One has elongated jaws for picking between the coral stems, another may specialise in cropping a particular kind of small crustacean. It is in the interests of each individual therefore to proclaim clearly among the confusion of swarming fish, that its particular niche is occupied so that no other individual of the same species will poach its territory. Equally, the colours will draw the attention of a female to the presence of a male of the only kind with which she can have a fertile union. In many environments, the need to advertise in this way is limited by the danger of becoming a conspicuous target for a predator. For the butterfly fish, this risk is small for, hovering over the coral, it can dart to safety among the stony fronds within a fraction of a second. So each species of the family, on the near-identical canvas of its body, carries a vivid and individual design based on stripes and patches, dots, eye-spots and zigzags.

As spawning time approaches, the need for species identification becomes particularly intense. Away from the reefs, in more dangerous and exposed waters, the males still often adopt brilliant colours, risking conspicuousness, in order to threaten rivals and attract females. Pigment granules diffuse within their skins as they become excited and they fight with their colours, circling one another and flexing and quivering their fins like bull-fighters' capes. They beat their tails and send pressure waves along the lateral lines of their rivals. They tear at the patterns on one another's fins. Eventually when one has had enough, he signals submission by contracting the pigment in one set of cells and expanding that in another so that his flank patterns change and he hoists the flag of surrender. The winner is now free to court his female. He then uses much the same repertory of colours and patterns and fin displays as he did for aggression, but in a female these trigger a series of different responses that eventually culminates in the laying of eggs.

The eyes of some fish enable them to see not only what is going on in the water around them but in the air above the surface. The archer fish is partial to flies and other insects that may settle on plants growing on the banks. It takes aim, compensating for the way that light bends as it passes from water to air, and squirts a jet of drops, knocking the insect from its foothold so that it falls into the water and can be eaten. A small fish from Central America is even more specialised. It has a horizontal division across its pupil which effectively gives it four eyes – the two lower halves for seeing underwater, the two upper for doing so in air – and the fish can swim along the surface looking for food above and below it at the same time.

Life in the darkness of the ocean depths

At the other extreme of the fishes' habitat, in the depths of the ocean, around 750 metres and below, there is no light by which fish can see one another's signals, so many

The colours of a fish

The colours of a fish are produced by pigment cells in the skin. Each contains granules of a particular hue which can be spread out in a sheet or concentrated into a tiny dot. The various cells, when expanded in different proportions, produce different shades, like colours mixed on a palette. So fish can swiftly change their colours and patterns to match their background or their mood. Over longer periods, some totally change their livery, as they mature or prepare for breeding, and nearly all lose their colours within minutes as they die.

KORAN ANGEL

GREEN SPOTTED BOX-FISH

ORANGE GROUPER

SEA POACHER (ABOVE)

SPOTLIGHT PARROT FISH (BELOW)   LONG-HORNED COWFISH (BELOW)

HARLEQUIN TUSK FISH (BELOW)   PURPLE QUEEN (BELOW)

GLASS-EYE SNAPPER (BELOW)

create their own. Some have modified cells that are capable of producing luminous chemicals. Others possess cultures of phosphorescent bacteria in special organs with flaps of skin over them which can be moved to expose or conceal the bacteria in a series of winks and flashes. So the depths of the oceans are full of lights moving rhythmically around and continually turning off and on. It is an obvious guess that these are social signals of some kind – instructions to the rest of the shoal, summons to mates – but much more work has to be done before their exact functions are properly understood. One category of luminescence, however, has a plain and unmistakable purpose. The deep-sea angler fish has a spine in front of its dorsal fin elongated into a thin thread which droops over the front of the mouth. On its end hangs a glowing green bulb. Other fish are drawn to investigate this swaying light, the angler suddenly opens its cavernous mouth – and engulfs one more meal.

And there are dark waters elsewhere. Some tropical rivers are covered with floating vegetation, and so full of rotting leaves that they are black and turbid. Here fish live that have developed a method of finding their way about that no other creature so far has emulated. They generate electricity within their bodies. Many small species do so – knife fish in South America, elephant fish in West Africa, so called because they have an elongated lip like a small probing trunk. If you want to discover them, all you need is two wires at the end of a pole leading to an amplifier, powered by a small battery and attached to a little loudspeaker. If you dip the end of the wires in a stream where such fish are searching for food in the muddy bottom, you will hear a series of clicks. These are the electric signals, translated into sound so that they are detectable by human ears.

The fish have modified muscles in their flanks which generate and transmit these electric discharges. Some species send out signals almost continuously, others emit short bursts. Each seems to have its own identifiable code. The transmission creates flow-patterns of current in the surrounding water. Any object with a conductivity different from that of the water will distort the pattern. The fish becomes aware of the change through receptor pores spaced out over its body and even in the darkest, most stygian waters, knows the shape and disposition of the objects around it.

The largest of such fish is the South American electric eel. It is not related to the true eels but looks superficially like them and so has acquired their popular name. It grows to a metre and a half in length and as thick as a man's arm. Often it makes its home in holes beneath a river bank or among rocks. Reversing into these holes for a lengthy creature like an eel must pose considerable steering problems. The eel does it with the aid of electricity. As you watch one tackling such a problem in a tank, you can detect the clicks of its discharges increasing as it identifies the outlines of the selected parking place behind it and slowly manoeuvres its great length into it without once touching the sides. But the electric eel has another set of batteries that produce not steady low-voltage direction-finding transmissions but sudden massive shocks so strong that if you pick up such a fish without the insulation of rubber gloves and boots, it can throw you flat on your back. The eel uses this kind of discharge for hunting. It is one of the very few creatures in the world that can kill by electrocution.

A mouth to match its stomach
The viperfish, about 25 centimetres long, gets its name from its huge fangs, elongated body and its expandable stomach that allows it to swallow creatures bigger than itself. At night, it is found close to the surface, but during the day it goes down as far as 2800 metres.

Fishing with a lighted lure
This angler fish (right) lives at depths of up to 4000 metres. Its dorsal fin carries a swelling at the end that glows brightly, probably powered by luminous bacteria. The angler can flick this forward to hang in front of its mouth, attracting inquisitive fish within range of its jaws. Another lure hangs beneath its chin.

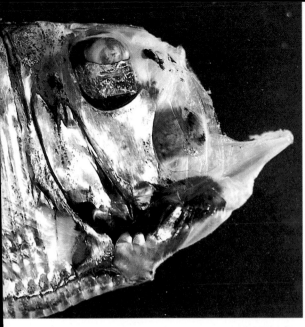

A living blade

The hatchet fish's eyes are telescopic and point permanently upwards (left). Its silver body, about 10 centimetres long, is shaped like an axe blade and has a line of luminous organs along its lower edge that glows brightly in the blackness of the ocean depths.

THE FISH WITH A FLASHLIGHT

Luminous bacteria live in special organs under each eye of the flashlight fish. They generate as much light as a weak torch, and allow the fish to see at night, communicate with other fish and lure prey.

Light organ fully visible *Organ rotates downwards* *The light 'goes out'*

The most splendid, valiant and efficient of fish

Today, five hundred million years after those jawless armour-laden creatures began to wag their tails and blunder over the muddy bottoms of the ancient seas, the fish have evolved into some 30,000 different species. Between them, they have colonised every part of the seas, lakes and rivers of the world. Their mastery of the waters is epitomised by that most splendid, valiant and efficient of fish, the salmon.

Five species of them visit North American rivers. They spend the bulk of their lives in the Pacific ocean. When they are small, they feed on plankton. As they grow larger, they take to eating fish. In August each year, the fish that have just reached adulthood travel towards the American coast. They assemble offshore and then begin to battle their way up the rivers, fighting and dodging the swift downward current, selecting with the help of the pressure-sensitive pores of their lateral lines, the reaches where the current is marginally slacker, resting in quiet pools, recovering their strength before tackling another stretch of rapids.

These rivers are not chosen at random. Each salmon remembers the precise taste of the waters in which it hatched, a flavour derived from the mix of minerals in its mud and the plants and animals that live in it. They can detect this flavour even when their home water is diluted to one part in several million. This memory draws them across several hundred miles of ocean, brings them to a particular bay and, as the scent gets stronger and stronger, up one special river and into one particular stream. We know that it is smell that guides them, for salmon with their nostrils blocked get lost. Unhampered, the accuracy of their memory and navigation is astounding. Many thousands of young fish have been marked soon after they hatched. Only one or two return to a river other than the one in which they first swam.

The compulsion to return may be strong, but the obstacles are huge. The move from saltwater to fresh in itself requires major adjustments to the chemistry of the body, but the salmon manages to make them. On their way upstream, they may encounter waterfalls. Their sharp eyes select the lowest part of the lip of the fall. Then, flexing their powerfully muscled silver bodies, they thrash their tails and leap from the water.

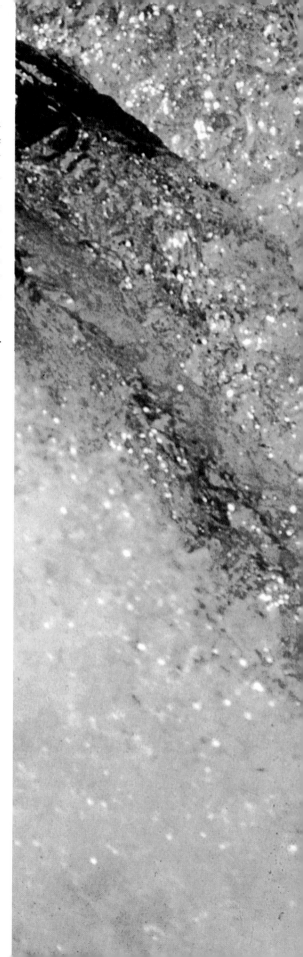

Last journey of the salmon

Sockeye salmon, vivid in their breeding colours (left), assemble in estuaries before beginning their arduous journeys up the rivers in which they were hatched (right). Once started on the journey they eat nothing. When they reach the shallows of the headwaters, they pair and lay their eggs in the gravel. Then, their breeding completed, they die.

They may have to jump again and again before at last they land in the pools at the head of the falls and can continue on their journey.

Eventually they reach the shallow stretches where their parents spawned and they lie there resting, their heads pointing upstream, flank to flank and so thick that the pale sand of the river bed is hidden by the black of their backs. Now, within a few days, the shape of their bodies changes with astonishing speed. They develop high humps on their backs. Their upper jaws become hooked and their teeth grow into long fangs. These are useless for feeding – but the time for feeding has long since passed. These teeth are for battle. The males wrestle and fight, seizing one another's jaws, striking at their opponents with their splayed teeth. The water is so shallow that their writhing backs break clear of the surface. At length, one wins and claims a scrape in the gravel. A female joins him. Swiftly eggs and milt are shed and sink beneath the gravel grains.

Now the adults are totally spent. They do not have enough energy even to heal their battered wounded bodies. Their scales fall off, the once powerful muscles dwindle and they die. Not a single one of the millions of fish that fought their way up the river ever returns to the sea. Their frayed bodies lie rotting in drifts on the surface of the streams and are washed up in piles on the sandbanks. Here and there, a last survivor makes a few final despairing flaps. Gulls gather in flocks to peck out eyes and strip the yellowing flesh.

But in the gravel, the eggs remain, a thousand or so from every female. They stay safe throughout the hard winter. Next spring they hatch. The fry remain in the streams for a few weeks, feeding on the flush of insects and crustaceans that appear in the warming waters. When they are fingerlings, they leave, following the current downstream to the sea. Some species will swim there for two seasons, others for up to five. Many will be eaten by other fish in the sea, but eventually the survivors will fight their way back up their own river to spawn and die in the very place where they were hatched.

Three-quarters of the world's surface is covered by water. Three-quarters of the world belongs to the fish.

MALES FIGHT FOR A PLACE TO MATE

THE END OF A GENERATION

IN THE SPRING, THE EGGS HATCH

6. THE INVASION OF THE LAND

Lungs and legs enable a swimmer to live on land, but most amphibians still need water to breed

One of the most crucial episodes in the history of life took place some 350 million years ago in a freshwater swamp. Fish began to haul themselves out of water and become the first back-boned creatures to colonise the land. To cross this frontier, they – like the first terrestrial invertebrates – had to solve two problems: first, how to move around out of water, and second, how to obtain oxygen from the air.

There is one fish alive today which manages to do both these things – the mudskipper. It is not closely related to those fish who pioneered the land, so any comparisons with them have to be made with caution, but even so it can give us a hint about how that momentous move was accomplished.

Mudskippers are only a few centimetres long and you can find them in mangrove swamps and muddy estuaries in many parts of the tropics, lying on the glistening mud well beyond the lap of the waters. Some may even be clinging to the arching aerial roots of the mangroves or clambering up the trunks. A sudden movement or an abrupt noise will send them skittering back to the safety of the water. They come out to feed on the insects and other invertebrates that swarm on the soft oozy surface of the mud. They move by suddenly flexing the hinder end of their body so that they give a little skipping jump. But they also have a steadier, more sober way of edging themselves forward with

A divided life

Typical amphibians spend the greater part of their lives on land but return to water to breed. There they produce young that in many ways resemble fish. They are descended from freshwater air-breathing fish and their body chemistry is still adapted to fresh water, so no amphibian lives in the sea and few can tolerate even brackish water. The most abundant are the frogs and toads, which have specialised in jumping by developing shortened backbones and elongated legs. There are 2600 species of these alive today and they are found wherever there is fresh water or moisture, even if it is only present for a short period every year or so. They flourish in the greatest numbers in the tropical rain forests, but some species live north of the Arctic circle in water that is only half a degree above freezing.

their front pair of fins. Each of these has a fleshy base supported internally by bones – the fin is, in effect, a rigid crutch. With it the fish can lever itself forward.

Such fins are similar, in principle, to those of a whole group of primitive bony fish that were living in that remote period when the move to land was first made. The most famous of them is the coelacanth.

The scientific sensation of the century

Many species of coelacanth have been found as fossils. They are not large – thirty centimetres or so in length. Some specimens have been preserved in miraculous detail with every scale and fin-ray present. A juvenile was uncovered in the rocks of Illinois with traces of its yolk sack beneath its belly, plain to see. They are most abundant in deposits about 400 million years old, but thereafter they become scarcer and none has been found in rocks younger than 70 million years. Since they were flourishing during the period when the land was invaded and since they certainly possessed limb-like fins, it seemed likely that they were the creatures from which the first land vertebrates were descended. Their fossils were therefore studied with great care to try and determine exactly how they moved and how they breathed. But scientists reconciled themselves to the fact that the answers to such questions would never be known with certainty since the fish had obviously become extinct long ago.

And then, in 1938, a trawler fishing off the coast of South Africa brought up a very strange fish. It was large, nearly two metres long, with powerful jaws and heavy armoured scales. After the catch had been landed at East London, the curator of the small local museum, Miss Courtenay-Latimer, came down to look it over. She noticed this peculiar fish and although she was not a fish specialist, she became convinced that it was of great importance. She wrote to Professor J. B. L. Smith of Grahamstown University, the greatest authority on African fish, describing it briefly. Before he could get to the specimen, its entrails had decomposed so badly that they had to be thrown away, so it was a gutted specimen that he eventually saw. In spite of this, and the fact that it was so large, he recognised it immediately as a coelacanth. He named it Latimeria and informed an astonished world that a creature thought to have been extinct for 70 million years was still alive.

The discovery was hailed as the scientific sensation of the century and a huge search for another specimen was mounted. Leaflets and posters carrying a picture of Latimeria and offering a huge reward were distributed among the countless fishing villages that dot the coasts of southern and eastern Africa. But without result. Then, fourteen years later, after it had seemed that this strange fish had appeared only to disappear totally, another was caught, not off South Africa but a thousand miles away in Anjouan, one of the tiny Comoro Islands that lie in the Indian Ocean midway between Madagascar and the coast of Tanzania. The first one, it seems, was a stray, for the fishermen of the Comores said that the coelacanth was no stranger to them. They caught one or two each season in depths of about two or three hundred metres. They did not often fish for them deliberately, for a coelacanth fights hard when it is hooked and a man might have to

struggle with one of them for many hours before it could be hauled on board his canoe. And after all that trouble, its flesh is oily and not particularly good to eat. Indeed, almost the most valuable part of the coelacanth anatomy, to the Comoreans, is its rough heavy scales. They are very useful for rubbing down inner tubes when mending a puncture.

Since that time, several dozen more coelacanths have been caught and, paradoxically, science now knows more about Latimeria than many an abundant fish. A pregnant female has been caught with young inside her attached to their yolk sacs, just like the Illinois fossil, showing that the species does not lay its eggs but gives birth to live young. But because it is so powerful a fish, such a doughty fighter and has to be dragged up from such depths, Latimeria very seldom reaches the shore alive. Many expeditions have gone to the Comores hoping to catch a living specimen. A British team managed to reach one that, although it had been hooked several hours before, was still just living when its captor got it ashore. They put it in a bath and filmed it from above the surface of the water as it moved feebly about, but they were unable to get any detailed shots.

We ourselves, on another expedition, searched for them, night after night, by lowering highly sensitive electronic cameras to the sea floor in areas where coelacanths have been most frequently caught, but without success. Then just before the last of us left the island, a fisherman brought one in, lashed to the side of his canoe. It, too, was nearly dead, but he was persuaded to release it in a bay long enough for it to be filmed with an underwater camera as it swam slowly above the bottom. And indeed, it did hold its stout pectoral fins away from the sides of its body, and it was not hard to imagine that had it been vigorous, it could have used them to help it move over the rocky sea floor of its true environment. What is more, it was also clear that, mechanically, such fins would be of real assistance out of water as in it, had the fish, like its ancient forebears, been living in shallow water and become stranded.

An answer to the problem of breathing on land

But what solution could the early fish find to the problem of breathing out of water? The mudskipper manages to do so by holding water in its mouth which it swills over the lining of its mouth with a rolling action of its head to extract the oxygen. It also absorbs some directly from the air through its moist skin. But these devices allow it to remain out of water for only a short time. Within a few minutes it has to return to wet its skin and take a fresh mouthful of water. Nor can the living coelacanth suggest an answer, for today it never leaves its deep waters. Once again, however, there is a living creature that has a solution.

Many of the swamps around the flood plains of African rivers turn to hard sun-baked mud during the dry season, yet one fish, the lungfish, manages to live in them and survive from season to season by breathing air. As the pools shrink, the lungfish burrows into the mud at the bottom. There it curls into a ball, wrapping its tail around its head, and secretes mucus to line its hole. As the sun bakes out the last moisture from the mud, the mucus turns to parchment. The bichir and other primitive freshwater fish have a pouch opening from the gut to enable them to breathe air. The lungfish has a pair

A fish that walks on land

The mudskipper seems to be more at home out of water than in it, provided its skin can remain moist. As the tide comes into a mangrove swamp, the mudskipper climbs up the roots (below), skipping with flicks of its tail or pushing itself forward with its leg-like pectoral fins. There it can continue feeding on small creatures. Its courtship is also carried on out of water, the male (left) displaying to the female, by erecting his coloured dorsal fin.

and now, out of water, it is totally dependent on them. In burrowing down, the fish made a tube through the mud an inch or so across. Air now passes down this to the mouth of the fish which is connected to tiny openings in the parchment cocoon. By pumping its throat muscles, the fish draws air down its throat to its pouches. The walls of these are thick with blood vessels which absorb gaseous oxygen. These organs are simple lungs and with their aid the lungfish can survive for several months, even years.

When the rains do finally return and water fills the pond again, the fish, within the space of a few hours, comes to life, wriggles free of its cocoon and the resoftened mud and swims off. In the water, it breathes with its gills like any normal fish, but like the bichir it uses its lungs too, rising every now and then to gulp air from the surface, a talent which is particularly valuable when the water in the pools becomes tepid and foul and loses most of its oxygen.

Four different species of lungfish are found in Africa, one in Australia and another in South America. They were, however, very much more abundant 350 million years ago and their fossils are often found in the same sort of deposits that contain coelacanths. Between them, these two kinds of fish possessed both the essential abilities that the ancient land-exploring fish must have required. But neither fish can be regarded as the one whose descendants eventually colonised the land permanently. Both are disqualified because the bones of their skulls are so different from those of the first fossil amphibians that the one cannot be derived from the other.

The ancestor of the amphibians
However, there is a third fish found in the deposits of that early and critical period. It belongs to the same broad group as the coelacanths and the lungfish. It has leg-like fins with fleshy bases like the coelacanth; it seems very likely that it had air-breathing pouches from its gut like a lungfish. Its skull, however, has the crucial feature which neither the coelacanth nor the lungfish possesses – a passage linking its nostrils with the roof of its mouth. All land vertebrates have this feature and it is this which confirms that this fish is indeed very close to the ancestral line.

This creature is called Eusthenopteron. Its fossils have been investigated by cutting them into thin slices, a technique that has revealed a great deal about its anatomy, even down to the details of the structure of its blood vessels. When the fins of fossil specimens are carefully dissected, the lobes at the base are found to be supported by one stout bone close to the body, two bones joined to it and finally a group of small bones and digits – the pattern that is found in the limbs of all land vertebrates.

But why should the descendants of Eusthenopteron have troubled to clamber about laboriously on the land? Perhaps, like the lungfish of today, they lived in pools that were seasonal and used lungs and legs to search for other water when their homes went dry. Perhaps, like the mudskipper, they were tempted out by a hitherto untapped source of food, for already at this period there were abundant worms, snails and the ancestors of insects. Maybe it was the emptiness of the land that attracted them: there were no reptiles, birds or mammals so it was a comparatively safe place for them. Perhaps it was

The missing millennia of the coelacanth
The similarities between a fossil coelacanth (right, above) and the living Latimeria (right, below) are so many and so close that there can be no doubt they are related. Both have heavy bone-based scales over their body, tassel-like fins with fleshy bases supported by internal bones and – particularly characteristic – a symmetrical, fringed tail, flanked above and below by smaller fins. The fossil forms, however, were much smaller. This specimen is only about one-sixth as long as the living species. The first coelacanth fossils occur in freshwater deposits laid down about 400 million years ago in many parts of the world. Later species are found in rocks that accumulated in shallow seas. None is found in any rocks younger than 70 million years. It had been assumed that this was because they became extinct then. We now know that it was for a different reason. They migrated into deeper waters, just beyond the edge of the continental shelves, an area of the earth's crust that hardly ever produces rock-forming deposits. So no fossils have been found. But coelacanths have remained there ever since, prowling over the rocks of the sea floor and, as the millennia passed, growing larger and larger. Finally, in 1938, a coelacanth was caught off the coast of South Africa. It was nearly 2 metres long, with powerful jaws and heavy scales. Not until 14 years later was it realised that coelacanths were caught regularly by fishermen of the Comoro Islands in the Indian Ocean.

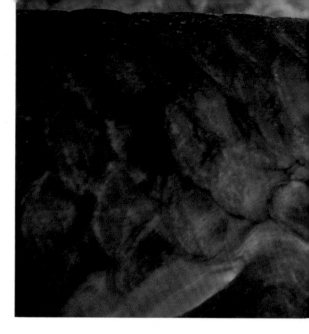

a combination of all these reasons. Whatever it was that lured or drove them there, these creatures, over the millennia, lumbering after their food, became more and more efficient at moving and breathing out of water.

The swamps through which they waddled were thick with great horsetail and club-moss trees. These eventually were fossilised as coal, and from coal-mines today come the bones of those first vertebrate inhabitants of the land – the amphibians.

Some of them must have been terrifying. They grew to a length of three or four metres and their jaws were spiked with lines of cone-shaped teeth. For the next hundred million years, they dominated the land. Eventually, they were eclipsed by the reptiles and much reduced in numbers. In consequence, amphibian fossils become very scarce indeed in later geological periods and there are long gaps in their fossil history. Modern forms differ from the early ones in many major ways and the connections between early and contemporary amphibians are therefore still a matter for speculation and argument.

The ancient amphibian pattern

The living amphibians that give the best impression of the appearance of the early ones are the salamanders and newts. Collectively these are known as the urodeles, 'tailed ones'. The largest of them lives in the rivers of Japan. It is a nightmarish creature with a flat spade-like head, tiny button eyes and a wrinkled warty skin that hangs in folds around its body. It grows to a length of about a metre and a half, only a quarter of the size of its ancestors but exceptional for contemporary amphibians. Most of them are very much smaller. More typical of the urodeles is the newt, a mere ten centimetres or so long.

The newt's legs, advanced though they are compared with the fin of a coelacanth or a mudskipper, are not very efficient. They are short and thin and to take a reasonable stride forward with its hind leg, the newt has to flex its body laterally. Most of its time is spent on land, hiding beneath stones or sheltering in damp mossy places searching for the worms, slugs and insects on which it lives. But it cannot stray far from water. For one thing, its skin is permeable and in consequence the animal, in a dry atmosphere, loses its body liquids very quickly and dies. To make matters worse, the newt, like other amphibians, lacks a mechanism for drinking with its mouth. It has to absorb all the liquid it requires through its skin. It must also keep its body moist to help it breathe. Its lungs are relatively simple and not totally sufficient for its needs, so its oxygen intake, like the mudskipper's, is supplemented by absorption through its wet skin. Both these requirements restrict it, and most amphibians, to moist places. But there is a third need that ties it to water: its eggs, like those of a fish, do not have waterproof shells, so it has to go back there to breed.

During its water-living phase in the breeding season, the newt becomes quite fish-like. It swims, with its legs tucked out of the way alongside its flanks, by sinuous movements of its body and by beating its tail. The male of some species develops a crest along his back like a dorsal fin and becomes brightly coloured as fish do during

The ancestor of all four-legged creatures?
This fish, Eusthenopteron (above), lived 400 million years ago in many parts of the world. It had lungs, heavy scales and muscular fins, as its contemporaries the lungfish did. It differed from them in having a canal connecting nostrils to throat, which links it to early amphibians. And the arrangement of bones in its fin bases resembles that of the first walking land animals.

courtship. When he displays, he beats water with his tail and flexes his crest, sending powerful currents towards the female or rivals. These they detect with lines of sensors on the head and along the sides of the body which are an inheritance from the fish and an equivalent of their ancient lateral line system.

The female lays a great number of eggs, attaching each individually to the leaf of a

The most primitive living lungfish

Of all living lungfish, the Australian species (left) most closely resembles the fossil ancestors. Its body is armoured with heavy scales and its paired fins have fleshy bases. It is not, however, able to survive total desiccation as its relations in South America can. If it is to live through the dry season it needs small pools, even though the water in them may become so foul that it has to depend upon its lung to get vital oxygen.

The first pattern for a limb

This pair of front fins of an Eusthenopteron (left) has been dissected to show the shoulder girdle and the internal bones of the left fin jointed to it. The right fin remains undamaged (top left of the picture). The bones of the limb itself appear against a white background. They are grouped in just the same way as those in the limbs of all land-living vertebrates.

water plant. When the young hatch, they are even more fish-like than their parents, for they have no legs and breathe not with lungs, which will develop later, but with feathery external gills. They are tadpoles.

Some salamanders in Central America exploit the possession of such a water-living larva to give themselves two alternative ways of spending their adult lives. One species living in a lake in Mexico, regularly changes to a land-living adult form in the normal fashion. But if there is a particularly wet season and its lake does not shrink and dry, then its larvae retain their feathery gills. They continue to grow well beyond the size at which they would normally change shape and become as big, if not bigger, than the land-living form. Eventually, while still retaining their tadpole appearance, they become sexually mature and breed.

In a nearby lake, a related creature has reverted permanently to the aquatic life of its ancestors. It always breeds in a larval condition, its external gills growing into great branching bushes on either side of its neck. The Aztecs, perhaps recognising how odd this was, gave it a name which means 'water monster' – axolotl. The fact that it is a salamander can be experimentally demonstrated by feeding it with thyroid extract. It will then lose its external gills, develop lungs and turn into a creature that closely resembles a burrowing salamander that lives in Florida. Farther north in the United States, one amphibian has reverted irrevocably to water-living – the mud puppy. It has both gills and lungs, lays its eggs in a nest in the bottom of a stream and remains in water throughout its life. No scientist has yet discovered any means of inducing this creature to change into a different form; but we need have no doubt that its ancestors were true amphibious salamanders.

Some salamanders have taken this reversion to a fish-like existence even further. They seem to be losing not only their lungs but their legs. The siren, a metre-long amphibian from the southern United States, has lost its back legs altogether and its front legs are not only greatly reduced in size but have no bones within them, merely cartilage, so that they are of no practical use in locomotion. The amphiuma, from the same part of the world, still possesses all four of its limbs but they are so minuscule that you have to look very carefully if you are not to miss them. Indeed, it is superficially so like a fish that it is known locally as the Congo eel.

This abandonment of both the major innovations made by the descendants of Eusthenopteron during their colonisation of the land occurs not only among those salamanders that have taken to water but even among some that spend their lives almost entirely on land. Many American salamanders have lost their lungs and yet manage to breathe adequately through their wet skin and the moist membranes lining their mouths. But this can only be done at the price of a restriction of body size. Breathing in this way will be more efficient if the body is of the size and shape that gives maximum skin area and minimum body volume and this, indeed, is just what is found among these lungless salamanders; their bodies are thin and elongated and none of them grows to more than a few centimetres in length.

One group have lost their legs altogether and taken to burrowing underground.

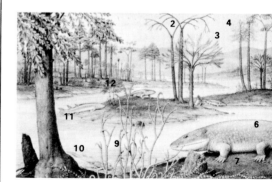

THE FIRST FOUR-LEGGED ANIMALS TO INVADE THE LAND

An amphibian called Ichthyostega was the first known four-legged animal to live on the land. Its fish-like body with well-developed legs is known from fossils found in Greenland.

This artist's reconstruction shows a landscape of about 350 million years ago, based on fossils collected in several European localities. Most of the trees are known from fossilised remains of specimens washed down by rivers. The terrain where they grew is not known, but there were probably rivers like the one illustrated, surrounded by trees such as the very common Archaeopteris whose leafy branches are shown in detail at the top left of the picture. The ground was covered by the tiny early club-moss Colpodexylon and small

plants such as Sawdonia and the creeper Sphenophyllum.

Hauling itself on to the island is a fish of the Eusthenopteron type, which could use its limbs to move on land as well as in water, indicating how amphibians evolved. In the foreground stands Ichthyostega, a fully developed amphibian with its fish-like body but strongly formed legs. Ichthyostega, which was about a metre long, is the earliest four-legged land animal to have been discovered.

The invasion of the land

The axolotl: a permanent tadpole

The development of this tadpole's breathing organs stopped before it grew lungs. But its sexual development continued, so that it breeds even though it has the feathery external gills of a tadpole. It is the Mexican axolotl.

Their anatomy is so specialised and so different from the urodeles that they are classified in an order of their own, the caecilians. They live only in warm parts of the world, the bulk of them in the tropics. Not only do they lack legs but there is no sign of an internal girdle of bones at either shoulder or hip. They also have an extremely elongated body. Urodeles usually have a dozen or so vertebrae in their spines; a caecilian, however, may have as many as 270. Eyes are of little use burrowing underground and often they have become covered in skin. Compensating for this loss of sight, some species have small extendible tentacles at the angle of their jaws which serve as sensitive feelers.

Caecilians are rarely seen for they seldom come to the surface except at night and even if they are accidentally dug up, they may well be mistaken for brightly coloured earthworms. But unlike earthworms, which eat rotting vegetation, the caecilians are carnivores. They have hunter's jaws and when they suddenly expose a huge gape, they can be quite alarming if you think you are handling an ordinary, inoffensive worm.

A fish-like larva

The eggs of all amphibians hatch into tadpoles, creatures that are more like fish than their parents, with finned tails and external gills. This newt tadpole is already changing and has developed fragile legs.

Frog and toads – 'the tail-less ones'

There are about 160 species of caecilians known and about 300 species of urodeles, but by far the most numerous amphibians alive today belong to a third group, the anurans, 'tail-less ones'. There are about 2600 of them.

In temperate parts of the world, there are two kinds of anurans: those with smooth moist skins which we call frogs, and those with dryer more warty skins, the toads. The distinction, however, is little more than skin deep. In the tropics, where the bulk of the anurans live, it is not nearly so clear, and there are intermediate forms which could be called frog or toad with equal accuracy. Instead of lengthening their bodies, like the caecilians, they have shortened them, their vertebrae having become fused together, and far from losing their legs, they have developed them enormously, and some have become prodigious leapers. The biggest anuran of all, the goliath frog from West Africa, is able to jump three metres or so. Spectacular though this is, many smaller frogs can easily outdo it, if their jumps are judged in relation to their body size. A few tree-living species can travel fifteen metres or so through the air, about a hundred times their body length, by becoming gliders. The web of skin that unites their toes has become greatly enlarged so that each foot is, in effect, a small parachute. When the frog leaps off the branch of a tree, these are spread so that instead of falling, it planes gently downwards, and usually to another tree.

The frog's leap is not merely a way of getting from one point on the ground to another. It is also a very effective method of escaping from an enemy – so explosive, so surprising, that catching a frog can be a difficult business, whether you are a human or a hungry bird or reptile. And as anurans, with their soft vulnerable bodies, are much sought after as food, they need all the defences they can muster. Many rely on concealment. Some match the green of the glossy leaves on which they crouch; others, camouflaged with blotches of brown and grey, are almost invisible, crouching among the leaf litter on the forest floor.

But some anurans defend themselves in a more active way. The common European toad, when it meets a snake, inflates its body and stands on tip-toe, a procedure that makes it appear to have grown suddenly and that seems to baffle most of the snakes that encounter it. The fire-bellied toad, when alarmed, suddenly throws itself on its back, so exposing its underside which blazes with a yellow and black pattern, a colour combination which is widely recognised in the animal world as a warning. Nor is this entirely bluff on the part of the firebelly. All amphibians have mucous glands in their skin which produce a slime that helps to keep it moist and some of these in the firebelly's skin produce a bitter-tasting poison. In Central and South America at least twenty kinds of frogs have developed this defence still further. The poison they produce from their skin is so lethal that it can paralyse a bird or a monkey immediately. It is of no value to the frogs, as individuals, if their attacker dies after they themselves have been eaten, so they have also developed the most striking, vivid colours – not just yellow and black, but scarlet, virulent green and purple. For this protective advertisement to be effective, it must be seen; so these frogs, unlike most others, are active not at night but during the day, moving boldly around the forest floor, confident and secure in their brilliant livery.

From the beginning of their history, the amphibians were hunters, preying on the worms, insects and other invertebrates that had preceded them on to the land. They remain so today despite the appearance of bigger and more powerful hunters which have compelled them to be more circumspect in their behaviour. Some indeed are still quite formidable. The horned toad of South America has a gape so big that it can with ease engulf nestling birds and young mice. But no amphibian can truthfully be described as nimble and for hunting they have to rely on something other than agility – their tongue.

The extendible tongue is an amphibian invention. No fish ever had one. It is attached not to the back of the mouth as ours is, but to the front. In consequence, the frogs and toads can stick it out much further than we can, simply by flicking it forward – a useful talent for a rather slow-moving hunter without a neck. Its end is both sticky and muscular so that a toad can use it first to grasp a worm or a slug and then to carry it bodily back to the mouth.

Many amphibians, including the horned toad, have very serviceable rows of teeth on their jaws, as their ancestors had, but these are used for defence or as a way of gripping the prey. They do nothing to break up the food into easily swallowed gobbets or to tease out the hard inedible bits. No amphibian can chew. This is the reason why toads, when they seize one end of a worm, methodically rake the length of it with their forefeet to remove any bits of sticks or earth that might be stuck to it. The tongue helps the process of swallowing by producing a lot of mucus which lubricates the food and prevents it scratching the delicate membranes of the throat. The tongue also assists in moving the food back along the floor of the mouth. So, it seems, do the eyes. All frogs and toads blink when they swallow. Their eye-sockets have no bony floor, so when they blink, the eye-balls are drawn down into the skull and make a bulge in the roof of the mouth which squeezes the lump of food to the back of the throat.

The amphibian's eyes are fundamentally the same in structure as those of their fish ancestors. Optically such eyes work just as well out of water as in it. The only modification needed to make them operate efficiently in air is some means of keeping their surface clean and smooth, so the amphibians developed the capacity to blink and a membrane that they can draw across the front of the eye-ball.

The amphibian develops a voice

The equipment they use to perceive sound waves in the air is, however, quite new. The fish's method of receiving sound through their bodies, amplified in some instances by the resonance of the gas-filled swim-bladder, does not work efficiently in air, so most frogs and toads have developed eardrums. These detect sound vibrations in the air very efficiently indeed.

While exploiting this ability to hear, the anurans developed a voice. Frogs and toads are most impressive singers. The lungs which blow air through their vocal chords are

The brilliant frogs

The spectacular colours of these South American frogs advertise to predators that they are highly poisonous and should be disregarded as potential meals. The poison glands in the frogs probably evolved from glands that produced a mildly disinfectant mucus. This mucus probably prevented infection from bacteria or fungi developing on the moist skins of the frogs, and must have been of great value to them from an early period.

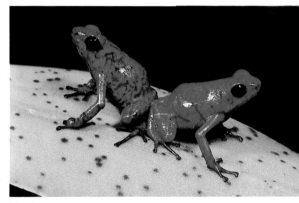

DENDROBATES SPECIOSUS (ABOVE)   ATELOPUS SPECIES (BELOW)

still simple and relatively feeble, but many frogs amplify the sound of their voices with huge swelling throats or resonating sacs bulging from the corner of the jaws. An assemblage of frogs, calling in a tropical swamp, can create such a noise that a human voice has to shout to make itself heard. The variety of sound produced by different species is enormous and amazing to anyone who has only heard frogs of the temperate regions. There are groans, metallic clicks, mewing and wails, belches and whinnies. It is intriguing to speculate, as you stand in a swamp listening to this astounding and deafening chorus, that, although much must have changed in the millions of years since the first amphibians appeared, it was an amphibian voice that first sounded over the land which, until then, had heard nothing but the chirps and whirrs of insects.

DENDROBATES AZUREUS

DENDROBATES HISTRIONICUS (ABOVE LEFT AND ABOVE RIGHT)

DENDROBATES SPECIES (LEFT)   AGALYCHNIS CALLIDRYAS (ABOVE)

The invasion of the land

The amphibians' chorus, rising from a pool or a swamp, is a prelude to mating, a summons to all other members of the same species to assemble and breed. The great majority of amphibians still mate in water. Though males usually grasp the females, the act of fertilisation still, with very few exceptions, takes place outside the body. Sperm swim to the eggs, as fish sperm does, and for this process, water is normally essential. Once this has happened, the adults usually return to land.

Caring for a family of limited size

Thus abandoned, the eggs are now beset by danger. Unprotected by a shell, they are easy meat for insect larvae and flatworms. Those that survive and hatch are then pounced on by water beetles, dragonfly larvae and many kinds of fish. The mortality is gigantic; but so is the number of eggs laid. A female toad may lay 20,000 eggs each season; perhaps a quarter of a million in her lifetime. Out of all these, only two have to live to maturity to maintain the level of the population. The strategy is an ancient one. Fish used it and still do. But it is an expensive one in terms of living tissue produced and it is not the only one possible.

Some frogs have adopted a different technique. They lay comparatively few eggs but look after them carefully, protecting them from predators. The Pipa toad is one of the most aquatic of the anurans, spending all its life in water. It is a grotesque creature

Colour for camouflage

The frogs' very considerable talent for producing colour in their skin is used not only for producing brilliant warning colours, but also for concealment. The little Megaphrys frog (right) lives on the floor of forests in many parts of Southeast Asia. Its colours not only closely match those of the leaf litter, but its markings also suggest leaf-ribs and spots of mould. Its outline is also broken up by peaks of skin over each eye. The result is near-perfect camouflage in its forest surroundings and excellent protection from passing predators.

Camouflage for a hunter

The South American toad, Ceratophrys, lurks beneath green leaves. Its gape is gigantic, and its jaws are armed with small but sharp teeth. It will engulf other frogs, lizards, young birds and mice.

A continuous pattern

When the Phrynohyas tree frog crouches on a tree, the patterns on its back and legs form a continuous band, so disguising its identity.

Clinging to a leaf by suction

Hyla tree frogs are spread around the world, including a species in Europe. Their headquarters, however, is South America. Nearly all have suction cups at the end of each toe, so they can cling to the smoothest leaf.

Leaping for a meal

A frog may sit on a water-lily leaf in a pond for hours on end, without movement, its body a perfect colour match for its background. When at last an insect such as a damsel fly flutters by, it suddenly launches a two-tier attack, leaping forward with a powerful spring of its hind legs and, as it reaches the farthest extent of its jump, shooting out its sticky tongue.

with a flattened body and a squashed-looking head. When they mate, the male grasps the female with his arms as most water-breeding anurans do. But then follows the most extraordinary and graceful ballet. The female kicks with her legs so that the pair soar upwards in an elegant slow somersault. As they descend, the female extrudes a few eggs which are immediately fertilised by the male's sperms that have been discharged into the water at the same time. Then, with delicate movements of his webbed hind feet, toes distended so that they form a fan, he gathers up the eggs and gently spreads them over the female's back. And there they stick. Again and again this arching leap is performed until a hundred or so eggs are fixed in an even carpet on the female's back. The skin beneath them begins to swell and soon the eggs appear to be embedded in it. A membrane rapidly grows over them and within thirty hours, the eggs have disappeared from sight and the skin on the female's back is smooth and entire once more. Beneath the skin, the eggs develop. After a fortnight, the whole of the female's back is rippling with the movements of the tadpoles beneath. Then after 24 days, the young break holes in the skin and swim swiftly away to seek safe hiding places.

Other pond-dwelling anurans find safety for their brood in less extreme ways. Several simply find or manufacture private swimming pools. This is not so difficult in the tropical rainforest where the rainfall is so heavy and so well spread throughout the year that the centres of many plants are permanently filled with water. Members of the bromeliad family are shaped like great rosettes with deep water-filled centres. Some grow, tall-stemmed on the ground. Others squat on the branches of forest trees with their roots dangling beneath them in the humid air. Their centres then become, in effect, miniature ponds high in a tree. No fish could possibly reach them. But frogs can and several species in South America have taken up permanent residence. They lay their eggs in these chalices and there the young go through their entire development, sharing their pool with nothing more dangerous than a few innocuous insect larvae. In Brazil, another small frog builds its own ponds on the margins of forest pools, constructing a crater ringed with a low mud wall about 10 centimetres high. The eggs are laid here and the tadpoles will stay in their privileged and exclusive water until rain raises the level of the main pool and floods their quarters or breaks down the walls.

When the first amphibians appeared, there was, of course, one comparatively safe place for their eggs and young – the land. At that time no other vertebrates were there to steal eggs and gulp the larvae, no risks comparable to those threatened in the water by shoals of hungry fish. If the amphibians could manage to deposit their eggs out of water, their young would certainly have greatly increased chances of survival. But there were problems. How could the eggs be prevented from drying out and how could tadpoles develop out of water? Whether the ancient amphibians overcame those difficulties we do not know. Had they done so they would certainly have greatly accelerated the rate at which they colonised the land. Today the attraction of the land for breeding is not so great, for the amphibians no longer have it to themselves. There are reptiles, birds and even mammals that relish amphibian eggs and tadpoles. Nonetheless, many frogs and toads still find it advantageous to follow this strategy.

A determined singer

Female frogs make only quiet calls or none at all. The males, however, at breeding time are powerful vocalists. They produce the sound by forcing air from their lungs through a larynx in the throat. Some then amplify it with resonators. This American spring peeper (right) uses the ballooning floor of its mouth. Others have a pair of bulging sacs at each side of the throat. These amplified calls can travel ten times as far as those produced by similar-sized species without sacs.

A protective eye-wiper

The eye depends for its efficiency on the smooth surface provided by a film of moisture. The frog's lower eyelid has a translucent fold that can be pulled up, sweeping the eye clean and lubricating it.

The invasion of the land

A pond up a tree

Bromeliad plants, which belong to the same family as the pineapple, live in the humid jungles of South America, sometimes growing trunks a metre or so high, sometimes perching on branches far above the ground with their aerial roots dangling in the moist air. The frequent rain keeps the centre of their rosettes filled with water and in these tiny pools lives a whole community – mosquito larvae, beetles, worms, and a particular species of small frog that is found almost nowhere else.

One European species, the midwife toad, spends most of its life in holes, not far from water. It mates on land. As the eggs are extruded the male fertilises them. A quarter of an hour later, he begins to take up the strings of eggs, twining them around his hind legs. For the next few weeks, he hobbles about with them wherever he goes. If his surroundings get dangerously dry then he moves to moister ones. Eventually, when the eggs are about to hatch, he hops down to the edge of the pool and dips his legs with their burden of eggs into the water. He stays there for the hour or so that is necessary for all the tadpoles to emerge and then returns to his hole.

The South American poison frogs have a variation of the same technique. Their eggs are also laid on moist ground and the males crouch beside them on guard. When the tadpoles hatch, they immediately wriggle to the male and climb on his back. His skin secretes a great deal of mucus which both keeps the young attached and prevents them from drying out. They have no gills, but obtain their oxygen by absorbing it through the skin of their body and greatly enlarged tails.

In Africa, there are frogs that manage to breed on the branches of trees. They select one that overhangs water. They couple and the female begins to excrete a liquid from

From egg to tadpole

The eggs of the European frog are enclosed in envelopes that swiftly absorb water and swell into a protective jelly. Each is a single gigantic cell, filled with food, which begins dividing very quickly, to produce in a week or so, depending on the temperature, the many millions of cells that constitute a free-swimming tadpole.

ABOVE: FIRST CLEAVAGE   BELOW: SECOND CLEAVAGE

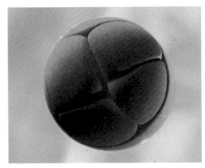

BELOW: THIRD CLEAVAGE

BELOW: A HOLLOW BALL OF CELLS

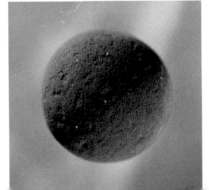

BELOW: 90 MINUTES AFTER THE FIRST CLEAVAGE

THE NEWLY LAID SPAWN

THE BEGINNING OF A SPINAL CORD   CLOSE TO HATCHING

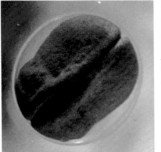

THE TADPOLE NEWLY EMERGED FROM THE JELLY

The invasion of the land

The frantic haste of the pyxie tadpole

The striped pyxie toad (below) lives in East Africa, where the rainy season may be very short, and rivers and marshes can be far distant. The young must therefore complete their development within a very brief period. As soon as rain falls, the female lays wherever she can find puddles. Some of her tadpoles, like those in the footprints of animals, dry out and die. Others cluster together in the drying pools and manage to keep the mud liquid by whipping their tails. Within a few days, some succeed in changing into tiny adults and are able to breathe air.

BELOW: DRIED PUDDLE BELOW: LIVING TADPOLES

BELOW: TOADLETS IN LIQUID MUD

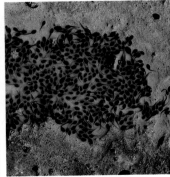

her vent which both she and her mate beat into a lather with their hind legs. The eggs are then laid in the resulting ball of froth. In some species the outside of the suds hardens into a dry crust, retaining the moisture within; in others, the female regularly descends to the pond or stream beneath, absorbs water through her skin and then returns to the egg-mass and moistens it with her urine. The eggs hatch and the young tadpoles develop within the froth until, at the appropriate time, the lower part liquefies and the tadpoles drop out and fall into the water below.

Other frogs avoid the need to provide water for their tadpoles by producing young that complete the whole of their development within the egg membrane. This, however, makes it impossible for them to feed during the larval stage, as free-swimming tadpoles can do, so they have to nourish themselves with specially large quantities of yolk. This, in turn, means that the female can only lay a relatively small number of eggs in a clutch. The whistling frog from the Caribbean, which practises this technique, lays only a dozen or so, which it places on the ground. Development is very rapid and within twenty days each egg contains a tiny froglet which pierces the egg membrane with a minute spike on the tip of its snout and so emerges having dispensed with external water altogether.

The most extreme and physically complicated breeding techniques are those in which the eggs and the developing larvae are kept moist by being retained actually within the body of the parent. The female of one South American frog, Gastrotheca, has a brood pouch on her back with a slit-shaped entrance. When the pair begin to spawn, the male, who is smaller than she is, climbs on her back and clasps her around the throat. She then raises her hind legs so that she is crouching with her nose down and her back tilted. One by one she extrudes eggs. The male fertilises them and they roll down a moist groove and into the brood sac. There they develop and hatch. One species of Gastrotheca produces about 200 young at a time. These emerge and are released into water as tadpoles. Another species, however, has only about twenty young but provides them with more yolk each and they remain within the sac until they become froglets. The female releases them by reaching forward with her hind leg, inserting her longest toe into the sac entrance and pulling it so that it enlarges and her young are able to clamber out.

The most bizarre of all these techniques, at least to our eyes, prejudiced as we are to a mammalian way of doing things, is that practised by Rhinoderma, a tiny frog that Darwin found in Southern Chile. When the females have laid their eggs, which they deposit on the moist ground, the males sit in groups around them on guard. As soon as the developing eggs begin to move within their globes of jelly, the males lean forward and appear to eat them. Instead of swallowing them, however, the eggs are taken into the vocal sac which is unusually large and extends right down the underside of the male's body. There they develop until one day the male gulps once or twice, suddenly yawns and a fully-formed froglet leaps out of his mouth.

The acme of parental care among amphibians, however, is that provided by a West African species of Nectophrynoides, the females of which retain their young inside

Breeding on a branch

One species of African tree frog mates on branches overhanging water. This female has attracted two males. She produces a foam, lays about 150 eggs in it, and protects it for three or four days while the tadpoles develop. They then drop into the water beneath.

A devoted father

The male midwife toad (below) collects 30–40 eggs from a female and may carry them for seven weeks before they are ready to hatch and can be taken down to a pond and released.

A nursery beneath the skin

The marsupial frog of South America (above) develops a pouch beneath the skin of her back into which her fertilised eggs are transferred. As the tadpoles get bigger, they wriggle so that her bulging back ripples.

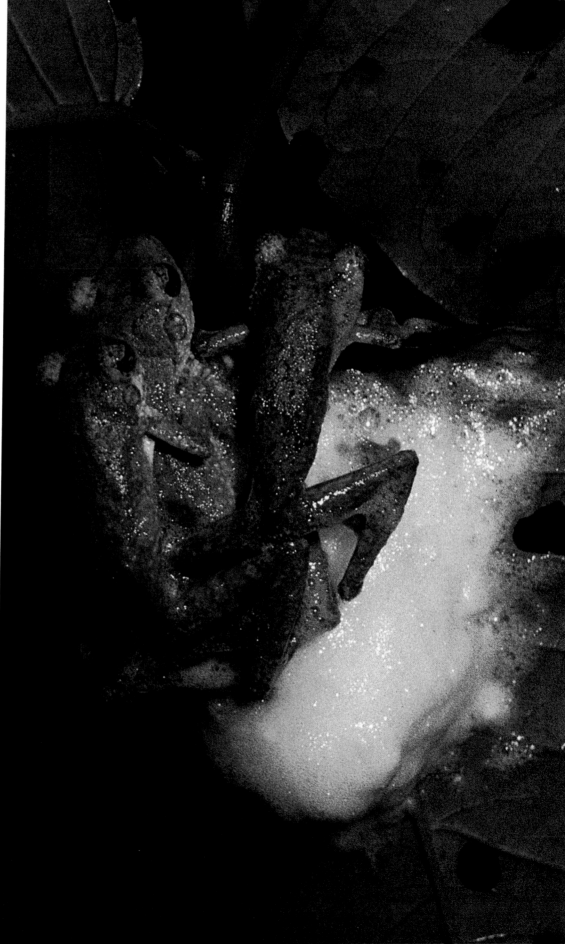

their bodies in a way that compares very closely with the technique of placental mammals. These toads are only about 2 centimetres long. Most of the year they are hidden in rock crevices. When the rains come, however, they emerge in great numbers and mate, the male clasping the female around the groin. Their vents are pressed together so that the sperm can make its way into the female. The fertilised eggs are not then laid but remain inside the female's oviduct. The tadpoles that develop from them are complete with mouths and external gills and they feed within the oviduct on tiny white flakes secreted from its walls, nibbling them just as though they were independent creatures browsing in a tiny pond. When, after nine months, the rains at last return, the female gives birth. Her stomach and oviduct do not have muscles which can contract and so expel her young as a mammal's womb has. She achieves birth, instead, by bracing her body against the ground with her forelegs and then inflating her lungs so that they swell into her abdomen and squeeze the young out by pneumatic pressure.

So by these and many more ingenious techniques, the anurans have minimised their dependence on moisture for mating and for hatching and rearing young. Their permeable skins, however, still dictate that their surroundings are to be moist if the animals are to avoid death by desiccation. But one or two species have succeeded in minimising even this requirement.

There could scarcely be a less promising environment for an amphibian than the desert of central Australia where sometimes several years may pass without any rain falling. And yet a few kinds of frogs manage to live even here. The water-holding frog, Cyclorana, appears above ground only during the brief and infrequent rain storms. Water then may lie on the rocks of the desert for several days, even a week or so. With frantic speed, the frogs feast on the great flush of insects that have also come with the rain. And they mate, laying their eggs in the shallow tepid pools. The eggs hatch and the tadpoles develop at a spectacular rate. As the rain water soaks away and the desert once again dries, the frogs, adults as well as young, absorb water through their skins until they are tightly bloated and almost spherical. Then they burrow deep into the still soft sand and excavate a small chamber. Here they secrete a membrane from their skin so that they resemble a plastic-wrapped fruit from a supermarket. This effectively prevents water-loss by evaporation through the skin, though the animal must doubtless lose some moisture by breathing, which it is able to do through tiny tubes attached to its nostrils and opening through the membrane. It can remain in this state of suspended animation for at least two years. The technique is very reminiscent of that used by the amphibians' far distant and antique cousin, the lungfish.

Nonetheless, the fact remains that even this frog is dependent upon rains arriving at some time and its active life is, in reality, condensed to that brief moment when the desert is wet. To survive, remain active and breed in areas where there is little or no rain and no open water at all, a creature must have both a watertight skin and a watertight egg. The acquisition of those two characters constituted the next great evolutionary breakthrough. It brought to an end the era of amphibians and it was introduced by the next great group to appear, the reptiles.

Living on a leaf
In some parts of the tropics, the rain forest is so humid and so regularly saturated by torrential rains that the surface of the leaves is continuously wet and frogs can live on them permanently. In Trinidad, one species even lays its eggs on a leaf (left), and the tadpoles hatching from them find all the moisture they require to sustain them through their development into froglets, without ever taking to open water.

A nocturnal hunter in the Panama forest

Protective coloration is most effective when its wearer remains motionless. Many frogs, so much sought after by reptiles and birds as food, crouch motionless and invisible during the day. Only at night does a traveller appreciate the great numbers that live in a forest, for then they hop about hunting insects which themselves swarm most abundantly during the darkness.

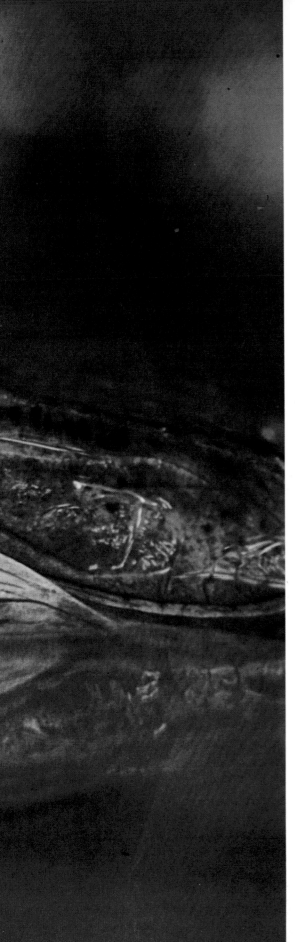

7. A WATERTIGHT SKIN

The reptiles' scaly skin prevented their bodies from drying out in the sun, and the shell around their eggs enabled them to breed away from water. So liberated, they spread over the earth

If there is one place on earth where the reptiles still rule, it must be in the Galapagos Islands, isolated in the emptiness of the Pacific, six hundred miles from the coast of South America. The reptiles reached them long before man and other mammals arrived four centuries ago. They must have drifted there as involuntary passengers on the great rafts of vegetation that float down the rivers of South America and are swept out to sea. Man has since introduced many other mammals, but even now there are small remote islands in the group where the rocks are still covered with herds of lizards, where giant tortoises lumber through the cactus and where you feel, as you land, that you have stepped back two hundred million years to a time when such creatures represented the pinnacle of evolution.

The Galapagos lie scattered across the equator, roasting in the sun. They are all volcanic. The larger ones rise almost 2000 metres, so high that they attract clouds and produce their own rain; their flanks, as a result, are thinly covered with cactus and straggling, dusty bush. The smaller islands, however, are largely waterless. Their extinct craters are surrounded by congealed lava, its surface rippled by the corded swirls and bubbles that formed when it oozed like treacle out of the vents. On the few occasions that rain falls here, it runs off the rock and disappears almost immediately. There are no trees or bushes to give shade, only a few fingers of cactus, furred with spines. The black lava, grilled by the sun, is so hot that it is painful to touch with your

---

An ancient eye regards a changed world

The reptiles dominated the world for 100 million years. Some grew to three times the weight of a bull elephant and stalked the land, browsing on vegetation. Others, with wings 10 metres across, glided through the skies. In the seas, yet others, the size of sharks, hunted for fish. Then 63 million years ago, their fortunes collapsed and most vanished. But not all. Crocodiles, like the owner of this eye staring from the surface of an African river, appeared long before the dinosaurs and even today dominate the rivers in which they live. They give some idea of the complex character of the creatures that once ruled the world.

LIVING WITH HOT SUN AND ICY SEA

The marine iguanas of the Galapagos Islands are unable to generate their heat internally, so they have adopted a daily routine to maintain efficient temperatures, despite extremes of heat and cold.

Warming up At dawn the iguanas lie sideways to the sun, exposing the maximum area of their bodies to its warmth.

Facing the sun As the sun rises higher, the iguanas turn to face it, reducing the surface area exposed to its heat.

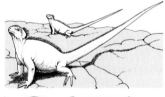

Cooling off If they become too hot they lift their bodies off the rocks to allow the wind to play over their bellies.

Finding shade In extreme heat, the iguanas crowd together into any shade provided by crevices in the rocks.

Food from the sea The iguanas enter the sea each day to eat seaweed. But they lose heat rapidly and cannot stay long.

Recovering On land again, they lie spread-eagled in the sun and wait for their bodies to warm up so they can digest their meal.

bare hand. An amphibian here would be shrivelled and killed within minutes. But the iguanas flourish. They can do so because, unlike amphibians, their skin is watertight.

There are two kinds of iguanas on the islands – the land iguanas which live in the scrub, and marine iguanas that swarm on the bare lava fields by the coast. Basking in the sun, for them, is not a trial to be endured but, for most of the time, an essential activity. The physiological processes of an animal's body, like all chemical reactions, are greatly affected by heat. Within limits, the higher the temperature, the quicker they proceed and the more energy they produce. Neither the reptiles nor the amphibians generate their heat internally; they draw it directly from their environment. As amphibians cannot expose themselves directly to the sun, because of the permeability of their skins, they must remain relatively cold and sluggish. But the reptiles have no such problems.

The marine iguanas follow a daily routine that maintains their bodies at the most efficient temperature. At dawn they assemble on the tops of lava ridges or clamber onto the eastern faces of boulders, lying with their flanks broadside to the rising sun and absorbing as much heat as possible. Within an hour or so their temperature reaches its optimum level and they turn to face the sun. Now their flanks are almost in shadow and the rays strike only their chests. As the sun climbs higher and higher, the risk of overheating grows. Although reptile skin has the crucial quality of relative impermeability, it does not possess sweat glands, so the iguanas cannot cool themselves by allowing sweat to evaporate. Indeed even if they could, this might not be a practical technique in an environment where water is so scarce. But they have to find some way of preventing themselves from simmering inside their skins.

Relief is hard to find. They stiffen their legs and hold their bodies off the baking black rock so that they absorb as little heat as possible from it, while what wind there is blows over their undersides as well as their backs. They pack themselves tightly into the few places where there is shade – in crevices beneath boulders or, better still, in the deep narrow gullies that are kept cool by the surging waves. The sea itself is too cold for comfort, for the Humboldt Current in which the Galapagos lie sweeps straight up from the Antarctic. The marine iguanas are compelled, however, to venture into it at some time every day to feed. Like many of their relations on the mainland of South America, they are vegetarians. No edible plants grow on the lava, but in the sea, just below high water mark, there are thick pastures of green algae. So, at some time during the middle of the day when their blood is almost as hot as they can stand and they are in danger of sunstroke, they risk a swim. They plunge into the surf, swimming strongly, beating their tails like giant newts. Some hang on the rocks near the sea's edge, gnawing the seaweed with the sides of their mouths. Others swim farther out and dive to forage along the sea bottom.

Now their requirements are reversed. Instead of needing to disperse heat, they must retain it for as long as they can. They have a sophisticated physiological mechanism to help them: they can constrict the arteries near the surface of their bodies so that the blood, temporarily limited to the centre of the body, remains warmer longer. If they become too cold, they will lose the strength to swim back through the surf or to resist the tug of the waves as they cling to the boulders and be smashed on the rocks. After a few minutes that danger point has approached. The temperature of their bodies has dropped some ten degrees and they have to return to land.

Back on the rocks, they prostrate themselves, all four legs outstretched like a spread-eagled human bather exhausted after a chilling swim. Not until their body temperature has risen again will they be able to digest the meal that lies in their stomachs.

As the sun starts to sink in the late afternoon, the risk of chilling returns and they assemble once more on the crests of the ridges to absorb as much as they can of the rays of the setting sun before the fall of night.

By such means, the iguanas manage to keep their bodies, for most of the time, very close to 37°C – almost exactly the temperature of the human body. Some lizards even maintain their blood two or three degrees hotter. Clearly the label 'cold-blooded', so often applied to reptiles, is a very misleading one. They are much better described as ectotherms – that is to say creatures that gain their heat from their external surroundings, as contrasted with endotherms, like mammals and birds, which generate it internally.

Refugees from the sun

At mid-day, the black lava rocks of the Galapagos are too scorchingly hot for even a sun-loving reptile like a marine iguana. The coolest places are in the deep shady clefts close to the sea's edge, where the air is chilled by the Pacific breakers. But the best ledges are much sought after and by the time the sun is high, most are densely crowded.

HOW EXTINCT ANIMALS ARE RECONSTRUCTED FROM FOSSILISED REMAINS

Disconnected bones can be assembled to create a skeleton of a long-dead creature. But how did it stand and move? Was its skin covered in fur or scales or feathers – or nothing at all? And most difficult of all: what was its colour?

It is not difficult to reconstruct the appearance of those extinct creatures that had hard shells. You do not need much imagination to fit together the two valves of an ancient mussel or to visualise a fleshy foot protruding between them; nor to replace the spines on the ranks of tiny knobs that cover the globular shell of a sea urchin preserved in chalk. But the problems become substantial when you try to rebuild backboned animals whose skeletons were not external but buried within their bodies. Their scattered and fossilised bones must be gathered and fitted together to make as complete a skeleton as possible. The way the limb bones hinge will give some idea of the animal's general posture. Most bones carry rough scars, bumps or pits which mark the places where muscles were once attached. From the placing and size of such features, a scientist can deduce the size of the vanished muscles and work out which way they stretched. So he can patiently clothe the assembled skeleton with imaginary flesh and form an impression of the vanished animal's bulk and contours.

But now he has to make more difficult judgments. What kind of skin covered the animal? Was it scaly, or hairy, or even naked? In a few rare and precious instances, he may discover direct evidence. The body of a dinosaur, found in the sandstones of Alberta, apparently dried out in the sun soon after its death some 70 million years ago, and mummified. As a result, its skin became so hard that it did not rot and when it was eventually entombed in the sand, the shape of every scale was preserved. From this one specimen, we can be fairly sure that this family of extinct creatures had a tough leathery hide studded with lines of bony scutes not unlike that of a living crocodile.

Colour – the greatest imponderable

The evidence of the nature of body covering, however, is seldom so direct. Sometimes judgments can only be made by a long – and indeed debatable – chain of reasoning. The shape of a creature's legs may suggest that it was able to run fast; and the deposits in which it was found may indicate that it lived in a cold environment. It is then a fair conclusion that it must have been able to generate its own body heat to produce the necessary energy. It follows that it must have had some way of conserving this heat. So the reconstructor may feel justified in giving it a covering of fur.

But what about colour? Did early fish display to one another by quivering multicoloured fins? Were the dinosaurs striped, or were the great plates on their backs or the horns on their heads accentuated with scarlet or livid blue skin? We do not know. No evidence of colour has ever been found. But the artist, trying to paint portraits of such creatures cannot escape a decision. To colour an animal uniformly brown may itself be misleading. The best he can do is to look at the nearest living relatives of his vanished subject and then make an informed guess.

Even when the evidence is marvellously complete, it is only too easy to make mistakes. The sandstones which lie between seams of coal are rich in plant remains. Among the commonest are the stems of a giant club-moss that was named by the early investigators, Lepidodendron. Other fossils were awarded such names as Stigmaria, Lepidostrobus and Aspidaria. It was many years before research established that all these three forms were, in fact, the remains of one and the same plant, Lepidodendron. The first was its roots, the second its reproductive cones, and the third was its stem in a particular state of decay.

Three questions answered *Reptilian eggs can only hatch in air, so swimming reptiles that lay them must return to land to nest. So how did ocean-going ichthyosaurs breed? Fossils of pregnant females (above) show they bore live young. This one has three within her ribs and a fourth half-born. What kind of skin did dinosaurs have? The tail of a duck-billed dinosaur (left) made an impression in the sand that entombed it which has survived even though the skin has gone. It reveals that the skin was scaly. How did the huge club-mosses in the ancient forests reproduce? With long cones (right) that sprouted from the end of the branches.*

Endothermy has many advantages. It makes possible the development of delicate and complex organs that would be damaged by fluctuations in temperature. It allows its possessors to remain active at night when the warming sun has disappeared. It even enables creatures to live permanently in cold parts of the world where no reptile can survive. But the price paid for such privileges is very high. Something like 80 per cent of the calories in our food, for example, goes towards maintaining our body temperature at a constant level. The ectothermic reptiles, by taking their heat directly from the sun, can survive on 10 per cent of the nourishment that a mammal of similar size would require. As a consequence, reptiles can live in deserts where a mammal would starve, and the marine iguanas flourish on quantities of vegetation that would not keep a rabbit alive.

The arrival of watertight eggs

The reptiles not only survive in waterless places, they manage to breed there too, so their eggs, like their bodies, must be watertight. Making them so is not complicated. A gland in the lower part of the oviduct secretes a parchment-like shell around the egg as it passes down. The embryo must breathe, so the shell has to be slightly porous to enable oxygen to pass in and carbon dioxide to pass out. This shell brings complications, however, as well as benefits. Clearly if it is dense enough to prevent the egg from drying out, then it is likely to prevent sperm getting in. Fertilisation must therefore take place within the female's body before the shell is deposited. To deal with this problem the male is equipped with a penis.

The form of this organ varies considerably between the different groups of reptiles. Only one reptile today lacks the organ, a strange lizard-like creature that lives in a few small islands in New Zealand, the tuatara.

The tuatara manages to achieve internal fertilisation in a manner that is reminiscent of some salamanders and frogs. When the pair come together, their genital openings are pressed closely together so that sperm from the male actively swims into the female's oviduct. Interestingly enough, the tuatara has another characteristic reminiscent of amphibians. It is active at temperatures even below 7°C, which is much lower than any lizard or snake would favour. It seems therefore to be a very primitive kind of reptile and the structure of its skull confirms this, for it resembles, in important ways, those of the earliest recognisable reptile fossils. Bones of a virtually identical creature have been found in rocks 200 million years old. The tuatara thus harks back, if not to the time when the reptiles first separated from the amphibians, at least to an early stage in their history when, at the dawn of their golden age, the reptiles were beginning to diversify into a huge variety of forms.

The basic four-legged, tough-skinned, egg-laying ectotherm now became adapted to life in all parts of the world except in polar regions. Some, the ichthyosaurs and plesiosaurs, became water-living with their legs modified into paddles. Others grew an elongated digit on each foreleg which supported sail-like flaps of leathery skin, and took to the air as pterosaurs. And the land was dominated by the dinosaurs.

Among the best known, the most abundant and the most perfectly preserved of all fossil reptiles are the ichthyosaurs which swam in the seas of 190 million years ago. Their fossils even show that they did not lay eggs like most reptiles but gave birth to live young; several superb specimens have been found in which the skeletons of the unborn young still lie within the ribs of their mother. One shows a baby, half-born, emerging tail first, as young dolphins do today. Yet our image of even this creature was for some years faulty. Investigators noted that the specimens they discovered had a downward kink in their spines. This was taken to be a chance breakage that had occurred during the process of fossilisation, and the first reconstructions were given a straight spine. Later, exceptionally good specimens were found in which the faint outline of the body profile could be distinguished. These showed beyond doubt that the bend was present in life and served to give strength to the lower lobe of the ichthyosaur's tail.

It is easy now to see the mistakes made during the last century. It is quite certain that we ourselves are making some today, but what they are will only be revealed by the steady accumulation of new evidence.

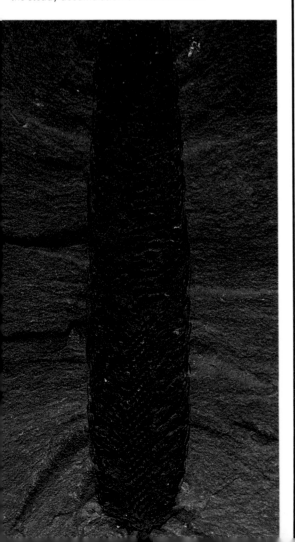

Procompsognathus ◁
'First elegant jaw'
Length: 90 centimetres

Scelidosaurus △
'Limb lizard'
Length: 4 metres

Dilophosaurus
'Two-ridged lizard'
Length: 6 metres
◁

Kentrosaurus △
'Prickly lizard'
Length: 5 metres

Heterodontosaurus
◁'Different-toothed lizard'
Length: 90 centimetres

Ceratosaurus △
'Horn lizard'
Length: 6 metres

Coelophysis ◁
'Hollow form'
Length: 3 metres

Diplodocus △
'Double beam'
Length: 26 metres

Megalosaurus
'Big lizard'
Length; 6–7 metres ▽

Plateosaurus
'Flat lizard'
◁ Length: 6 metres

Ornitholestes
'Birdcatcher'
Length: 1·5 metres △

Camptosaurus △
'Bent lizard'
Length: 5 metres

Compsognathus △
'Elegant jaw'
Length: 60 centimetres

THE TRIASSIC PERIOD
225–195 million years ago

THE JURASSIC PERIOD
195–136 million years ago

DINOSAURS: THE DIVERSE REPTILES THAT DOMINATED THE WORLD FOR 100 MILLION YEARS

Scolosaurus
'Crooked lizard'
Length: 6 metres ▷

Hypsilophodon △
'High-ridge tooth'
Length:
2 metres

◁ **Brachiosaurus**
'Arm lizard'
Length: 26 metres

Polacanthus
'Many spined'
Length: 4 metres
▽

Ornithomimus ▽
'Bird imitator'
Length:
4 metres

Pachycephalosaurus
'Thick-headed lizard'
◁ Length: 6—8 metres

Camarasaurus
'Dome lizard'
◁ Length: 18 metres

Parasaurolophus
'Abnormal crested
lizard'
◁ Length: 10 metres

Corythrosaurus
'Helmet lizard' ▷
Length: 9 metres

Tyrannosaurus
'Tyrant lizard'
Length: 13 metres
◁

Psittacosaurus
'Parrot lizard'
Length: 2 metres
△

Deinonychus
△
'Terrible claw'
Length: 3 metres

◁ **Monoclonius**
'Single shoot'
Length: 6 metres

Protoceratops
'First horned face'
Length: 2 metres
▷

Styracosaurus
'Spiky lizard'
Length: 6 metres
▽

Spinosaurus
'Spine lizard'
Length: 11 metres △

THE CRETACEOUS PERIOD
136—64 million years ago

Dinosaurs varied from delicate, bird-like creatures to giants of 75 tonnes. Some ate plants, some ate flesh. But despite their diversity all of them suddenly perished.

During the 100 million years when dinosaurs ruled the earth, hundreds of types evolved, and many became extinct before the end of the dinosaur era. They ranged from the tiny carnivorous Procompsognathus, which walked only on its hind legs, to the giant herbivore Brachiosaurus, which walked on four legs and weighed 75 tonnes. The dinosaurs drawn here are arranged in the geological periods in which their fossils first occur. The giant dinosaurs – Diplodocus, Camarasaurus, and Brachiosaurus – were all herbivores, and were at their peak during the Jurassic period. They were preyed on by two-legged carnivores, such as Megalosaurus, Dilophosaurus and Ceratosaurus. During the Cretaceous period these predators became bigger. The largest of all were Tyrannosaurus of North America and Mongolia, and the amazing Spinosaurus of Egypt, with a 'sail' on its back which may have been a temperature regulator.

Climatic change
Pachycephalosaurus are thought to have fought each other by banging their thickened skulls together. Why did this great group of reptiles finally die out? The most probable answer is that when the world suffered a drop in temperature the huge herbivores simply died of cold, and the carnivores – deprived of prey – perished from starvation.

A watertight skin

A parade of dinosaurs

The richest known deposits of dinosaur remains lie in the midwestern states of North America. In Texas, the Paluxy River, a tributary of the Brazos, is slowly meandering across a layer of mudstones. This was once the mud flat of an estuary. One day at low tide several dinosaurs wandered across it. One was a theropod, a carnivorous species that walked erect on its hind legs. The line of its three-toed footprints is still clear along one side of the present-day river, with a furrow thrown up by its tail swinging between them. Farther down, the river has eroded more of the overlying rocks to expose in the same layer four immense circular prints nearly a metre across that were made by one of the huge plant-eating species. As the water ripples above them, it is easy to imagine that the river bed is not stone but still mud and that these giants were striding through the water only hours before.

At Dinosaur National Monument a museum has been built around a cliff face where a single layer of stone, some four metres thick, has yielded fourteen different species of dinosaur. Some were no bigger than a chicken. Others were the biggest land-living creatures the world has ever seen. Thirty complete skeletons have been taken away but bones of many more remain. The rock which now forms the cliff-face was once a sandbank in the middle of a river. Gigantic rotting carcasses of dinosaurs floated down, beached on the sandbank and were dismembered there partly by putrefaction and partly by smaller dinosaurs that came to feast on carrion. All the long bones, such as those from the limbs and sections of backbone, lie pointing in roughly the same direction and from them we can deduce which way the river ran. The whole deposit seems to have been laid down in the space of not more than a hundred years or so. It is an astonishing demonstration of how abundant these creatures once were.

Why did some species grow to such a great size? There are at least two possible reasons. The teeth of some of the biggest, such as Apatosaurus (which used to be called Brontosaurus and was some 25 metres long and may have been 30 tons in weight), make it clear that they were vegetarians. The plants of the period, ferns and cycads, have tough fibrous fronds which would certainly have required a great deal of digestion. The teeth of Apatosaurus and its relatives, though very numerous, were simple and peg-like – far less efficient grinders than the molars of modern herbivores like cows and antelopes – and the pulping of the food had, therefore, to be done in the dinosaur's stomach. There are indications that some species swallowed pebbles to act as millstones within their heaving stomachs just as today, on a much smaller scale, some birds use grit in their gizzards. But they must have relied primarily upon the biochemical and bacteriological powers of their digestive juices. At all events, it is very likely that the process took a considerable time. The herbivorous dinosaur's stomach, therefore, had to be huge to serve as a storage vat where the food could be held while the lengthy process of fermentation took place. A huge stomach requires a huge body to carry it. Carnivorous dinosaurs, like Tyrannosaurus, would, in turn, have to have considerable stature to be able to prey on the giant herbivores.

The second advantage of great size to the dinosaurs is connected with the recurring

Tracking across 80 million years

Tracks can tell a hunter a great deal about the weight, size and speed of an animal he is following. Dinosaur footprints can be almost as revealing to the student of fossils. The distance apart gives an idea of the animal's stride and therefore its height; the depth suggests its weight, and the placings of the feet its gait. A furrow, swinging between the footprints, may reveal that it had a long tail. Fossil tracks, however, do pose one problem that seldom troubles a modern hunter – the identity of the animal that made them. It is not easy to link bones with footprints. These tracks in Texas were probably made by a giant carnivorous dinosaur that walked on its hind legs, Acrocanthosaurus.

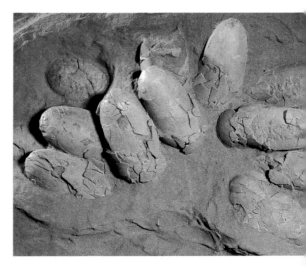

The nest of a dinosaur

Fossilised eggs like these have been found in some numbers in the Gobi Desert, in groups of up to 18 arranged in three concentric rings. Fragments of embryonic bone in some of the eggs, together with the skeletons of newly hatched young near by, make it clear that these are the nests of a small short-horned dinosaur, Protoceratops, that grew about 2 metres long.

problem for all reptiles, temperature control. The bigger a body, the longer it retains its heat and the less susceptible it is to short-term variations in the temperature of its environment. Since their vegetable food was so poor in nutritive value, the herbivores had to eat a great deal of it and spend much of their time feeding, so an indifference to small temperature changes must also have been very valuable to them.

Temperature control may also explain the extravagant body form of some species. The Stegosaurus carried along its back a twin line of staggered diamond-shaped plates. It was once thought that these were a kind of armour, but close examination of the bone surface has shown that in life each plate was covered with skin thick with blood vessels. The animal may therefore have controlled its temperature in the same way as the marine iguanas do today. If it stood broadside to the sun, its blood would heat very quickly as it flowed over the plates; if it faced the sun – and particularly if there was any kind of breeze – the plates would become very efficient cooling radiators.

The end of the dinosaur dynasty
The bones of many of the smaller dinosaurs make it clear that they were able, at least on occasion, to move very swiftly. From that we can deduce that, at least at times, their blood temperature was quite high. It may be that many were able to generate heat within their bodies. To what extent they were able to maintain a temperature constant within a few degrees at all times is a question that is much debated. All contemporary endotherms are equipped with some kind of heat insulation above or just below their skins – hair, fat or feathers. Without it, the demands on their energy would be intolerable. No reptile skin has such insulation today; nor is there any evidence that the dinosaurs were better provided for.

Problems of body temperature may well have brought about the fall of the dinosaur dynasty. Their end is portrayed with graphic clarity in the rocks of the Montana badlands. Here, horizontal beds of sandstones and mudstones, that were laid down 60 to 70 million years ago, have been sliced and gouged by the melting snows of winter and the violent storms of summer into a wilderness of pinnacles, buttes and gullies. On the striped faces of the crumbling cliffs, trickles of brown fragments, like water stains from a dripping tap, show where fossil bones are weathering out. Among them are the remains of Triceratops, a huge horned dinosaur. In life, it grew to eight metres or so in length and a weight of nine tons. Its immense skull carried three horns, one above each eye and one on the tip of its nose, and a great bony frill that projected from the back of its head to protect the neck. It was a vegetarian, champing cycads that grew in the swamps. Its brain, one of the largest possessed by any dinosaur, weighed about a kilogram. It seems probable therefore that it was not only huge and powerful but, compared with other creatures alive at the time, relatively intelligent. But that did not save it.

Just above the level at which its most recent bones are found, a thin deposit of coal rules a black, precise line that can be traced in cliff after cliff across Montana and over the Canadian border into Alberta. It must represent a short-lived but widespread

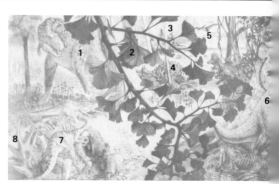

A FOREST WHERE DINOSAURS ROAMED

This reconstruction of a North American forest, shortly before the end of the age of reptiles, shows the major types of dinosaurs that ruled the landscape, and the vegetation that grew there.

Towards the end of the age of reptiles, about 75 million years ago, a diverse group of dinosaurs and other reptiles inhabited the forests and plains of western North America. The vegetation of that time included plants that still survive, including ginkgo trees and magnolias. There were a few small mammals, and turtles and salamanders swam in the streams. But the dominant animals on land were the dinosaurs. The duck-billed Corythrosaurus and Parasaurolophus stood 8 metres tall and fed on ferns and leaves. They lived in groups, and their bizarre crests may have functioned as resonators, enabling them to communicate over long distances. The horned Styracosaurus and the slow-moving Scolosaurus were armoured against attacks by predators such as the giant tyrannosaur Albertosaurus, which grew over 8 metres long and weighed several tons. Ornithomimus, the ostrich dinosaur, probably fed mainly on insects and fruits, using its three-fingered hands to turn over logs and perhaps scavenge meat from carcasses.

A watertight skin

swamp forest, and it marks the death of the dinosaurs. Immediately below it you can find the remains not only of Triceratops, but of at least ten other species of dinosaur. Above it there are none.

There have been many suggestions as to what brought the dinosaurs to their end. The more extreme require some kind of global catastrophe. They can be disregarded because, after all it was only the dinosaurs that disappeared, not the whole of animal life – or even all the reptiles. Another theory suggests that the mammals, which at this time were on the brink of their great expansion, began to compete with the dinosaur for food and, perhaps because of their superior intelligence, were so successful that the dinosaurs were displaced and exterminated. The Montana fossil beds show why this could not have been so. They contain not only gigantic bones but minute ones, bones so tiny that the naked eye has great difficulty in finding them unaided. Fortunately, a species of ant in the area comes to the fossil hunter's aid. It builds low smooth mounds over its nests which it roofs with carefully selected gravel chips of a particular size. If you search through them you find that some are not stone but tiny cone-shaped teeth. These belonged to a shrew-like creature only a few centimetres long, one of the very first of the mammals. Mammals had already been in existence for many millions of years, but no sign of any bigger species has been found living at the same time as the dinosaurs. It is just possible that such a small creature could have preyed on dinosaur eggs, but it seems extremely unlikely that it could have done so with such intensity that it exterminated a single species, let alone the entire dinosaur group. Nor is it credible that it robbed the dinosaurs of their food or in some way out-manoeuvred them with its greater intelligence.

The Montana badlands provide evidence of yet another but more convincing explanation. In beds a little way above the final black marker of coal, there are some excellently preserved fossilised tree stumps. Triceratops and other dinosaurs of the time had lived in forests of cycads and ferns. These stumps belonged to a very different tree, Sequoia, the coniferous redwood. Today, and almost certainly then, the redwood preferred a cool climate. Its presence here is only one element in a great body of evidence which shows that about 63 million years ago, coinciding very closely with the disappearance of the dinosaurs, the world went through a great change of climate. It got colder.

This may very well have killed the dinosaurs. While it is true that a big body retains its heat for a long time, it is also true that it takes a very long time to regain it once it has been lost. Even if some of the dinosaurs had the ability to generate heat internally to some degree, a succession of bitterly cold nights could have drained a big dinosaur of its heat beyond all recovery. With its body badly chilled, it might not be able to summon sufficient energy to move its huge bulk and browse. So a steady cooling of the climate and an increasing seasonality producing severe winters, as there are now in Montana, may well have led to the extermination of the large herbivores. With them would go the carnivores that hunted them and were therefore dependent upon them. The pterosaurs,

The last of the great dinosaurs
The skull of a Triceratops lies exposed in a cliff in Montana. The nearest horn has been eroded away, the second is visible in the rock behind and the nose horn is hidden in the cliff.

huddled on their cliffs, would be even more severely affected. The ichthyosaurs and plesiosaurs did not figure in this crisis. Their line, for some reason, had died out many millions of years earlier.

There were two ways to escape the effects of this increasing cold which are both practised by various reptiles alive today. One is to find a crevice in rocks or to bury yourself so that you are beyond the reach of the worst frosts and then fall into a state of suspended animation and hibernate. But that was only possible if you were small. Apatosaurus or Tyrannosaurus had no chance of doing so. The other was to take to the water. Since water retains heat much longer than air, the effects of a sudden cold snap are much reduced and the consequences of a long cold season can be avoided by swimming on migration to warmer latitudes. This was a way open to big creatures. It is not without significance that the three main types of reptile that survive today from the period of the dinosaurs – the crocodiles, the lizards, and the tortoises and turtles – can take advantage of one or other of these expedients.

Crocodiles: the largest modern reptiles

The crocodiles are the largest of all living reptiles. Males of the huge sea-going species that lives in Southeast Asia have been reported to be over 6 metres long. Fossil crocodiles appear in the rocks at about the same time as dinosaurs and species very like the monsters of today lived alongside Apatosaurus and doubtless preyed on smaller antelope-sized dinosaurs. If anyone supposes that this dinosaur-ruled world was one of puny-brained animals lumbering clumsily about, reacting in a simple, slow-witted way to one another, then watching crocodiles today will quickly show how false that picture must be.

The Nile crocodile spends most of its days basking on sandbanks, maintaining an even body temperature in much the same way as the Galapagos iguanas. Its problem, however, is not as acute as the iguanas', for being so much bigger, it is less affected by short-term variations. It also makes particular use of an additional technique for cooling. It opens its mouth and gapes so that air plays over the soft skin inside the mouth which is much thinner than the hide that covers the body. At night, it moves down into the warm waters of the river. Although crocodiles are inactive for long periods, on occasion they can run very fast indeed. Recent work has shown that their social lives are very much more complex than had been suspected. The males establish a breeding territory, patrolling a patch of water not far from a beach. They bellow and fight any other males that come to dispute with them. Courtship takes place in the water. As the female approaches, the male becomes greatly excited. His roars increase to such an intensity that his flanks vibrate and throw up clouds of spray. He lashes his tail and claps his huge jaws in frenzy. Actual mating lasts only a couple of minutes or so as the male clasps the female with his jaws and their tails intertwine.

The female digs a hole well above the waterline on a site that she may use all her life. She lays at night, producing 40 eggs in several batches. The depth to which she buries them varies according to the nature of the soil, but it is always sufficiently deep for the

A watertight skin

temperature not to vary more than 3°C. The holes are never made in places that are exposed to full sunshine throughout the day. Other species go to even greater lengths to ensure that their eggs remain at an even temperature. The saltwater crocodile builds a mound of vegetation as a nest and sprays urine over it when the heat gets too intense. The American alligator also piles up vegetation, lays her eggs in it, and regularly turns it

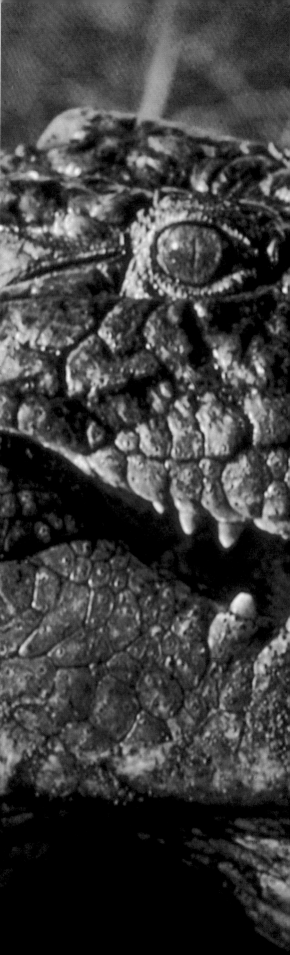

Crocodile care
The Nile crocodile (above), like all reptiles, must lay her eggs on land, for the embryo cannot breathe if the shell is in water. Both parents guard the eggs from predators for 90 days (left).

The ride to the nursery
As the young emerge (above) the parents delicately lift them in jaws that can shear the leg from an antelope and carry them to nursery areas.

A watertight skin

Life in the crocodile nursery
In the nursery, the mother stays with her babies while they play around and over her, feed and grow; for marabou storks, vultures, ospreys and other crocodiles will eat them if they get a chance. Young reptiles are capable of independence as soon as they hatch, and baby crocodiles soon catch dragonfly larvae, beetles and even small frogs in their needle-like teeth.

over to provide the eggs beneath with moisture and a constant heat from the rotting foliage.

It is in the care it gives its offspring that the crocodile's behaviour is most complex and surprising. When the eggs of the Nile crocodile are close to hatching, the young within begin to make piping calls. These are so loud that they can be heard, through shell and sand, from several metres away. In response, the female begins to scrape away the sand covering the eggs. As the young struggle up through the sand, she picks them up with her jaws, using her huge teeth as gently and delicately as forceps. A special

pouch has developed in the bottom of her mouth and in it she can accommodate half a dozen babies. When she has collected such a number, she carries them down to the water and swims away, with her jaws half-closed, the young piping and peering through the palisade of teeth. The male helps and within a short time the young have been ferried to a special nursery area in the swamp. Here they remain for a couple of months, hiding in small holes in the bank and hunting for frogs and fish while their parents laze in the water close by, keeping guard. It is difficult not to believe that the dinosaurs themselves had similarly complicated forms of courtship and parental behaviour.

Assembling to breed

South American freshwater turtles, at the beginning of their breeding season, make immense journeys along the rivers to reach their breeding sites on sand banks or river islands. Here they assemble in vast numbers before mating and laying their eggs in communal nests.

ARMOUR PLATING ON LAND AND SEA

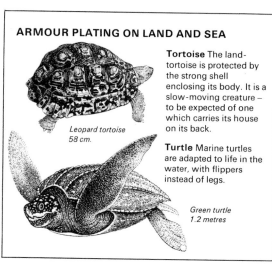

Leopard tortoise 58 cm.

Tortoise The land-tortoise is protected by the strong shell enclosing its body. It is a slow-moving creature – to be expected of one which carries its house on its back.

Turtle Marine turtles are adapted to life in the water, with flippers instead of legs.

Green turtle 1.2 metres

The armour-plated tortoise

The tortoises have an ancestry just as ancient as the crocodiles. Very early in their history, they invested in defence. The crocodiles had strengthened their skin with small ossicles beneath the scutes of their backs. The tortoises took even more extreme measures, enlarging the scales into horny plates and reinforcing them from below with bone so that their bodies became enclosed within a virtually impregnable box into which they could withdraw their head and limbs should danger threaten. It is by far the

A watertight skin

The ornamented skin of the reptiles

The reptiles' scales, like our own nails, are dead and can easily be grown into extravagant shapes. Beneath the scales, their skin, like that of amphibians and fish, contains pigment cells which many species can dilate. With these two elements, the reptiles have developed many spectacular ornaments and patterns that serve a great variety of functions – camouflage, the recognition of their own kind, the battles of courtship, threats against aggressors, and even the collecting of water.

most effective armour developed by any vertebrate and has certainly served the tortoises well for they have remained virtually unchanged from that day to this. The one major variation on the basic pattern arose very early in their history. One group took to the water and became the turtles. It was a logical move for a creature with heavy bulky armour that made movement on land laborious and energy-consuming, but one of their newly acquired reptilian talents prevented them from becoming totally at home there. The shelled egg that had enabled their ancestors to become independent of water was useless in it. The membranes beneath the shell by which the embryo breathes through the shell pores, function by gaseous exchange. In water, the system does not work and the young would drown within their shells. So the female turtle, every breeding season, has to forsake the open ocean, swim to coastal waters and then, one night, haul herself up a sandy beach, excavate a hole and lay eggs, just as her land-living relations do.

MOLOCH LIZARD, AUSTRALIA

GREEN IGUANA, SOUTH AMERICA

BEARDED DRAGON, AUSTRALIA

JACKSON'S CHAMELEON, EAST AFRICA

HELMETED LIZARD, SOUTH AMERICA

KNOB-TAIL GECKO, AUSTRALIA

Shells: a liberating innovation

When they wrapped their eggs in shells, the reptiles no longer needed water for breeding. Their young, like this gopher tortoise, could develop in the tiny pond inside the egg and emerge as miniatures of their parents.

Lizards: most numerous of reptiles

The third group of survivors, the lizards, are now very much more numerous than either the crocodiles or the turtles. They have also changed to a much greater degree from their ancestral pattern. There are now many different families – iguanas, chameleons, skinks, monitors and several others. They have all protected their invaluable watertight skin by developing their scales. The Australian shingleback skink has a covering of stout polished ones that fit together with the neatness of chain mail; the Gila Monster from Mexico is clothed in rounded black and pink ones resembling beads; the African sun-gazer grows them long and spiny like rococo armour. Scales, like our own finger-nails, are made of a dead horny material and gradually wear away. The lizards have therefore to replace them, often several times a year. A new set grows beneath the old which are then sloughed off.

Crests and dewlaps for use in arguments

Many male lizards carry extravagant head ornaments, often accentuated with colour, like those of the angle-headed lizard (left). These they brandish during arguments with one another. Such eye-catching decorations, however, risk attracting hunters. The little anolis lizard (above) minimises the risks by having a retractable dewlap that is only exposed when necessary.

A watertight skin

Relief for burning feet

This little lizard lives in one of the hottest places in the world, the Namib Desert of South-West Africa. Here the sand gets so hot that it is apparently painful to even the scaled feet of a reptile. The lizard gets relief by lifting its legs alternately to cool them and sometimes (below) even raising all four at the same time and resting its belly on the sand which, having been shaded by its body, may be slightly less searing.

Scales are, it seems, more quickly responsive to evolutionary pressures than bone and they serve the lizards in many ways apart from straightforward protection against wear and tear. The marine iguanas have a crest of long ones along their spine so that the males, when they display in territorial competition, appear particularly big and formidable. Some chameleons, the most heraldically dramatic of all reptiles, have grown their head scales into horns – single, double, triple or even quadruple. The thorny devil, a tiny highly specialised lizard from the central Australian desert which lives entirely on ants, has each scale enlarged and drawn out to a point in the centre. Few birds could relish such a thorny mouthful and to that extent, they must be a very effective defence, but the shape of the scales also serves another and most unusual function. Each is scored with very thin grooves radiating from the central peak. During cold nights, dew condenses on them and is drawn by capillary action along the grooves and eventually down to the tiny creature's mouth. Perhaps the most specialised scale of all is that developed by the geckos. These small tropical lizards can run up walls, scuttle upside down over ceilings, even cling to vertical panes of glass – and do all these tricks with such ease that it is tempting to think that they use suction in some way. But scales are responsible. Those on the underside of the toes carry pads formed from enormous numbers of microscopic hairs, invisible to the naked eye. Each hair is so tiny that it can only be seen through the electron microscope. When pressed hard it engages on the tiniest roughnesses, even those that occur on the surface of glass. The mass of hairs in the pad thus provide the gecko with a foothold.

Throughout their history, the lizards like the salamanders of the New World seem to have had a tendency to lose their legs. Several skinks today represent different stages of the process. Australian ones, like the blue-tongue or the shingleback, have, at best, diminutive legs which are scarcely sufficiently strong or big to hoist their stout bodies above the ground. The European slow-worm, another lizard, has no legs at all, though internally it still carries relics of shoulder and hip bones. The snake-lizards of South Africa, even within their single genus, show many intermediate stages of limb reduction. One has all four legs, each with five toes; another, very small limbs with only two fully developed toes on each; and a third has hind legs with one toe apiece and no external front legs at all.

Snakes: the reptiles that lost their legs

A hundred million years ago, this process of limb reduction took place among a group of ancient lizards. Its consequence was the appearance of the snakes.

The exact identity of this ancestral group is still in debate. The loss of their limbs, however, seems to have been connected with the assumption of a burrowing life. There are several clues that suggest that the snake's ancestors once lived underground. There the delicate drum of the ear can be easily damaged and hearing is not, in any case, of much value. So burrowers tend to lose their ears. No snake has an eardrum and the bone that in other reptiles transmits vibrations from an ear drum is connected instead to the lower jaw so that snakes are virtually deaf to sounds transmitted through the air but can,

The constrictors

The pythons and the boas are primitive snakes which still retain several relics of their four-footed less-elongated ancestors. They have small isolated vestiges of their hip bones buried in their flesh and relics of the hind legs, which are visible as spurs. In females, these spurs are small and easily overlooked, but in the male they are quite large and are used during mating. These snakes also retain two lungs, whereas in all other kinds the right lung is extended into a long thin tube, but the left lung does not develop at all. Neither do pythons and boas have venom. Having seized their prey with their jaws, they kill by wrapping themselves around it and squeezing. This may burst their victim's blood vessels. The victim is also prevented from breathing so that eventually it will die of suffocation. The pythons live in Africa, Asia and Australia, the boas in South America and Madagascar. Superficially, it is difficult to tell the two families apart and each contains species that parallel one another very closely. The emerald boa (right) comes from Peru, but in New Guinea there is a python of almost exactly the same colouring, size and habit. The difference between the two, however, becomes plain at breeding time. All species of python lay eggs. All the boas, however, give birth to live young. The constricting snakes include the biggest of all snakes — the reticulate python of Asia and the anaconda, a largely water-living boa from South America, which may both grow to over 10 metres in length.

A watertight skin

A killer in hiding

The dwarf puff adder can bury itself in sand within a single minute to ambush creatures running over the surface, such as small rodents and lizards. It lies buried with its eyes exposed, waiting its moment to strike.

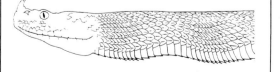

HOW A SNAKE MOVES IN A STRAIGHT LINE

Snakes move not only by sideways undulations but also by sending muscular contractions along their undersides. The belly scales catch on the ground and provide traction.

instead, detect vibrations such as those produced by a footstep that travel through the ground.

Their eyes too, in the opinion of some authorities, provide further evidence. They differ considerably in structure from any other reptilian eye. If the snake's ancestors had been burrowers, then their eyes, like those of any other burrower, would have tended to degenerate. But if, before they were lost altogether, their owners had returned to a life above ground, then sight would once again be needed and the vestiges would redevelop. So the snake eye would have a structure peculiar to itself. This explanation is very persuasive but not yet universally accepted.

No one doubts, however, that the snakes once had legs. Indeed, a whole group of them, the pythons and boas, still retain internal relics of their hip bones, and show external signs of them – two spurs on either side of the vent. Above ground, without legs, the snakes had to develop new means of getting about. They flex their flank muscles in alternate bands so that their body is drawn up into a series of S-shaped curves. As the contractions travel in waves down the body the flanks are pressed against obstacles on the ground such as stones or plant stems and the snake is able to push itself forward. In short, it wriggles. If it is put on a surface completely free of any irregularities to provide purchase, the technique fails and the snake simply writhes helplessly.

Several snakes that live in sandy desert have developed a variation of this technique and practise it so quickly that it is baffling to watch and extremely difficult to describe comprehensibly. It is called side-winding. The snake's body is again contracted into an S-shape but it only touches the ground at two points which travel rapidly down the body. The movement starts behind the head. The snake lifts its head and bends it into a curve at the point where it touches the ground. The muscle contraction making the bend travels rapidly down the body, keeping contact with the sand beneath while the forepart and head remain raised. By the time the wave is halfway down, the neck drops once more and momentarily touches the sand as a new wave begins again. The result of all this is that the snake moves rapidly forward, leaving behind a series of bar-like tracks in the sand, orientated at about 45° to the direction in which the snake has actually travelled.

When a snake hunts it is often very important for it to be able to advance with a minimum of movement so as not to attract the attention of its victim. The snake lies with its body quite straight and pointing directly at its prey. The scales on its underside are shaped like narrow rectangles running across the width of the body and overlapping one another with their free edges to the rear. The snake is able to hitch these scales up and forward in groups by contracting its belly muscles. The back edges catch on the ground and as the contractions pass downwards in waves, the snake advances smoothly and silently with no lateral movement whatsoever.

If the ancestral snakes did indeed spend a period below ground, their prey is likely to have been small and limited to invertebrates such as worms and termites and perhaps the early burrow-living shrew-like mammals. When they came above ground, after the mammals had begun to evolve into the forms we know today, their scope became very

A side-winder edges its way up a dune
*Two snakes, living in deserts on opposite sides of the
world, have developed the technique of side-winding – a
rattlesnake in the south-western United States and an
adder in South-West Africa (below). Both are highly
venomous night-time hunters. They seldom move during
the day and warn off creatures that might disturb their
rest, the rattler by shaking the hollow scales on the end
of its tail, the adder by hissing loudly and inflating
itself to double its normal thickness.*

much greater. Maybe it was, indeed, just this that tempted them back there. A few boas
and pythons now grow to such a length that they can tackle creatures as big as goats and
antelope. Having seized their prey with their mouths, they swiftly coil themselves
around it and then kill it by tightening their coils so that their victim cannot expand its
chest to breathe. It dies by suffocation rather than crushing. With the backward
pointing teeth engaging on the prey, the snake draws its food in by working its loosely
connected jaw. The long process of swallowing may take several hours and leave the
snake in a state of bloated immobility.

The more advanced snakes kill, not by constriction, but by poison. One group, the
back-fanged snakes, deliver the venom by means of specially adapted teeth near the
back of the upper jaw. The poison glands lie above these teeth and the venom simply

Two ways of delivering venom

The vine snake (above) is one of many that have back fangs — long teeth at the back of the mouth which carry grooves down which poison can flow. To be effective, they have to be worked into a wound, so back-fanged snakes, having struck, usually hang on. The rattlesnake (right) is a more efficient killer. Like pit vipers, mambas, sea-snakes and cobras, its huge stabbing fangs are at the front of the mouth and inject poison deep in the flesh of their victims. After one swift bite, such snakes withdraw and wait to allow their virulent venom to take effect.

The beginning of a long meal

The boomslang of Africa is a back-fanged snake. This one has caught a chameleon and started the lengthy process of swallowing it. The lower jaw is connected to the upper by an elastic ligament which has stretched to accommodate its huge mouthful. The snake slowly works its jaws from side to side, gripping with its backward-pointing teeth on one side while it disengages the other and inches it forward, until eventually the whole chameleon has been swallowed. The flesh will be quickly digested and even the bones demineralised and broken down. Only the horny parts of an animal – hair, feathers, scales or horns – seem resistant to the snakes' potent digestive juices.

trickles down a groove in the tooth. Once the prey has been bitten the back-fanged snake may have to maintain its grip and chew, rocking its jaw from side to side until the fangs are at last driven into the victim's flesh carrying their poison with them.

More advanced snakes have more refined ways of killing. Their fangs are placed at the front of the upper jaw and have an enclosed canal through which the poison flows. Cobras, mambas and sea-snakes have fangs that are short and immobile, but those of vipers are so long that most of the time they have to be kept hinged back, lying flat along the roof of the mouth. When the snake strikes, its mouth opens wide, the bone to which the fangs are attached rotates, bringing the fangs down and forward so that they will stab the victim immediately. When they pierce the flesh, the venom is injected down them, like serum from a hypodermic needle.

The snakes were the last of the great reptile groups to appear and the most sophisticated of them are the pit vipers. The rattlesnakes of Mexico and the south-west of the United States belong to this group and exemplify the perfection to which the reptilian pattern can be taken.

Like many other snakes, and some amphibians and fish before them, the rattlesnakes give their eggs maximum protection by retaining them inside the body. That reptilian innovation, the shell, is reduced to a thin membrane so that the embryos, as they lie inside the oviduct, not only feed on their yolk but draw sustenance from their mother's blood diffusing from the walls of the oviduct pressed against them. It is a process which parallels, in essence, the device of the placenta that is used by the mammals.

Nor does the female rattler abandon her young once they emerge fully formed from her vent. She actively guards them. Intruders are warned off with the sound of her vibrating rattle. Each time she sheds her skin, one special hollow scale remains fixed to her tail, so that a fully grown rattler may have as many as twenty of them.

A rattlesnake hunts mostly at night and does so with the aid of a sensory device which has no parallel elsewhere in the animal world. Between the nostril and the eye is the pit which gives the group as a whole its name. It detects infra-red radiation, that is to say heat, and is so sensitive that it responds to a rise of three hundredths of one degree centigrade. What is more, it is directional and enables the snake to identify the source of the heat with precision. So, with the aid of its pits, the rattlesnake is able to detect the presence of a small ground squirrel crouching motionless half a metre away even in total darkness. The snake glides smoothly towards it on its belly scales in near-silence; once within range it strikes, shooting its head forward at a speed of 3 metres a second; and then its huge paired fangs inject its victim with a dose of extremely virulent poison. It must surely be one of the most efficient killers in the animal world.

Because, like all reptiles, it can absorb the sun's energy directly, its food requirements are small. A dozen or so meals a year are quite sufficient for it. Not for the rattlesnake the incessant daily search for food to which the endothermic mammals, even in a desert, are committed. Nor does it need, like them, to spend its days cowering in crevices and holes, panting with the heat, waiting for the cool night to fall before it can venture abroad. Curled up among the stones and cactus, it is the master of its environment and fears nothing. The reptiles, by virtue of their water-tight skins and eggs, were the first vertebrates to colonise the desert. In some places, some of them still own it.

A specialist in egg-eating

One group of snakes eat nothing but eggs. Their teeth are small and few. Instead they have a remarkable shell-cutting device within their body. Here an egg-eater tackles a quail's egg. First its jaws dislocate and stretch apart to a spectacular degree. The lining of the mouth has abundant deep pleats which expand and glands which squirt saliva to lubricate the egg shell. Once the egg is inside its gullet, the snake bends its neck downwards so that special sharp spikes, projecting from the underside of its spine like the teeth of a saw, cut a slit in the egg shell, so releasing its contents. The snake then tightens its muscles, crushes the shell and regurgitates the fragments which are still held together by the membranous lining of the shell.

A killer searches for food

The lidless eyes of a bamboo viper stare unblinkingly at its prey. Without ears, it is deaf, but its flickering tongue tastes the air, carrying back molecules of scent to a sensory pit in the palate; and two pits in front of the eyes can, even in total darkness, detect the tiny rise in temperature caused by the warm body of a little rodent crouching half a metre away.

8. LORDS OF THE AIR

Reptiles followed the insects into the skies. One group developed feathers, reduced their weight and became such accomplished aeronauts that now they inhabit the air from Pole to Pole

The feather is an extraordinary device. Few substances can equal it as an insulator and none, weight for weight, whether man-made or animal-grown, can excel it as an aerofoil. Its substance is keratin. The same horny material forms a reptile's scales and our own nails, but the exceptional qualities of a feather come from its intricate construction. A central shaft carries on either side a hundred or so filaments; each filament is similarly fringed with about a hundred smaller filaments or barbules. In downy feathers, this structure produces a soft, air-trapping fluffiness and, therefore, superb insulation. Flight feathers have an additional feature. Their barbules overlap those of neighbouring filaments and hook them onto one another so that they are united into a continuous vane. There are several hundred such hooks on a single barbule, a million or so in a single feather; and a bird the size of a swan has about twenty-five thousand feathers. Almost all the characteristics that distinguish birds from other animals can be traced one way or another to the benefits brought by feathers. Indeed, the very possession of a feather is enough to define a creature as a bird.

When, in 1860, in Solnhofen in Bavaria, the delicate and unmistakable outline of a single isolated feather, seven centimetres long, was found impressed in a slab of limestone, it caused a sensation. It lay on the rock, as eloquent as a Red Indian sign, proclaiming that a bird had been there. Yet these limestones dated from the days of the dinosaurs, long before birds were thought to exist.

The sediments from which they had formed were deposited on the bottom of a

---

The key to the birds' success
Birds regularly renew their worn-out feathers. Most do so once a year. Those that wear special decorations for courtship do so twice, alternating breeding and non-breeding plumage. Moulting usually takes about two months, new feathers growing beneath the old and pushing them out. Flight feathers are lost in a regular order and symmetrically on each side so that the bird's flight, though impaired, is nonetheless balanced. A few birds, such as shearwaters and some ducks, lose all their flight feathers at once and, for a period, are flightless.

The oldest-known feather

This single feather, found in 1860 fossilised in the Solnhofen limestones, was the first hint that feathered creatures had existed at the same time as the dinosaurs. The fact that both birds' feathers and reptilian scales are composed of the same substance, keratin, suggests strongly that one is derived from the other.

shallow tropical lagoon enclosed by a reef of sponges and lime-depositing algae. The water was tepid and poor in oxygen. Cut off from the open sea, there were few if any currents. Lime, partly from the disintegrating reef and partly produced by bacteria, was deposited as ooze on the bottom. Such conditions suited few animals. Those that did stray there and died, fell to the bottom and lay undisturbed in the still water as they were covered by the slowly accumulating ooze.

The Solnhofen limestones have been quarried for centuries because their fine even grain makes them excellent for building and ideal for use in lithographic printing. They are also immaculate blanks for nature to impress with the fine detail of the evidence of evolution. The stone, if it is thoroughly weathered, splits along the bedding planes so that a block can be opened into leaves, like a book. When you visit one of the quarries, it is almost impossible to resist the temptation to turn the pages of every boulder that you see, knowing that no one has ever looked at them before and that whatever they contain will not have been exposed to daylight for a hundred and forty million years. Most, of course, are blank, but every now and then, the quarrymen find fossils of a near-miraculous perfection – fish with every bone and shining scale in place, horseshoe crabs lying just where they died at the end of their last furrow through the silt, lobsters with even their finest antennae intact, small dinosaurs, ichthyosaurs and pterodactyls, lying with the bony scaffolds of their wings crumpled but unbroken and the shadow of their leathery flight membranes plain to see. But in 1860, that beautiful and enigmatic feather was the first indication that birds had been living in such company.

To what kind of bird had it belonged? Science, on the strength of the feather alone, called it Archaeopteryx, 'ancient bird'. A year later, in a quarry close by the first, searchers discovered an almost complete skeleton of a feathered creature the size of a pigeon. It lay sprawling on the rock, its wings outstretched, one long leg disarticulated, the other still connected with four clawed toes, and all around it, dramatically and indisputably, the clear impress of its feathers. It was certainly apt to call it an 'ancient bird' but it differed substantially from any known living bird. The long feathered tail that flared out behind it was supported by a bony extension of its spine; and it had claws, not only on its feet but on the three digits of its feathered forelimbs. It was almost as much a reptile as a bird and its discovery within two years of the publication of *The Origin of Species* was a providentially timed confirmation of Darwin's proposition that one group of animals developed into another by way of intermediate forms. Indeed, Huxley, Darwin's champion, had predicted that just such a creature must have existed, and had prophetically described its details. Even today, there is no more convincing example of such a link.

Since that first skeleton was found, two more Archaeopteryx have been discovered in the Solnhofen district, one even finer than the first with a complete skull. This added a most important detail. The animal had possessed bony jaws lined with teeth. A fourth specimen was recognised only a few years ago in a Dutch museum. It too had come from Solnhofen – six years before the first acknowledged skeleton – but because the impression of its feathers was faint and difficult to see, it had been mistakenly

Feathered reptile or toothed bird?

The most complete specimen of Archaeopteryx so far found is this one discovered in the Solnhofen limestones in 1877 (right). The feathers on its wings and tail are plain to see – and so are the reptilian characters of toothed jaws, bony tail and clawed fingers.

A clawed wing

Alone among living birds, the young hoatzin has true claws on its wings. It uses them to hold on as it clambers around in the branches near its nest. Within a few weeks, however, it will shed them.

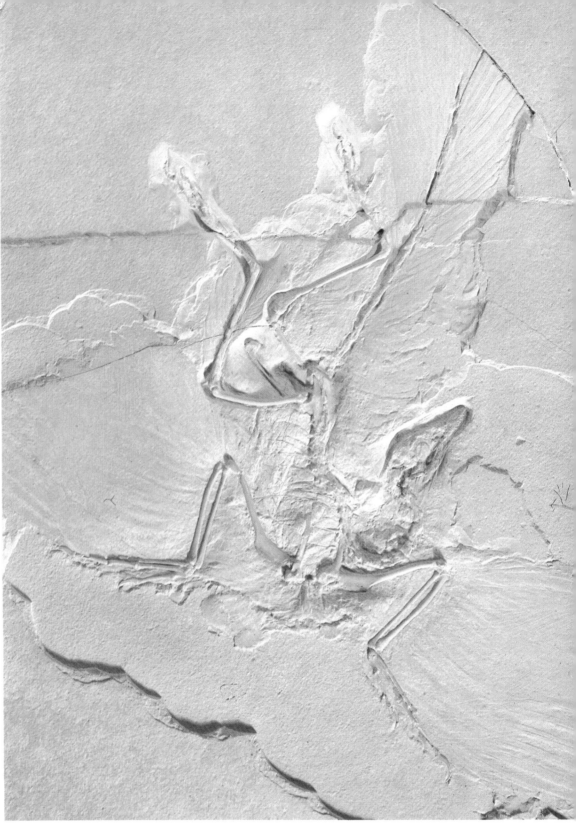

203

catalogued as a small pterodactyl, an indication of how reptilian a character Archaeopteryx has, even in the eyes of experts.

These fossils, between them, have provided us with detailed knowledge of Archaeopteryx's anatomy. Feathers covered its whole body, except for the legs, head and upper neck. Undoubtedly these insulated it very well and so dealt with the problem of maintaining a high body temperature which had caused so many difficulties for its dinosaur cousins. With such a warm coat, Archaeopteryx must have been able to move at speed even during the cool hours of the day.

The feathers on its wings, however, cannot be accounted for in such a straightforward way. Flapping flight requires powerful wing muscles and these, in all flying birds, are attached to a deep keel on the breast bone. Archaeopteryx had no such structure. So its wing beat could only have been feeble and quite insufficient to get it into the air. It has been suggested that it used its feathers as a kind of net, holding its wings outstretched and so trapping insects in them. A more straightforward and believable explanation is that its ancestors were tree-climbers. Their feathers, initially developed from reptilian scales to provide insulation, grew larger and larger and eventually enabled Archaeopteryx to glide from branch to branch, in much the same way that gliding lizards are able to do today, with the aid of membranes stretched out from the flanks of their body. Archaeopteryx was certainly well able to climb. One of its four toes pointed backwards and could be opposed to the others so that the animal had a powerful grasp. And the claws on the front of its wings would also have been of considerable assistance in clinging to branches.

One living bird provides a demonstration of just how effective such a method of climbing can be. The hoatzin is a curious heavily-built bird, the size of a chicken, that lives in the swamps of Guyana and Venezuela. Its nests are roughly-built platforms of twigs, built above water, often in mangroves. When the young first hatch they are naked and extremely active. Watching them is not easy. A bump from the bows of a canoe against the mangrove branches is almost unavoidable, and if the nest shakes the young will scramble feverishly off their twig platform and onto the branches. If they are disturbed any further the chance of seeing them at all is likely to be lost, for they will abruptly launch themselves into the air, dive into the water and swim energetically into the tangle of mangrove roots where you will never be able to follow them. But with luck, you may have seen how they cling so adhesively to twigs and clamber from one to another. They have two little claws on the front edge of each wing, relics of the time when their reptilian ancestors had not wings but forelimbs with separate digits. It is not at all difficult to see in these naked young birds a hint of the way Archaeopteryx moved through the branches of its dinosaur-haunted forests.

When hoatzin chicks grow up, they lose these vestigial claws. The adults are poor flyers, flapping heavily and laboriously along the rivers. They do not seem able to cover more than a hundred metres or so before they have to crash into the vegetation and rest. Nonetheless, they are unquestionably very much more accomplished in the air than Archaeopteryx ever was, for they, like all modern birds, have a skeleton that, during the

The malleable beak

Birds' beaks are constructed of keratin, a lightweight substance, and have responded quickly to evolutionary pressures. Each species has one with a shape appropriate to its food. The oyster catcher uses its bill for opening molluscs and probing in the sand, the bald eagle for tearing flesh, and the hummingbird for sipping nectar from flowers.

OYSTER CATCHER

BALD EAGLE

HUMMINGBIRD

past 140 million years, has become greatly modified for flight.

The overwhelming priority for every flyer is to keep weight to a minimum. Archaeopteryx's bones were solid, like a reptile's; those of true birds are paper-thin or hollow, often supported inside with cross-struts which closely resemble those designed to strengthen the wings of aeroplanes. Birds' lungs are extended into air-sacs which bulge into the body cavity so filling space in the lightest possible way. The heavy extension of the spine that formed the basis of Archaeopteryx's tail has been replaced with stout-quilled feathers requiring no bony support of any kind. A weighty jaw, laden with teeth must have been a particular handicap for any creature trying to fly, for it would tend to unbalance the animal and make it very nose-heavy. Modern birds have lost it and have developed instead another lightweight construction of keratin, the beak.

The multifarious uses of the beak

Even the best beak cannot chew and most birds still have a need to break up their food. They do it with a special muscular compartment of the stomach, the gizzard, which lies in the middle of their bodies, roughly between the wings where it causes the minimum

A team of fishermen

Pelicans are very sociable birds and fish in teams using a variety of techniques. Sometimes they form a line across a lake or a lagoon and advance towards the shore beating their wings, driving the fish in front of them into shallow water where they can be scooped up. In deeper waters, the birds encircle a shoal of fish and then, with remarkably accurate timing, dip their huge bills in unison and net the fish. The baggy skin of the bill probably serves another purpose as well. In hot weather, the birds vibrate it so that moisture evaporates from the surface and so cools their blood.

Bills for courtship

The puffin changes the shape of its bill annually. As the breeding season approaches, a brightly coloured plate grows around the base and the tip becomes bright red. The birds display their newly ornamented beaks to one another, shaking their heads, sometimes smacking their beaks together. After breeding, the red fades, the basal plates are shed and the beak becomes narrower.

The beak as a sieve
The flamingo filters tiny organisms from lake water by using its tongue to pump water through plates lining its beak. Its chick, however, does not develop this complicated beak until it is several weeks old.

problems of balance and trim when the bird is flying. The beak itself has to do no more than gather the food.

The keratin of the beak, like that of the reptilian scale, seems to be easily moulded by evolutionary pressures. Just how quickly it can be changed to suit the diet of its owner is vividly shown by the honey-creepers of Hawaii. The ancestor of these birds was probably a sparrow-sized creature with a short, straight beak that lived in continental America. A few thousand years ago, a flock of them must have been carried out to sea by a freak storm. They eventually reached the Hawaiian islands, and there found lush forests empty of other birds for the islands are volcanic and were formed comparatively recently. To exploit the many kinds of food now at their disposal, they rapidly evolved into different species, each specialised for a particular diet with the beak shape that was best suited to gather it. Some have short thick bills for seed-eating, others have hooked and powerful ones for tearing carrion. One species has a long curving bill for extracting nectar from lobelia blossoms; another has an upper mandible twice the length of the lower which it uses to hammer bark and lever it off in its search for weevils; yet another has crossed mandibles, a form apparently that enables it to extract insects from buds. Darwin had noted similar variations in the bills of the finches of the Galapagos Islands and regarded them as powerful evidence for his theory of natural selection. He never had the luck to visit Hawaii. Had he done so, he might well have concluded that the honey-creepers illustrated his arguments even more convincingly.

Elsewhere in the bird world, where the evolution of beaks to suit a particular purpose has gone on for much longer, there are even more extreme forms. The sword-billed hummingbird has a probing beak four times the length of its body to suck nectar from the deep-throated Andean flowers. The macaw has a hooked nut-cracker of such strength that it can split that most intractable of nuts, the Brazil nut. The woodpecker uses its beak like a drill to excavate wood-boring beetles. The flamingo's crooked beak has inside it a fine sieve through which it pumps water with its throat and so collects tiny crustaceans. The skimmer has a lower mandible almost twice the length of the upper so that it can fly low over a river with the lower mandible just cutting the surface of the water. When it touches a small fish the bill snaps shut instantaneously and the fish is caught. The list of odd bills is virtually endless and ample proof of the malleability of the keratin beak.

Significantly, most of these foods – fish, nuts, nectar, insect larvae, sugar-laden fruit – are full of calories. Birds favour them because flying is an extremely energetic business. To ensure that energy in the form of heat is not wasted, insulation is of the greatest importance. So feathers are essential to a bird not only to provide aerofoils on the wings but to enable it to generate enough energy to flap them.

Feathers: unrivalled for keeping out the cold
As insulators, feathers are even more efficient than fur. Only a bird – the penguin – can survive on the Antarctic ice-cap in winter, the coldest place on earth. The penguin's feathers are devoted entirely to this task. They are filamentous and trap the air in a

Different beaks, different diets

Several species of bird can live alongside one another provided they eat different foods, and that difference may be clearly visible in their beaks. This lake in Brazil supports large colonies of spoonbills and scarlet ibis. The ibis probe in the mud with their long beaks, the spoonbills catch small crustaceans and fish by swinging their beaks from side to side.

A careful toilet

Water birds nearly always bathe while afloat. Cleanliness is essential but a total drenching would damage their waterproofing and dangerously reduce buoyancy. So what may appear to be a haphazard splashing is, in fact, a carefully controlled activity. The bird ducks its head so that water runs down its neck and back, and shakes its wings loosely in the water, as this pelican is doing, to produce an overall spray, while the feathers are held out from the body so that each receives its proper share. When the right amount of wetting has cleaned the feathers, the bird anoints them with oil.

208

continuous layer all round the body. This, reinforced by a thick coat of fat just beneath the skin, enables the hot-blooded penguins to stand about in a blizzard in temperatures of forty degrees below freezing and remain there for weeks on end, even without stoking their internal warmth with a meal. And when man goes there, the most luxurious and effective way he has yet devised of keeping his own body warm is with feathers taken from an Arctic duck – eiderdown.

How birds keep their feathers in prime condition

The feathers on which a bird's life is so dependent are regularly moulted and renewed, usually once a year. Even so they need constant care and servicing. Their owners wash them in water and ruffle them in dust. Disarranged feathers are carefully repositioned. Those that have become bedraggled or have broken vanes are renovated by careful combing with the beak. As the filaments pass through the mandibles and are pressed together, the hooks on the barbules re-engage like teeth of a zip-fastener to make a smooth and continuous surface again.

Most birds have a large oil-gland in the skin near the base of the tail. The bird takes the oil from it with its beak and anoints its feathers individually so that they are kept supple and water-repellent. Some birds, including herons, parrots and toucans, lack the gland. They condition their feathers with a fine talc-like dust, powder-down, that is produced by the continuous fraying of the tips of special feathers which grow sometimes in a clump, or are scattered through the plumage. Cormorants and their relatives the darters, although they spend a great deal of their time diving in water, have feathers so constructed that they get thoroughly wet, but this is to their advantage for by losing the air trapped beneath them, they become much less buoyant and so can dive in pursuit of fish with greater ease. When they have finished fishing, they have to stand on the rocks, wings outstretched, drying themselves.

The skin beneath the feathers must be a most attractive place for fleas, lice and other parasites. It is warm, snug and out of sight. There are plenty of such creatures to afflict a bird, so birds regularly erect their feathers and probe around the base of their quills to pick off lodgers. Jays, starlings and jackdaws and several other species actively encourage insects to crawl over their skin, probably as an aid in this de-lousing process. The bird will squat on an ant nest with feathers ruffled and spread, so that the disturbed, angry ants swarm all over it. Sometimes it even picks up individual ants with its bill, holding them firmly but gently so that they are not killed and jabs its skin and strokes its feathers with them. The ants usually chosen for this are those which eject formic acid when irritated and this would undoubtedly kill parasites. The behaviour may have originated as a matter of personal hygiene, but now some individual birds seem to do it for pleasure and will 'ant' with all kinds of things that might give their skins exciting and pleasurable stimulation – wasps, beetles, smoke from a fire, even lighted cigarette ends. Anting sessions may go on for half an hour or so, the bird sometimes falling over itself excitedly in its attempts to stimulate parts of its body that are difficult to reach.

Feathers for insulation

Feathers provide birds with the insulation they must have to maintain a high body temperature. For no birds is this more important than penguins. Having abandoned flight in favour of swimming, their feathers can be devoted solely to retaining body heat. Instead of sprouting from restricted areas as they do on nearly all other birds, they cover the penguin's body uniformly. They are also short and fine and together form a dense, completely waterproof coat very like fur. As a result, king penguins, like these chicks in Antarctica, can survive some of the coldest conditions on earth.

All this toiletry takes up a considerable part of the bird's non-flying time. The reward comes when it takes to the air. The immaculately arranged feathers not only form perfect aerofoils on the wings and tail, but those on the head and the body fulfil the equally valuable function of streamlining the contours so that there is a minimum of eddying and drag when the bird is in flight.

Wing shapes for different types of flight

Bird wings have a much more complex job to do than the wings of an aeroplane, for in addition to supporting the bird they must act as its engine, rowing it through the air. Even so the wing outline of a bird conforms to the same aerodynamic principles as those eventually discovered by man when designing his aeroplanes, and if you know how different kinds of aircraft perform, you can predict the flight capabilities of similarly shaped birds.

Short stubby wings enable a tanager and other forest-living birds to swerve and dodge at speed through the undergrowth just as they helped the fighter planes of the Second World War to make tight turns and aerobatic manoeuvres in a dog-fight. More modern fighters achieve greater speeds by sweeping back their wings while in flight, just as peregrines do when they go into a 130 kph dive, stooping to a kill. Championship gliders have long thin wings so that, having gained height in a thermal up-current they can soar gently down for hours and an albatross, the largest of flying birds, with a similar wing shape and a span of 3 metres, can patrol the ocean for hours in the same way without a single wing beat. Vultures and hawks circle at very slow speeds supported by a thermal and they have the broad rectangular wings that very slow flying aircraft have. Man has not been able to adapt wings to provide hovering flight. He has only achieved that with the whirling horizontal blades of a helicopter or the downward-pointing engines of a vertical landing jet. Hummingbirds have paralleled even this. They tilt their bodies so that they are almost upright and then beat their wings as fast as 80 times a second producing a similar down-draught of air. So the hummingbird can hover and even fly backwards.

No other creatures can fly as far as fast or as long as birds. The swift is, indeed, the swiftest, one Asian species being capable of speeds of 170 kph in level flight and flying every day about 900 kilometres to collect the insects that are its only food. So extreme is its adaptation to an aerial existence that its feet are reduced to little more than tiny grasping hooks. Its scimitar-curved wings are so long that sitting flat on the ground it cannot beat them properly and it can only get into the air with any ease by launching itself from a cliff or the side of its nest. It even copulates in mid-air. A female, flying high, holds out her wings stiffly and a male comes from behind, alights on her back and, for a few moments, the two glide together. They never alight between breeding seasons so that they spend at least nine months of the year continuously on the wing. Even that, however, is excelled by the sooty tern which, after it leaves its nest for the first time has not been seen to alight or settle on the water until it nests three or four years later.

Many species of birds make long annual journeys. The European stork travels every

The magnificent terns
Terns are masters of flight. They can hover high above the sea taking aim on a fish and then spear it with a precision dive. They may spend months continuously on the wing at sea. The Arctic tern flies from the Arctic to the Antarctic and back every year. The fairy tern (above) is pure white and one of the loveliest.

autumn down to Africa and returns to Europe in the spring navigating with such
accuracy that the same pair, year after year, will occupy the same nest on the same roof
top.

    The greatest traveller of all is the Arctic tern. Some nest well north of the Arctic
Circle. A chick hatching in northern Greenland during July will, within a few weeks, set
off on an 18,000 kilometre flight that takes it south, down the western coasts of Europe
and Africa and then across the Antarctic Ocean to its summer grounds on the pack ice
not far from the South Pole. It may then, during the Antarctic summer, driven by the
incessant westerly gales, circle the entire Antarctic continent before heading back

The changing shape of a wing

*The condor (left, above) is one of the heaviest flying
birds, but its immense wings provide such a huge air-
catching surface that its sink-rate is very low and it can
soar for hours with scarcely a wing flap. By separating
the feathers at the end of the wings into slots, it can
glide at very low speeds without stalling. When it needs
to fly faster it brings the feathers together and makes
the wings more pointed. The brown pelican (left) can
also make crucial changes to its wing shape. Alone of its
family, it fishes by diving. Once it has seen the prey, it
folds its wings to shorten their effective length and so
increase its speed as it hurtles down into the sea.*

The hushed flight of the owl
The owl pounces silently on its prey, for its wing feathers have soft fringes, clearly seen on this small owl, which suppress the noise of the wing beat. The feathers bordering its ear-slits are short and stiff and grow on movable flaps, so the owl can change the shape of the ear opening and focus its hearing on a particular spot.

A use for the rudiment of a thumb
As this white-crowned sparrow beats its wing down, the tiny bastard wing on the leading edge, a relic of the thumb, which carries a few feathers of its own, separates, reducing turbulence and preventing stalling. **213**

north the next May, leaving once more for southern Africa and heading north back to Greenland. So it experiences both the Antarctic and the Arctic summers when the sun scarcely dips below the horizon, and sees more daylight each year than any other creature.

The energy spent by such migrants in their vast journeys is gigantic, but the advantages are clear. At each end of their routes they can tap a rich food supply that exists for only half the year. But how did they ever discover that such sources existed so far apart? The answer seems to be that their journeys were not always so long. It was the warming of the world at the end of the Ice Age eleven thousand years ago that began to stretch them. Before that time birds in Africa, for example, might fly briefly a little to the north to the edge of the ice-cap in southern Europe where, for a few months in summer there were insects in quantity and no permanent local population to feed on them. As the glaciers began to retreat, new strips of land became liberated from the ice and colonised by insects and berry-bearing plants. So each year, birds were able to find food by flying farther and farther until their annual journeys involved travelling thousands of miles. Similar climatic changes are likely to have been responsible for extending the movements of those migrants in Europe and North America which fly in an east-west direction to the centre of the continents during the summer and back for the winter to the coastal regions that are kept warmer by the sea.

But how do the birds manage to find their way? There seems to be no single answer: they use many methods. Some we are beginning to understand; some mystify us; and there may be some that depend on abilities we have not yet suspected. Many birds certainly follow major geographical features. Summer migrants from Africa fly along the North African coast, converging on the Strait of Gibraltar and cross there, where they can see Europe ahead of them. Then they follow valleys, flying over recognised passes through the Alps or the Pyrenees and so arrive at their summer homes. Others take an eastern route by way of the Bosphorus.

But all birds cannot use such straightforward methods. The Arctic tern, for example, has to fly at least 3000 kilometres across the Antarctic Ocean with no land to guide it. We know that some birds, flying at night, navigate by the stars for on cloudy nights they tend to get lost and if they are released in a planetarium where the constellations have been rotated so that they no longer match the position of the stars in the heavens, the birds will follow the visible and artificial ones.

Day-flying birds may use the sun. If they are to do so, they must be able to compensate for the shift of the sun across the sky each day and that means that they must have a precise sense of time. Still others appear to be able to use the earth's magnetic field as a guide. So it seems that many migrating birds must carry in their brains a clock, a compass and the memory of a map. Certainly, a human navigator would need all three if he were to match the journeys that a swallow can make within a few weeks of its hatching.

And yet even these abilities seem insufficient to account for the skills of some birds. In a famous case, a shearwater was taken from its nest on the island of Skokholm in west

The drawbacks of a flamingo's legs

Flamingos' extraordinarily long legs and necks enable them to wade and feed in deep water, but they are a handicap in the air. The birds fly with necks outstretched and legs trailing, and though they can achieve speeds of about 55 kph, they are not very manoeuvrable and must be vulnerable to attack by eagles. Perhaps for this reason, they seldom fly over land by day, and the long migration journeys that some species make are undertaken at night.

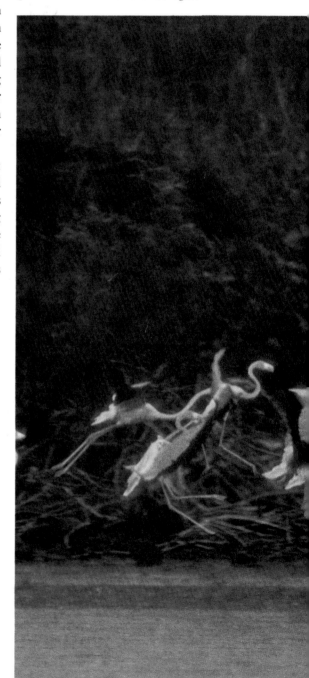

Hovering before a meal of nectar

The hummingbirds are tiny. Allen's hummingbird weighs only about 2 grams. They are the most accomplished hoverers of all birds. They can hang absolutely stationary in front of a flower and then gently advance so that the straight bill enters the depths of the bloom to sip nectar, their main food. They can also fly at great speeds and sometimes, during their aerial manoeuvres, they beat their wings so swiftly that they make the hum which gives the birds their name.

Wales and sent by aircraft to Boston in the United States, 5100 kilometres away. There it was released. It was back in its breeding burrow $12\frac{1}{2}$ days later, a time so short that the bird must have flown in a direct and purposeful way. How it knew where it was and how to get back home, we still have no idea.

When feathers become banners, proclaiming a message

The feathers that keep a bird warm and enable it to fly are of service to it in yet a third way. Their broad surfaces, easily erected or folded away, serve splendidly as banners with which to send messages. For most of their lives the majority of birds have much to gain from remaining inconspicuous, and feathers can provide the colours and patterns necessary for perfect camouflage. But each year, at the beginning of the breeding season, birds have an over-riding need to communicate with one another. As male meets male in territorial dispute over nesting sites, dramatic feather crests are raised, coloured chests pouted and wing patterns spread, in a long series of ritualised threats and arguments. These visual signals are usually reinforced with vocal proclamations. Both kinds of signals carry the same three messages – a declaration of species; a challenge to any male of that species to dispute the ownership of the territory; and an invitation to a female to join him.

The nature of the country a male bird inhabits and his general character may make one medium of communication more suitable than the other. Shy birds that normally live unobtrusive lives in woodland or thick forest tend to use only the minimum of visual signals and concentrate instead on pouring out a specially long and elaborate song. If you hear marvellous cascades of notes, full of liquid trills and thrilling swoops, the singer is likely to be a plain-liveried unspectacular creature – a bulbul in Africa, a babbler in Asia, a nightingale in Europe. Conversely, the most gorgeously caparisoned birds – peacocks, pheasants, parrots – are those that are so self-confident, so untroubled by the fear of enemies, that they have no hesitation in exposing themselves in prominent places to show off their adornments. Since their main signal is a visual one it is no surprise that such birds usually have calls that are short, uncomplicated and harsh.

A declaration of the species of the sender is obviously important to prevent birds wasting their time in courting and coupling with partners with whom there can be no fertile union. In a few cases, this is done entirely by song. A human ornithologist and a female bird may be equally baffled about the identity of a small brown warbler lurking in an English hedgerow. Neither may be sure exactly who he is, judging solely from his appearance. It is only when he begins to sing that either can tell whether he is a willow warbler, a wood warbler or a chiff-chaff.

Usually, however, identity of species is proclaimed by the plumage, a fact that a heartless experimenter can demonstrate by painting an eye-stripe or a wing-flash on a bird so that it looks like a related species and successfully deceives a genuine member of it. Identification becomes a particular problem when many related species live in the same area and there is danger of confusion between them. This was the problem that produced the brilliant and varied colours of the closely related butterfly fish on the coral

The faithful dancing albatross

Albatrosses spend most of their lives out at sea and only settle on land to breed. As they assemble, they begin elaborate courtship ceremonies, standing facing each other and clapping their bills, duelling and lifting their heads to bray and gurgle. The incubation of their single egg takes two to three months and each time one returns from feeding at sea, the pair display to one another. They may live for 30 years or more, and once pairs are formed they stay mated for life, even though the partners may not meet again until, usually in alternate years, they come back to breed at exactly the same nest site. Below is the courtship dance of the Galapagos albatross.

FENCING WITH BEAKS

BEAK CLAPPING

CALLING WITH HEAD RAISED

THE FORWARD STRETCH ANSWERED BY SHOULDER PREENS

A BOW TO END THE SEQUENCE — AND INDICATE THE NEST SITE

Courting boobies

A pair of boobies, even in a crowded colony of many thousands of superficially identical birds, recognise one another and constantly reinforce the bond between them by repeating their beak-sparring ritual (right).

reef. Similarly, if extravagant feather patterns and bright colours are found in many closely related birds, it may well be an indication that these birds often share the same habitat. Some of the most vividly coloured birds in Australia are the parakeets and finches. In both groups, several species do indeed live in the same patch of country. All over the world, ducks of different species mingle together in large assemblages on open water in spring. The drakes of each species develop for the occasion highly characteristic patterns and colours on their heads and wings so that the females can recognise them. That the prevention of confusion is a major function of these colours is shown by the fact that when only one species of duck manages to colonise an island, and remains there long enough to develop into an individual form, it is always a much drabber version of its mainland original. There is no longer any need for such a drake to send vivid signals about who he is: there is no other bird around with whom his females could confuse him.

At the same time as proclaiming their species, individual birds must also declare their

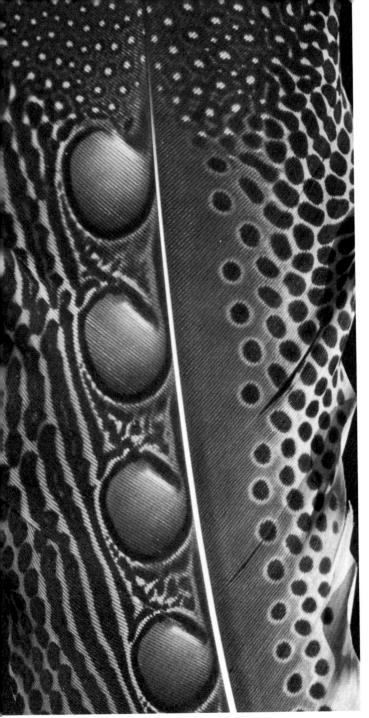

An evolutionary mystery

The enormous wing feathers of the male argus pheasant seem to represent a line of huge protruding eyes, each one shaded to give a three-dimensional impression. The meaning of the decoration has yet to be explained.

sex to one another. Ducks do so with their head patterns for only the drakes develop them. In many species, however – among them, sea birds and birds of prey – the male and female look the same throughout the year. Their sexual identity therefore has to be conveyed by their song and behaviour. The male penguin has a particularly charming way of discovering what he wants to know about his uniformly-suited companions. He picks up a pebble in his bill, waddles over to a bird standing alone and solemnly lays it before it. If he gets an outraged peck and the squaring up for a fight, he knows he has made a dreadful mistake – this is another male. If his offering is met with total indifference, then he has found a female who is not yet ready to breed or is already paired. He picks up his spurned gift and moves on. But if the stranger receives the pebble with a deep bow then he has discovered his true mate. He bows back and the two stretch up their necks and trumpet a celebratory nuptial chorus.

One of the loveliest of the European water birds, the great crested grebe is much more elaborately costumed than the penguin. In spring, both sexes grow long chestnut-brown tippets on their cheeks, a deep brown ruff beneath the beak and a pair of horn-like tufts of glossy black feathers on the head. But again both male and female look alike. Their courtship consists of almost every manoeuvre imaginable that would show off these head adornments to good advantage. The response an individual bird gets to particular gestures tells it whether it is displaying to another bird of the same or the opposite sex. The two stretch their necks up high and twist their heads rapidly from side to side, their tippets fanned wide. They dive and pop up in front of one another. They collect strands of water plants in their beaks and present them to one another, neck stretched low over the water. And at the climax of all these ceremonies, they suddenly rear up, side by side, treading water with their feet until it looks as though they are standing on the surface, twisting their heads ecstatically from side to side.

Their courtship lasts for many weeks and elements of it are continually repeated throughout the breeding season when the birds greet one another or change places on the nest. It is as though the identically-plumaged partners need to keep reassuring one another of their respective identities and the relationship between them. Even so, there are possibilities of confusion. When it comes to copulation, grebes are notorious for getting muddled and the female may well mount the male instead of being mounted.

Close similarity of plumage is a strong indication that the birds are monogamous and that both partners share in preparing for and rearing their family. Many species, however, have some visual indicator of their sex, even if it is only a small detail like the moustache of a bearded tit, the black bib of a sparrow or the different-coloured eye of a parrot. Courtship will include displays in which the owner of this badge flaunts it in front of the partner who lacks it.

Some groups of birds have developed this sexual difference in plumage to an extraordinary degree and it is they who have brought the feather to its highest pitch of fantastication. The males of pheasants, grouse, manakins and birds of paradise grow feathers of great size and sensational colour and become so obsessed with displaying their costumes that they do little else. Their females are drabs who appear at the display grounds for a brief coupling and then return to lay their eggs and care for their young entirely by themselves, leaving the male still absorbed in his strutting and pirouetting, awaiting his next female visitor.

Among the most elaborate of all feathers are those grown by the male argus pheasant on his wings. Some may be over a metre long and are lined with huge eye-spots. He clears a display ground in the Borneo forest and shows off to the female by raising both wings above his head in a towering shield.

The island of New Guinea, north of Australia, contains some forty different species of birds of paradise. It is difficult to know which has the more spectacular plumage. The King of Saxony Bird, the size of a thrush, sprouts two long quills from his forehead, each bearing a line of enamelled blue pennants; the Superb Bird has an immense emerald shield which it can expand until it is as broad as the bird is tall; the Twelve Wired Bird has a shimmering green bib and a huge inflatable yellow waistcoat with bare quills, the wires of its name, curling down behind it.

Watching such birds display their ornaments is one of the most thrilling and heart-stopping experiences the bird world has to offer. The New Guinea forest is, for the most part, dark and wet. Great trees soar above to cut out most of the light. But you may suddenly come across a patch of floor that has been swept clear. The leaves and litter

The inflating sage grouse

At breeding time, male sage grouse assemble in groups of over 400 and display to one another. Each erects dramatic feathers in his tail and around his neck, and inflates huge air sacs hanging down his chest. These sacs not only look extremely impressive but also amplify his booming calls, and when after each bout a male deflates them they make a loud plopping noise.

Wings for display

Although the sun bittern of South America (below) has large wings, it hardly ever flies. Both sexes have similar plumage. During courtship, they seek a clearing and there, in a pool of light, hold their wings rigidly outstretched, displaying to their mates.

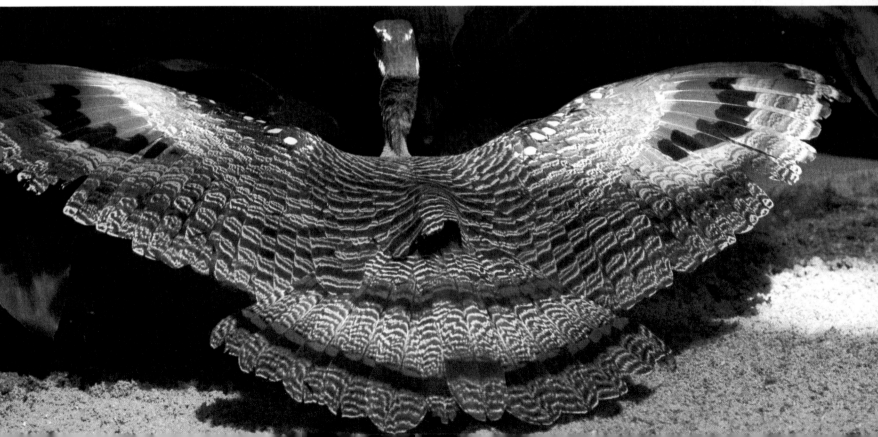

that once covered it are piled up around the sides. It is difficult to believe that the clearing has not been done by a human being, but if you wait, the creature responsible will appear. The Magnificent Bird is the size of a starling. From his tail emerge two naked quills that curl into circles; over his shoulders he has a golden cape; on his breast, a green shield fringed with the finest shimmering blue lines. The feathers on his head and around his beak are so fine and lustrous that they look like rich black velvet. He may pause in the trees for a few minutes, hunched on a branch, assessing the situation. Then he abruptly flies to one of the saplings that grow in his court. Gripping it with both feet, he points his bill vertically upwards, spreads wide his glinting golden collar and expands his chest plumes, swelling them and contracting them so that they appear to throb, while at the same time making a buzzing noise and gaping his beak to expose the green lining of his throat. He may do this many times a day, usually in the mornings, for months on end, as will his many rivals, each with their own courts distributed through the forest, each aiming to attract females.

The most celebrated of all the birds of paradise are those with long gauzy plumes sprouting from beneath their wing coverts. There are several species, each with plumes of a different colour, yellow, red or white. These birds display communally. Their dances are held in particularly prominent trees that may have been used for the purpose for decades. One special branch in the crown will have been stripped of leaves and twigs. Soon after dawn, a flash of yellow catches your attention in the lower branches. The birds are beginning to assemble for their daily ritual. They are about the size of crows with iridescent green bibs, yellow heads and brown backs. Their golden plumes, even though they are folded, hang down on either side, doubling the length of their bodies. Soon there may be half a dozen males skulking in the undergrowth, some tentatively flicking their plumes over their backs. Eventually, one will fly up to the display branch. With a raucous shriek, he bows his head low, stropping the branch with his bill. He claps his wings above his head, throws his plumes up in a shimmering fountain of colour and scuttles up and down the branch. His passion stimulates the others to join him and soon there may be a dozen of them in the tree, shrieking and displaying, awaiting their chance to perform on the dancing branch.

A sudden movement in the shaded darkness of the branches nearby may draw your eye from this marvellous spectacle. There, plain and brown, is the hen bird. She flits across to the dancing branch and the male jumps aggressively onto her back. His plumes fall. The union lasts a second or two. Then she flies away to return to the nest that she has already prepared for her now fertilised eggs.

The birds that display colourful treasures to their mates
The male birds of paradise carry their cumbersome plumes for several months, but when the season ends, they shed them. To have to renew such large-scale accoutrements each year must make considerable demands on a bird's resources. One related group of birds in New Guinea, with similar appetites for display and polygamy, manage their affairs in what seems to be a more economical way. The bower birds achieve their

The plumed dancers
There are over 40 different kinds of birds of paradise. The Greater Bird (right) is one of a small closely related group of species, the males of which display together in the same tree.

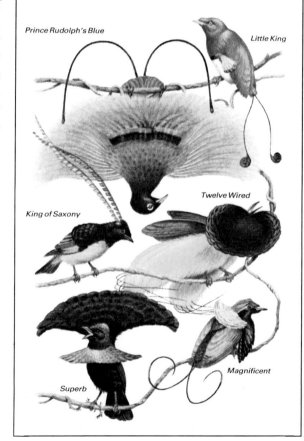

THE CONSEQUENCES OF POLYGAMY

The birds of paradise have abandoned monogamy. Instead, the males devote their energies during the breeding season to attracting as many females as they can by display. They take no part in nest-making or rearing the chicks. This competition by display has led to an extraordinary fantastication of plumes and display postures. The different species vary so widely that it is difficult to believe that they all belong to the same family. But it is only the males that develop these amazing costumes. The females remain drab and their relationship with one another is much more obvious. Indeed, the females of all the varied species pictured below, with the exception of the Blue Bird, are remarkably similar, all having plain brownish-red upper parts and pale underparts, patterned by narrow dark bars.

Prince Rudolph's Blue

Little King

King of Saxony

Twelve Wired

Superb

Magnificent

results by displaying with sticks, stones, flowers, seeds and any brightly coloured objects they can find, provided that they are of a particular colour. The males construct bowers in which to display such treasures. One species stacks twigs around a sapling to form a maypole which it decorates with fragments of lichen. Another constructs a roofed grotto with two entrances in front of which he assembles flowers, mushrooms and berries, each neatly stacked in its own pile.

Other bower birds live farther south in Australia. The male Satin Bower Bird, a dark glossy blue and about the size of a jackdaw, constructs an avenue of twigs a foot or so apart and twice his height. He usually builds it running north and south, and at the northern sunnier end, he assembles his collection. There may be feathers from other birds, berries, even pieces of plastic. Their substance does not matter – only their colour. They must all be either a yellowy-green or, preferably, a shade of blue that closely matches the glint of his shining feathers. Not only does he collect such objects from far and wide and steal them from the collections of neighbours, but he sometimes mashes blue berries with his beak and uses a piece of vegetable fibre to paint the walls of his bower blue with the juice.

One way you can bring a Satin Bird down to his bower is to add to his collection an object of a quite different colour, such as a white snail shell. He usually returns very quickly and indignantly removes the aesthetically offensive object, picking it up with his bill and throwing it aside with a flick of his head. His female is, once again, a dull-looking creature. As she tours the bowers in the district, each male busies himself excitedly with his jewels, rearranging them, picking them up in his beak as though to show her their quality and calling excitedly. If he lures her to the bower, mating takes place close by or actually between the avenue walls, accompanied by a great flapping of the male's wings, sometimes so violent that the bower walls are damaged.

Constructions of the bower birds

Many birds build, but all their constructions are nests except for those of the male bower birds. They build avenues and maypoles to impress females. The male satin bower bird decorates his bower with blue objects. The nest for the eggs is built elsewhere by the female. The male may never see it.

FIVE WAYS OF TEMPTING A MATE

Male bower birds of Australia and New Guinea build elaborate bowers – ranging from complex huts to simple clearings – to attract females.

Pyramid and hut
The golden bower bird builds a pyramid of twigs (far left) around a tree, connected to a smaller pyramid nearby. The striped gardener bower bird makes a hut with a fenced garden (left).

Arena Lauterbach's bower bird builds an arena of sticks with four walls inclining outwards. He decorates the area with bright objects.

Blue motif This male satin bower bird uses a blue feather to attract a female into his bower which is decorated with blue shells, feathers and flowers.

Display ground. Archbold's bower bird makes a simple clearing for a display ground, which he strews with shells, ferns and beetles' wing covers.

222

An egg arrives

The pied-billed grebe lives on ponds and marshes in North America. It is an enthusiastic nest builder, piling up rafts of rotting vegetation which it anchors to reeds and bulrushes. Some years it will build several in a season. The grebe's egg, when it emerges, is a pale green-blue, but as it dries a chalky layer develops over its surface which conceals the original colour. It does not remain white for long, for it soon absorbs brown stains from the nesting material. So the half dozen or so eggs in a complete clutch can be dated. The older they are, the darker they will have become.

The actual mechanics of mating used by birds seem clumsy. The male with only few exceptions, has no penis. He has to mount rather precariously on the female's back, steadying himself by clinging onto her head feathers with his beak. She twists her tail to one side so that the two vents are brought together and the sperm, with a certain amount of muscular assistance from both partners, is transferred to the female. But the process can hardly be described as neat. The female has to remain very still or the male topples off and only too often, it seems that the union is unsuccessful.

When birds are most vulnerable

All birds lay eggs. This is the one characteristic inherited from their reptilian ancestors that no bird anywhere has abandoned. In this the birds are unique among vertebrates. Every other group has a few forms that have found it advantageous to retain eggs inside their bodies and so give birth to live young – sharks, guppies and seahorses among fish; salamanders and marsupial frogs among amphibians; skinks and

THE COMMUNAL OSTRICH NEST

There are more breeding ostrich hens than cocks, so about one-third of the hens have no mates. These unattached ('minor') females mate with a territorial cock and lay their eggs in the nest which he shares with his 'major' hen. She allows them to do so: the more eggs that are in the nest, the smaller are the chances that any of her own will be taken by predators. Most hens lay eggs in more than one nest, and so increase the chances that some will be hatched and reared.

Laying the eggs Three to twelve hens, having mated with the same cock, lay up to 45 eggs in one nest.

The choice The 'major' hen arranges the eggs so that she incubates about 21, including all her own.

Discarded Surplus eggs are pushed to the edge of the nest where they do not hatch.

The chicks When the eggs have hatched, the chicks are protected by both parents.

A crèche Chicks from several nests later merge into a crèche of up to 100, escorted by only a few parents.

rattlesnakes among the reptiles. But no bird has ever done so. Perhaps this is because a large egg inside the body, let alone a clutch of several, would be too great a load for a female to carry in flight throughout the weeks necessary for development. So as soon as the egg within her is fertilised, the female lays it.

But now the birds must pay the penalty for having developed the hot blood necessary for flight. Reptiles can bury their eggs in holes or under stones and then abandon them. Their eggs like the adults themselves, need no more than the normal heat of their surroundings to survive and develop. But the embryos of a bird have hot blood like their parents and if they get badly chilled, they will die.

Birds therefore have to incubate their eggs and that is a very dangerous business. It is the only time in the lives of most of them when they cannot escape their enemies by freely taking to the air. Their eggs and their young keep them sitting until the last possible moment and sometimes beyond. If they are driven to leave, their eggs and young are put at risk. Yet the nest has to be accessible so that the parents themselves can take turns in incubating and leave it to collect food for themselves and the young.

Some birds can and do nest in places that other animals find impossible to reach. Only a bird could get to a ledge in the middle of a vertical sea cliff. But there is danger even there. The risk of the egg rolling off is minimised for most birds that nest on ledges by the production of eggs that are pointed at one end and which, if they do roll, merely go around in a circle. But some sea birds are robbers themselves and unless parents are careful, gulls may come and peck holes in their eggs and eat the contents.

Plovers and birds that live on sandy, gravelly shores have no alternative but to lay their eggs out in the open, for no cover exists. Their eggs are coloured to match the gravel so closely that their destruction is likely to come not from some predator that has noticed them, but from some other creature, like a blundering man, who has failed to do so and trodden on them.

Most birds, however, safeguard their eggs and young by laboriously building some kind of protection. The woodpecker excavates or enlarges holes in trees; the kingfisher bores into river banks, flying at the face with its mandibles slightly parted until it has chipped enough of a dent for it to create the foothold it needs to work with real speed. The sparrow-sized tailor bird in India sews together the growing leaves of a tree by piercing holes in their margin and tying them with separate knots of plant fibre. This forms an elegant and virtually undetectable cup within which the bird constructs its downy nest. The weaver bird, a member of the sparrow family, tears strips from palm leaves and, hanging upside down, deftly weaves them into a hollow ball, sometimes with a long vertical tube to serve as an entrance. The oven bird lives in open country in Argentina and Paraguay, where trees are few and much sought after as homes. So it fearlessly uses fence posts and bare branches as sites and builds out of mud a near-impregnable nest, the size of a football which resembles in miniature the oven made by local people. The entrance is large enough to admit a paw or a hand but a cross wall between the two internal chambers baffles any further plunder, for the hole through it is tucked away out of line of the main entrance. Hornbills nest in holes in trees, and the male takes extreme measures to keep raiders away from the eggs and the female who is incubating them. He walls her up by building a mud wall across the entrance leaving only a tiny hole in the centre. Through this he passes food to his long suffering mate and nestlings. Cave swiftlets in southeast Asia nest in caves but since there may not be enough suitable ledges, they construct artificial ones with their glutinous spittle, sometimes mixed with a few feathers or rootlets. These are the nests that the Chinese, for some reason, believe make the most delectable of soups.

Some birds enlist the unwitting aid of other creatures in deterring raiders. An Australian warbler habitually builds its nests alongside those of hornets; a kingfisher in Borneo lays its eggs actually within the nest of a particularly aggressive species of bee; and many parrots dig holes for themselves inside the brown nests of tree termites.

One family of birds has, in the most ingenious way, managed to avoid the hazardous duty of sitting on its eggs throughout the incubation period. The mallee fowl of eastern Australia lays its eggs in a large mound built by the male. The core is composed of rotting vegetation and the whole is covered with sand. The breeding season is a very long one, spread over five months, and during all this time, the male has to remain in constant attendance probing the mound with his bill to test the temperature. In spring the newly-gathered vegetation at the centre is decaying rapidly and producing so much heat that the mound may get too warm for the eggs within it, in which case he industriously removes sand from the top to allow heat to escape. In summer, there is a different danger: the sun may strike the mound and over-heat it. Now he must pile more sand on top as a shield. In autumn, when the decaying core has lost much of its strength, he removes the top layers to allow the sun to warm the centre where the eggs are and then covers it in the evening to retain the heat.

Another member of the family living farther east on Pacific islands, has developed a specialised variation of the system. It buries its eggs in the ash on the flanks of volcanic cones and allows the lava far beneath to supply the necessary heat for its eggs.

Several species, of which the cuckoo is the most famous, have dodged the perils and labours of incubation altogether by depositing their eggs in the nest of some other bird and allowing them to rear its young. To avoid having their eggs thrown out by the foster

Balanced building

The hermit hummingbird builds its nest from spiders' webs and attaches it to the surface of a dangling leaf. This lop-sided support might bring the risk of a capsize when the bird alights. To prevent this happening, the bird weaves little pieces of earth into the long trailing underside of the nest, to act as counter-weights.

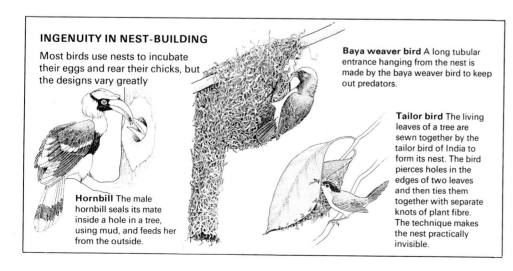

INGENUITY IN NEST-BUILDING

Most birds use nests to incubate their eggs and rear their chicks, but the designs vary greatly

Baya weaver bird A long tubular entrance hanging from the nest is made by the baya weaver bird to keep out predators.

Tailor bird The living leaves of a tree are sewn together by the tailor bird of India to form its nest. The bird pierces holes in the edges of two leaves and then ties them together with separate knots of plant fibre. The technique makes the nest practically invisible.

Hornbill The male hornbill seals its mate inside a hole in a tree, using mud, and feeds her from the outside.

Royal penguins and their chick

Royal penguins (below) live in vast colonies. The male first establishes a breeding site and attracts a female to it. She lays two eggs, but the first, which is smaller, is rejected. Both parents incubate the second. When it hatches, the male stands guard over the chick while the female collects food at sea and regurgitates it in front of the youngster.

Incubating on ice and snow

The king penguin (right) has no nest. As soon as the female lays her single egg, the male puts it on top of his feet, covers it with a fold of his feathered belly skin and so protects it from the cold winds and the snow and ice beneath. The female also shares in incubating duties and between them the pair keep the egg warm for 54 days. When it hatches at last, the young chick remains on the parents' feet, while they take turns in feeding it and protecting it from marauding skuas and gulls.

parents they have had to develop a coloration of their eggs to match those of the species they parasitise, so each race of cuckoos restricts itself to certain species as nurses.

The process of incubation is not a straightforward one. The very fact that the bird's body feathers insulate it so well means that they form a very effective heat screen between its body and its eggs. Many therefore develop a special modification for brooding. Just before incubation starts, a group of feathers on the underside are moulted and the exposed skin becomes pink with distended blood vessels just below the surface. The eggs fit neatly into this patch and so are warmed very efficiently. But not all birds produce this patch by moulting. Ducks and geese make one mechanically by plucking their own feathers from their breasts. The blue-footed booby, which has bright blue feet and uses them in its displays, lifting them in an irresistibly comic fashion as it high-steps around its partner during courtship, now puts them to good use as incubators. It keeps its eggs warm by standing on them.

At last, the young hatch, chipping their way out of their shells with a small egg-tooth on the tip of the bill. Many of those that nest on the ground are covered with down when they emerge and this gives them excellent camouflage. They run away from their nest almost as soon as they are dry to search for food under their mother's supervision. Hatchlings of species that nest above ground in protected or inaccessible nests are often naked and helpless and have to be fed by their parents.

As the days pass, blue, blood-filled quills appear on the skins of the young and at last the essential feathers sprout. Young eagles and storks, as they fledge, may spend days standing on the edge of their nests, beating the air with their wings, strengthening their

A winter crèche

When king penguin chicks are a few months old, they leave their parents and form nursery groups, thousands strong. The parents go off to sea to fish. The young will remain in these crèches throughout the winter while their parents return every two or three weeks with a crop full of food for them. The chicks will beg from any returning adult but, amazingly, the parents can identify their own chick among the huge throng and will surrender food to no other. Even so, the chick's weight falls steadily throughout the winter and many of the smaller ones die before spring arrives and abundant food supplies are at last available.

muscles and practising the movements necessary for flying. Gannets on their narrow cliff ledges do the same thing, though they prudently face inwards when they do so, just in case they become too successful too early. Such preparations, however, are the exceptions. Most young birds seem to be able to perform the complex movements of flying with virtually no practice. Some that are raised in holes, like petrels, manage to fly several kilometres at their first attempt and almost all young birds become accomplished aeronauts within a day or so.

The birds that abandoned flight

Astonishingly, despite their unrivalled skill in the air and all their adaptations necessary to perfect it, birds appear to abandon flight whenever possible. The older bird fossils dating some thirty million years after Archaeopteryx included gull-like forms which were skilled flyers with a keeled chest bone and no bony tail. In essentials they were modern birds. With them, however, lived a huge swimming bird, Hesperornis, which was nearly as big as a man. It had already ceased flying. Fossils of those other highly successful non-flying birds, the penguins, also appear around this time.

The tendency to become grounded can still be seen in operation today. When a species of land bird colonises an island that no four-footed predators have been able to reach, sooner or later, it seems to develop into a flightless form. Rails on the islands of the Great Barrier Reef run in front of intruding feet like domestic chickens and only flutter feebly into the air on extreme provocation. The cormorants of the Galapagos have such small wings that they cannot get in the air even if they try. On the islands of the Indian Ocean, huge flightless pigeons evolved, the dodo on Mauritius and the solitaire on Rodrigues. Unfortunately for them, their islands did not remain without predators for ever. A few centuries ago, man arrived and within a short time exterminated them both. In New Zealand too, there were no predators before the arrival of man and several bird groups there evolved flightless forms. The moas, the tallest birds that have ever existed, standing over three metres high, were hunted to extinction by early man. Only their small secretive relatives, the kiwis, survive from the whole group. There is also a strange flightless parrot, the kakapo, and a giant flightless rail, the takahe.

This relapse to a ground-living life is an indication of the great demands that flying puts on a bird's energies and the amount of food it needs in consequence. If life can be led in safety on the ground, then this is a much easier option and the birds take it. It must have been the harassing by their dinosaur relatives that drove Archaeopteryx into the trees in the first place and the threat of hunting mammals that has kept its descendants there ever since.

But in between these two periods, there was an interregnum of a few million years when the dinosaurs had disappeared and the mammals had not yet developed into forms sufficiently powerful to dominate the land. It seems that the birds did then make a bid to claim the ruling position for themselves. Fifty-five million years ago, an immense flightless bird called Diatryma stalked the plains of Wyoming. It was a hunter. Taller than a man, it had a massive bill fully adequate to butcher quite large creatures.

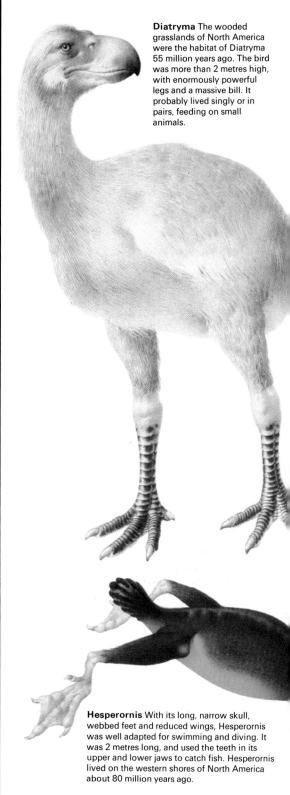

Diatryma The wooded grasslands of North America were the habitat of Diatryma 55 million years ago. The bird was more than 2 metres high, with enormously powerful legs and a massive bill. It probably lived singly or in pairs, feeding on small animals.

Hesperornis With its long, narrow skull, webbed feet and reduced wings, Hesperornis was well adapted for swimming and diving. It was 2 metres long, and used the teeth in its upper and lower jaws to catch fish. Hesperornis lived on the western shores of North America about 80 million years ago.

Phororhacos This bird was a dominant predator in the grasslands of Patagonia 20 million years ago, for there were no large mammalian predators to compete with it. It stood about 2 metres high.

FLIGHTLESS BIRDS OF THE PAST

When flight was not needed for protection, some birds lost their wings and became powerful land-dwellers.

After they first evolved over 140 million years ago, birds rapidly developed their power of flight – perhaps, in some cases, as protection from dinosaurs. Some birds, however, later abandoned flying. Hesperornis, an expert diver, took up life in the sea, living on fish. After the dinosaurs had died out 65 million years ago, the giant Diatryma ruled the land in North America. Later, mammals became dominant, but flightless birds continued to live in some isolated places such as islands.

Aepyornis The remains of Aepyornis – 'the elephant bird' – have been found mainly on the island of Madagascar. They date from about 70,000 years ago, but it is unclear when they died out. Their extinction may have been hastened by man's hunting. Aepyornis reached a height of 3 metres and probably fed on fruit, roots and invertebrates in the forests. Its eggs, which are still sometimes found in the sand dunes of southern Madagascar, may have been incubated by the sun-heated sand.

Dinornis Giant moas inhabited New Zealand until about 200 years ago, when the last of them were exterminated as a result of hunting by man, and agriculture. Dinornis, the largest type of moa, was a vegetarian which inhabited forested regions. Its remains, some of them remarkably well preserved, date from about 40,000 years ago. Dinornis had a strong skeleton, powerful legs, fluffy feathers, a relatively small head and bill, and no wings. The biggest was over 3 metres tall.

The Dodo This was a large, flightless pigeon which, in the absence of predators, lived on the island of Mauritius until it was exterminated, largely by visiting sailors, in the 17th century.

Diatryma disappeared after a few million years, but giant flightless birds still survive elsewhere – ostriches, rheas and cassowaries. They are not close relatives of Diatryma but they have ancient lineages and are descended from stock that once flew. That can be deduced from the fact that they still retain many of the adaptations for flight – air sacs in the body, toothless keratin beaks and, in some instances, partially hollow bones. Their wings are not reduced fore-legs but simplified versions of limbs that once beat the air and the feathers that grow on them are arranged in the patterns appropriate for flight. The keel on their breastbone, however, has virtually disappeared for now it has only to provide attachment for the feeblest of muscles. The feathers, since they are not needed for flight, have lost their barbules and have become merely fluffy appendages that are used in display.

The cassowaries in particular can give us some idea of how formidable a creature Diatryma must have been. Their feathers have lost most of their filaments and are more like coarse hair. Their stubby wings are armed with a few curving quills as thick as knitting needles. On their heads they have a bony casque with which they force their way through the thick vegetation of the New Guinea jungles where they live. The bare skin of their head and neck is livid purple, blue or yellow and hung with scarlet wattles. They feed on fruit but they also take small creatures such as reptiles, mammals or nestling birds. Apart from venomous snakes, they are by far the most dangerous creatures on the island. When cornered, they lash out with savage kicks that can rip open a man's stomach and many people have been killed by them.

Cassowaries are solitary creatures. As they prowl through the forest, they often make a threatening, booming rumble which carries for considerable distances. It hardly sounds like a bird at all. Closer to, you may be able to detect the outline of an animal, as tall as a man, moving in the undergrowth. A glittering eye peers through the leaves; and then suddenly the huge creature stampedes away, crashing by brute force through bushes and saplings. You need no convincing that if large carnivorous birds developed a taste for blood, they could be very dangerous animals.

Yet in the end, birds like Diatryma were not clever enough hunters. One group of animals escaped them. They were small insignificant creatures at that time but they were very active. Like the birds, they had developed warm blood but they insulated themselves not with feathers but with fur. They were the first mammals. It was their descendants, in the end, which inherited the earth and kept the birds, by and large, in the air.

A killer bird

Few birds are capable of killing a man, but the cassowary can and does. It has abandoned the power of flight and has taken to a life on the ground. In the jungles of Australasia, where it lives, it is by far the biggest animal, rivalling even man, and it will attack anything that interferes with it, with powerful kicks.

How feathers create colours

Colour can be produced by structure. Some feather filaments have walls so thin they split light like an oil film and change colour with their angle. Some are filled with microscopic bubbles which reflect light. Their colour will disappear if they are doused with liquid and return when they dry. Yet others, like these macaw feathers (right), contain pigments and retain their colour even when they are wet and viewed from any angle.

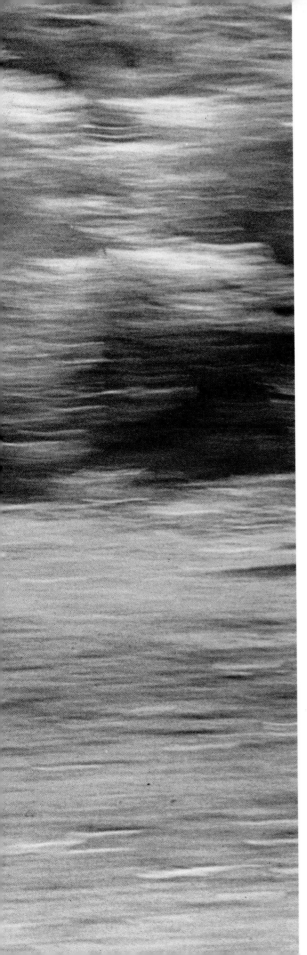

9. EGGS, POUCHES AND PLACENTAS

A complex animal requires considerable sustenance during its development, and mammals provide it in several ways

At the end of the eighteenth century, the skin of an altogether astounding animal arrived in London. It had come from the newly established colony in Australia. The creature to which it had belonged was about the size of a rabbit, with fur as thick and as fine as an otter's. Its feet were webbed and clawed; its rear vent was a single one combining both excretory and reproductive functions, a cloaca, like that of a reptile; and most outlandish of all, it had a large flat beak like a duck. It was so bizarre that some people in London dismissed it as another of those faked monsters that were confected in the Far East from bits and pieces of dissimilar creatures and then sold to gullible travellers as mermaids, sea dragons and other wonders. But careful examination of the skin showed no sign of fakery. The strange bill which seemed to fit so awkwardly on to the furry head, with a flap like a cuff at the junction, did truly belong. The animal, however improbable it might seem, was a real one.

When complete specimens became available, it was seen that the bill was not hard and bird-like as it had first seemed when the only evidence was a dried skin. In life it was pliable and leathery so the resemblance to a bird could be discounted. The fur was much more significant. Hair or fur is the hallmark of a mammal, just as feathers are of birds. It was clear, therefore, that this mystery animal must be a member of that great group which contains creatures as diverse as shrews, lions, elephants and men. The function of a mammal's hairy coat is to insulate the body and enable it to maintain a

The symbol of a continent

The kangaroo is the most famous and the largest of all the marsupials of Australia, but it is only one of over 150 different kinds. Some are as small as mice. Others resemble squirrels, moles, rabbits, badgers and ant-eaters. In the past there were species that looked like wolves, and even one the size of a rhinoceros. All these marsupials share a particular method of breeding, in which they give birth to their young at a very early stage and rear them outside the body on milk, sometimes within the protection of a pouch. But though the marsupials are thought of as characteristically Australian, another 70 or so species live outside the continent.

233

high temperature, so it followed that this new creature must also be warm-blooded. And, presumably, it also possessed a third characteristic of mammals and the one that gives the group its name, a mamma, a breast, with which to suckle its young.

The Australian colonists had referred to the creature as a 'water-mole' but science had to have something that sounded a little more scholarly. There were many extraordinary features to inspire a vivid name, but the one invented for it was the rather dull one of Platypus which means no more than 'flat-footed'. Soon afterwards, it was pointed out that the name was invalid anyway as it had previously been given to a flat-footed beetle, so a second one had to be devised and the animal was re-labelled Ornithorhyncus, 'bird-bill'. This is the scientific title it still bears. To most people, however, it remains a platypus.

It lives, then as now, in the rivers of eastern Australia, swimming energetically and buoyantly, often cruising along the surface, paddling with its webbed fore-feet and steering with its hind. When it dives, it closes its ears and tiny eyes with little muscular flaps of skin. Unable to see as it grubs around on the river bed, it feels for fresh-water prawns, worms and other small creatures with its bill, which is rich in nerve endings and very sensitive. As well as being an adept swimmer it is also a powerful and industrious burrower, digging extensive tunnels through the river banks sometimes as much as 18 metres long. To do this, it rolls back the webbing of its fore-feet into its palms and so frees the claws for work. Here the female constructs an underground nest of grass and reeds. From one of these came more sensational news about the animal. It was claimed that the platypus laid eggs.

Many zoologists in Europe regarded this as being altogether too absurd. No mammal laid eggs. If eggs were found in a platypus nest, then they must have been deposited there by some other visiting creature. They were described as being nearly spherical, about the size of marbles and soft-shelled, in which case they were probably those of a reptile. But local people in Australia insisted that they belonged to the platypus. Naturalists argued heatedly about the issue for nearly a century. Then in 1884, a female was shot just after she had laid an egg. A second one was found inside her body on the point of being extruded. Now there could be no doubt. Here was a mammal that did indeed lay eggs.

Further surprises were to come. When, after ten days, these eggs hatch, the young are not left to find food for themselves as all young reptiles must do. The female develops on her belly some special glands. They are similar in structure to the sweat glands that the platypus, like most mammals, has in its skin to aid in cooling the body if it gets over-heated. But the sweat these enlarged glands produce is thick and rich in fat; it is milk. It oozes into the fur and the young suck it from tufts of hair. There is no nipple, so the platypus cannot be said to have a true breast; but it is a beginning.

That other important mammalian character, endothermy or warm-bloodedness, also seems to be incompletely developed. Nearly all mammals keep their bodies at temperatures between 36°–39°C. The platypus' temperature is only 30°C and fluctuates very considerably.

An egg-laying mammal

Only a century ago, the platypus was much hunted, for its fur is dense and soft and coats made from it were greatly valued. As a result the animal became very rare. Now total protection has restored its numbers. It is quite abundant in some rivers in south-east Australia and Tasmania, but is seldom noticed, for it is only active at dawn and dusk and seldom makes any noise apart from an occasional splash. The animals excavate immense many-branched tunnels in the river banks. Those built by the female usually climb steeply upwards into the bank for 5 or 6 metres before continuing horizontally for as much as 18 metres. This design allows the animal to emerge close to the water but minimises the risk of flooding the burrow. The female builds the nest chamber at the far end, lining it with reeds and leaves which she carries there under her tail. After her eggs are laid, she stays with them for several days without eating. When she does eventually leave to feed, she plugs the tunnel behind her with one or more barriers of soil which she renews when she returns, sealing herself in. The tunnels are, in places, very narrow and fit tightly around the platypus. This, it seems, is important for the animal's health, for as it squeezes through all the water is removed from its thick fur, and its body, which in any case has a very low and variable temperature, is not chilled by water-logged fur.

Eggs, pouches and placentas

One other creature in the world can parallel this mixture of primitive mammalian and reptilian features and that, too, comes from Australia, the spiny ant-eater. The history of its naming is a repeat of that of the platypus. Science first called it Echidna, 'spiny one', only to discover that that name had been bestowed previously on a fish. So it was renamed Tachyglossus, 'swift-tongued'. But once more it was the first name that stuck. The animal looks like a large flattened hedgehog with an armoury of spines on its back embedded in a coat of dark bristly hair. It can dig itself into the ground with swimming movements of its four legs which excavate so efficiently and with such strength that on anything but the hardest surface, the echidna simply goes down vertically and within a few minutes all that can be seen of it is an impregnable dome of extremely sharp spines. The animal is not primarily a burrower. It goes to ground largely as a defensive measure. Most of its time it spends either asleep in some unobtrusive corner or waddling through the bush searching for ants and termites. When it finds a nest of them, it tears it open with the claws of its front legs and licks up the insects with a long tongue which flickers in and out of the tiny mouth at the end of its tube-like snout.

This snout and its spines, like the bill of the platypus, are specialised characters that befit it for its particular way of life. In evolutionary terms, they are recent acquisitions. Fundamentally, the echidna is very similar to the platypus. It has hair; its body temperature is very low; it has a single vent, the cloaca; and it lays eggs.

In one detail of its reproduction, it differs. The female keeps her eggs not in a nest, but in a temporary pouch which develops on her underside. It is said that when the moment for laying arrives, she curls round and manages to deposit her eggs directly into her abdominal pouch, thus exhibiting a gymnastic ability one might not have suspected in such a comfortably plump creature. The shells of the eggs are moist and stick to the hair in the pouch. After seven to ten days, they hatch. Thick yellowish milk exudes from the skin of the mother's belly and the young suck it up. They remain in the pouch for some seven weeks by which time they are about 10 cms long and their spines have begun to develop. This presumably makes them uncomfortable passengers as far as their mother is concerned. At any rate, the mother now scratches them out and deposits them in a den. She continues to feed them for several more weeks, encouraging them to suckle by prodding them beneath her body with her snout and arching her back so that her abdomen is clear of the ground. The young then lift their heads and fasten their little jaws on tufts of her hair.

The only food a reptile mother provides for its baby is the yolk in its egg. From this small yellow ball, the young creature must build a body that is sufficiently complete and strong to make it totally independent as soon as it emerges from the shell. It must then go and seek food for itself – nearly always of the same kind as it will live on for the rest of its life. The platypus uses a method that has much greater potential. Its eggs have a small amount of yolk in them but by providing its young as soon as they hatch with a continuous supply of special easily-digested food, the milk, it enables them to have a much longer development. This is a major change in maternal technique and one that

236

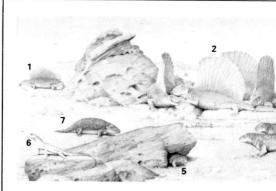

SAIL-BACK REPTILES: FORERUNNERS OF THE MAMMALS

In the arid landscape of Texas, 270 million years ago, lived the pelycosaurs, a group of reptiles which later gave rise to the mammals.

Pelycosaurs are an early group of reptiles which lived in areas where vegetation was probably sparse. Edaphosaurus, an herbivorous type, is shown in this reconstruction feeding on an early, scrubby conifer. The 3 metre long Dimetrodon, a carnivore, probably hunted smaller reptiles and amphibians, possibly including the lizard-like Araeoscelis. Pelycosaurs had sails on their backs which probably functioned as temperature regulators, absorbing and radiating heat quickly. This technique of heat control foreshadowed more effective devices developed later by mammals, which produced their heat internally and dissipated excess amounts by the evaporation of sweat. Pelycosaurs later lost their sails, indicating that they may have begun to produce their heat internally.

The reconstruction includes three types of amphibian. Eryops probably stayed near the water, but Seymouria and Diadectes were extremely reptile-like in appearance and probably had to return to water only to breed.

has been crucial, in even more sophisticated versions, to the ultimate success of the whole mammal group.

The body design of the echidna and platypus is undoubtedly of great antiquity, but we have no hard evidence to indicate which fossil reptiles were their ancestors. Our knowledge of many of the candidates is based to a considerable degree on teeth. These, one of the most durable parts of any animal's anatomy, and therefore frequently preserved as fossils, are very informative about an animal's diet and habits. They are also highly characteristic of a species and similarities between teeth are strong evidence of genealogical relationships. Inconveniently, when the platypus and echidna became specialised for underwater foraging in one case and ant-eating in the other, they both lost their teeth. Assuredly their ancestors had them for young platypus still produce three tiny ones soon after birth, but they are lost within a very short time and replaced with horny plates. Nor is there any fossil evidence of any consequence about their ancestors. So we have virtually nothing to help us link these creatures to any group of fossil reptiles. Nonetheless, it is a reasonable guess that the kind of breeding techniques the platypus and echidna use today were developed by some reptile groups in the process of their transformation into mammals.

But which reptiles were they? The hallmarks of today's mammals – hair, warm blood and milk-producing glands – do not fossilise. We can only deduce their presence. As we have already seen, some dinosaurs, such as Stegosaurus, undoubtedly developed very effective methods of absorbing heat quickly from the sun. But they were not the first reptiles to do so. An earlier group, the pelycosaurs, also managed to do this. One of them, Dimetrodon, grew long spines from its backbone which supported a sail of skin. This must have served as a solar panel much as the Stegosaur's plates did. But the interesting thing about the pelycosaurs is that while their dynasty thrived, the sail-like crests disappeared. It seems extremely unlikely that even if there were a warming of the climate, the forces of evolution would allow an animal to lose such a valuable method of heat control unless it was able to replace it with something more efficient. It is therefore supposed that the pelycosaurs and their successors, the therapsids, were to some degree endothermic. The therapsids were only a metre or so long. Endothermy, particularly in such small creatures, needs some form of body insulation if it is to be effective, so it could be that some of these creatures were covered in fur.

How teeth helped mammals develop

There are other clues to suggest that some of the therapsids were on the way to becoming mammals. Generating heat in the body, in a proper endothermic manner, absorbs a lot of energy and would have required an increase in daily food and a speeding up of the digestive processes. One way of achieving this is to replace the typical reptilian teeth, which are simple and peg-like and do little more than grip, with specialised cutters, grinders and mashers that can break up the food mechanically. This is exactly the change that can be traced in the teeth of therapsids.

But even supposing that they were both warm-blooded and hairy, would that make

An echidna vanishes
An echidna needs only a minute to disappear downwards. It can dig into all but the hardest ground. Once below the surface no animal will risk painfully pricked paws or muzzle to dig it up; so there it stays until danger has passed. The claws of an echidna are not only digging instruments. One on each hind leg is particularly long and is used for the hazardous process of preening between the long and extremely sharp spines that cover the animal's back and sides. Its jaws have no teeth and are prolonged into a thin horny beak which has a tiny mouth at the end from which the long sticky tongue emerges.

them mammals? The question, of course, is to some extent an artificial one. These categories are man's inventions, not nature's. In practice, ancestral lines merge imperceptibly into one another. The anatomical characters which, grouped together, man may choose to regard as diagnostic, may individually change at different speeds so that one feature may develop while the remainder of an animal's anatomy remains relatively unmodified. Furthermore, the environmental conditions that stimulate such change may produce similar responses in several dynasties. Indeed, there seems no doubt that warm blood was acquired at various times by several quite separate reptilian groups. It may therefore be that the line of reptiles from which the platypus and echidna stemmed was not the same as that which was to give rise to other mammals.

Whatever the exact shape of the genealogical tree, at least one group of the reptiles completed the transition to mammal status some 200 million years ago. A small fossil, discovered in 1966 in southern Africa, is the earliest near-complete specimen of a mammal that has so far been found. This creature was only about ten centimetres long and somewhat shrew-like. Details of its jaw and skull link it firmly with true mammals. Its teeth were specialised for eating insects and there is no doubt in the minds of those scientists who have examined it that it must have been both warm-blooded and furry. At the moment we cannot tell whether it laid eggs like a platypus or gave birth to live young and suckled them by means of a breast. The mammals, however, had now certainly arrived.

Even so, the next great developments among the land animals did not come from them. Instead, the dinosaurs began their dramatic expansion. Although the little mammals were quite over-shadowed in both numbers and size, they survived, saved by their warm blood, which allowed them to be active at night when the great reptiles became torpid. It must have been then that they emerged from hiding and hunted for insects and other small creatures. This situation prevailed for a vast period of time – 135 million years – but eventually, the fortunes of the dinosaurs waned and when they finally disappeared, sixty-five million years ago, the little mammals were poised to take over.

The marsupial and its strange 'little bag'

Among them were creatures that were very like the opossums that today live in the Americas. The Virginia opossum is a large rat-shaped creature, much be-whiskered, with an untidy shaggy coat, button eyes and a long naked tail which it can wrap round a branch with sufficient strength to support its own weight for a little time at least. It has a large mouth that it opens alarmingly wide to expose a great number of small sharp teeth. It is a tough adaptable creature that has spread through the Americas, from Argentina in the south to Canada in the north. There it endures such cold temperatures that on occasion its large naked ears get frost-bitten. It wanders around the countryside with a raffish buccaneering air, eating fruit, insects, worms, frogs, lizards, young birds – almost anything that might be considered edible.

The most extraordinary thing about it, too, is the way it reproduces. The female has a capacious pouch on her underside in which she rears her young. When the first opossum was brought to Europe from Brazil in the early sixteenth century by the explorer Pinzon who had served under Columbus, no one had ever seen anything like it. The King and Queen of Spain were persuaded to put their fingers inside the pouch and wonder. Scholars gave the structure a name, marsupium, 'little bag', and so the opossum became the first marsupial to be known in Europe.

There was no doubt that the young were reared in the marsupium, for they were often found there, minuscule naked pink creatures clinging to the teats with their mouths; but how did they get there? Some said at the time, and some country folk in America still maintain, that they are, literally, blown into the pouch. The opossums mate, according to the story, by rubbing noses. The young are conceived in the nostrils and in due course the female sticks her nose in her pouch, gives a hefty snort and blows out the lot of them. The story doubtless arose because the female opossum, just before the young appear in the pouch, pokes her nose into it and carefully licks it clean to prepare for their arrival.

The truth is scarcely less fantastic than the fable. Opossums, like the echidna and platypus, have a single cloaca closed by a sphincter muscle into which the anus and the urino-genital vent both open. They copulate and the male fertilises the female's eggs internally, but the young embryos that result have only tiny yolk sacs to supply them and they are expelled into the world after twelve days and eighteen hours, the shortest gestation period known in any mammal. Blind pink morsels no bigger than bees, they are so unformed that they cannot justly be called infants or babies, and are referred to instead by the special name of neonate. The female may produce as many as two dozen of them at a time. As they emerge from their mother's cloaca, they haul themselves through the fur of her belly to the opening of the pouch, a distance of about 8 cm. It is the first and the most hazardous journey of their lives and half of them may well die on the way. Once they reach the warmth and security of the pouch, each fastens on to one of the thirteen nipples and starts to take milk. If more than thirteen complete the journey, the latecomers, finding no vacant teat, will starve and die.

Nine or ten weeks later, the young clamber out of the pouch. They are now fully formed, the size of mice, and cling to their mother's fur in what seems to be a most precarious fashion. In the early eighteenth century, a famous illustration of a South American opossum showed the young with their tiny tails neatly wrapped around their mother's tail which trails behind her. As this was copied by one illustrator after another, this posture became transformed into one in which the mother arches her tail over her back and the babies in a neat row strap-hang from it by theirs. When museums came to mount opossum skins, they consulted books and understandably mounted their specimens in this engaging posture, so giving further strength to the story. It is, however, only another of the fables with which this odd creature seems to be surrounded. Young

Playing possum
If attacked, an opossum often feigns death – 'plays possum'. It becomes paralysed and lies with its eyes closed, mouth open and breathing scarcely detectable (right), so that its attacker may assume it is dead. Many creatures behave in this way but few so dramatically. Whether the behaviour is of any real value in protecting an opossum's life is uncertain.

A full load for a busy mother
Baby opossums remain with their mother for about three months, clambering through her straggling, untidy fur. Only about half a dozen of the original 24 or so babies (or neonates) survive to this stage. This mother has a bigger than average litter of seven. Once they have left her, she will mate again, and so raise another family within the same year.

240

opossums are not nearly so orderly. They clamber all over their parent, clinging to her long fur, sometimes beneath her, sometimes on her back, with as much abandon and contempt for normal safety as children cavorting in an adventure playground. It is three months before they leave her and set off on an independent life of their own.

There are seventy-six different species of opossum in America. The smallest is mouse-sized and does not have a pouch. Its young, no bigger than grains of rice, cling to the teat between their mother's hind legs and hang there like a diminutive bunch of grapes. At the other end of the scale, the water opossum is almost the size of a small

otter. It has webbed feet and spends much of its time swimming. Its young are saved from drowning by one of the more elaborate of pouches. It is closed by a sphincter, a ring-shaped muscle which shuts the entrance like the draw-strings of a purse. The young inside are able to endure several minutes of submergence and breathe air with a concentration of carbon dioxide in it that would stifle most creatures.

The earliest mammalian fossils that have been certainly identified as being marsupial were found in South America and it may be that the group originated here. But the greatest assemblage of marsupials today live not in America but in Australia. How could they have got from one continent to the other?

The continents drift apart, and animals become isolated

To find an answer to that question, we have to return to the period when the dinosaurs were still at the height of their dominance. At that time, the continents of the world were in contact with one another. They may even have been grouped together in one gigantic land mass. So it is that fossils of closely related dinosaurs have been found in all of today's continents, in North America as well as Australia, in Europe as well as Africa. The early mammal-like reptiles must have been similarly widespread. But towards the end of the dinosaurs' reign, this great land split into two – a northern supercontinent comprising today's Europe, Asia and North America; and in the south, another made up of South America, Africa, Antarctica and Australia.

The primary evidence for this grouping and the subsequent splitting and drifting is geological. It comes from studies of the way in which today's continents fit together, the continuities of the rocks between their opposite edges, the orientation of magnetic crystals in rocks which show the position they held when they first formed, the dating of the mid-ocean ridges and their islands, drillings in the ocean floors and other sources.

The distribution of many animals and plants adds corroborative evidence. Giant flightless birds provide a particularly clear case. As we have seen, they appeared very early in the history of the birds. One group, which included the ferocious Diatryma, evolved in the northern supercontinent. All of these are now extinct. In the southern supercontinent, another different family appeared which fared much better. These were the ratites – the rhea in South America, ostrich in Africa, emu and cassowary in Australia and kiwi in New Zealand. The distribution of these birds had been a great puzzle. They are so similar that it seems very probable that they are descended from a single flightless ancestor. But how could descendants that could not fly spread between these widely separated lands? The former existence of the southern supercontinent dissolves the difficulty. The birds had simply walked to different parts of it and remained there, evolving further into the different forms we know today, while the land mass separated into its constituent continents.

Fleas, too, support the case. These parasitic insects travel with the animals they live on but readily develop into new species and move on to new hosts. Some families of highly characteristic fleas are found only in Australia and South America. It seems inconceivable that had their hosts carried them through Europe and North America,

An American marsupial mouse
About 40 different species of mouse opossum are found between Mexico and Argentina. They are like mice in both size and general appearance, but they have a very different diet, living largely on insects.

the only alternative route, they would not have left relatives among other furred creatures on the way.

There is also botanical evidence. The southern beech, a forest-forming tree related to but quite distinct from the European beech, flourishes only in the temperate lands of the southern hemisphere. This distribution is now easy to explain.

The great southern land-mass eventually began to break up. Africa separated and drifted northwards. Australia and Antarctica remained joined to one another and were linked, either by a land bridge or a chain of islands, to the southern tip of South America. At this point, it seems, the marsupials were developing from the early mammal stock. If this took place in South America, as some evidence suggests, then they spread across into the Australian-Antarctic bloc.

Meanwhile, primitive mammals were also evolving in the northern supercontinent. They were to develop a different way of nourishing their young. Instead of transferring them at a very early stage into an external pouch, they retained them within the body of the female and supported them by means of a device called the placenta. We can examine this technique later. For the moment it is enough to recognise that this different branch of the mammals existed.

The South American marsupials flourished greatly while they had the continent to

An Australian marsupial mouse

This creature, like its American parallel, is also an insect-eater, and produces tiny neonates the size of rice grains. Some species have pouches. Others manage to rear their minute young without any such protection.

A marsupial cat on a nocturnal hunt

The quoll comes from south-eastern Australia. It is a savage nocturnal hunter that preys on rodents and birds as well as insects. A large proportion of the female's offspring die within a few hours of birth, for she produces some 24 young and has only six teats in her pouch.

themselves. A huge wolf-like form appeared and also a leopard-like carnivore with sabre-like canine teeth. But the fragments of the southern supercontinent were drifting apart and South America was moving slowly northwards. In due course, it connected with North America by way of a land bridge in the neighbourhood of Panama. Down this corridor came the placental mammals to dispute the possession of South America with the marsupial residents. In the course of this rivalry, many species of marsupials disappeared, leaving only the tough, opportunist opossums. Some of these invaded the land of the invaders and managed to colonise North America, as the Virginia opossum has done today.

The marsupials that lived in the central part of the southern supercontinent, however, did not survive at all. This great block of land became Antarctica. It drifted over the South Pole where it was so cold that it developed an immense ice-cap and life on the land became insupportable. The creatures on the third section of the supercontinent, however, were more fortunate. This was Australia. It drifted north and east into the emptiness of the Pacific basin and remained totally separate from any other continent. So its marsupials have evolved in isolation for the last fifty million years.

The marsupial fossils of Naracoorte

During this vast period, they developed into a great number of different types in order to take advantage of the wide range of environments available to them. You can see the remains of some of the spectacular species that once existed in the limestone caves of Naracoorte, 250 kms south of Adelaide. These caves have been famous for years because of the beauty of their stalactite formations, but in 1969, a faint breath of air, filtering up through boulders at the far end of the main chamber, hinted that there might be hitherto unknown sections beyond. Excavations revealed a narrow passageway which eventually led to the greatest assemblage of marsupial fossils yet found.

After an hour of crawling on hands and knees, wriggling through tight rock squeezes and worming down narrow winding chimneys, you come at last to two low galleries. You can only enter them by inching through a narrow tunnel on your stomach. Before you stretches a long gallery not much more than a metre high with a ceiling hung with straw-like stalactites. The air is so humid that your breath turns to mist in front of you and a party of half a dozen could, in a few minutes, cause the entire gallery to fill with fog. The floor is covered with a soft red silt, carried down here by floods of a subterranean river that has long since disappeared. With the mud, it brought the bones of marsupials. Some were animals that had lived in the upper cave. Others appear to have been creatures of the surrounding forests that had accidentally fallen down swallow holes at the cave's entrance and been killed. The bones lie strewn thickly on the mud – leg bones, shoulder blades, teeth and, most dramatic of all, skulls. All are a delicate pale cream colour as though they were specimens straight from an anatomist's cleaning bath. Most are so fragile that they crumble at a touch and can only be safely lifted if they are jacketed in foam and plaster.

There are the remains of a huge marsupial the size and shape of a rhinoceros, of an

Gliders of the marsupial world

The marsupial gliders of Australia (above) and the flying squirrels of North America have paralleled one another so closely that it is almost impossible to tell which continent one of them comes from without handling it. Both are magnificent gliders, soaring for over 100 metres on their flying membranes.

The gliding flower-seekers

Some marsupial gliders feed on leaves. Others, including the sugar glider (left), feast on blossom of the eucalyptus. The female glides with her young in her pouch for two months, but later leaves them in a nest.

immense kangaroo with a neck like a small giraffe that browsed on the branches of trees. The character of one creature here is still under discussion. It was originally thought to be a carnivore for its back teeth are elongated into formidable shearing blades with which it might have sliced through the flesh and bones of its prey. Because of its size, it was called a marsupial lion. Now studies of its front legs have shown that they were well suited for clinging so it may actually have been a tree climber and used its fearsome-looking back teeth merely to cut hard fruits.

These creatures died about 40,000 years ago. The factors that ultimately brought about their extinction are still uncertain. It may be that the animals were affected by changes in the climate. Australia, after it had broken away from Antarctica, continued to drift northwards. Indeed, it is still doing so and as fast as it has ever done, at a rate of about five centimetres a year. The shift brought about a gradual warming and drying of the continent.

The marsupial wolf that preyed on sheep

Great numbers of marsupials still survive, of course. Today there are a dozen main families with, between them, nearly two hundred species. Many of these creatures parallel the placental forms that evolved in the northern hemisphere. When colonists from Europe came to Australia, they naturally enough gave the marsupials the names of the European creatures they most closely resembled. In the temperate forest of the south, for instance, the colonists found little furry, pointed-nosed long-tailed creatures and called them, understandably, marsupial mice. The name is not really appropriate for these are not rodents, timidly nibbling grain, but savage hunters that will set upon insects quite as large as themselves and crunch them to pieces. There are carnivorous marsupials that will tackle reptiles and nestling birds and are called marsupial cats. Until very recently there was also a marsupial wolf, the thylacine. This creature was a very efficient hunter. It took to feeding on the newly introduced sheep and so was itself hunted and eventually exterminated by farmers. The last identified living one died in the London Zoo in 1933, but there is still a chance that a few might survive in the remoter parts of Tasmania.

In two instances, the parallels between placental and marsupial forms are so close that if you came across one of them in a zoo you would find it almost impossible to tell which it was without handling it. The sugar glider is a small leaf- and blossom-eating marsupial that lives in eucalyptus trees. It has a parachute of skin connecting its fore and hind legs which enables it to glide from branch to branch. It looks almost exactly like a North American flying squirrel. A burrowing way of life demands particular structures and both marsupial and placental burrowers have developed them. Moles of both kinds have short silky fur, reduced eyes, powerful digging forelegs and a stumpy tail. The female marsupial mole, however, has a pouch and one which, fortunately for her young, opens backwards so that it does not fill with earth as she burrows through her tunnels.

Not all marsupials have such close placental equivalents. The koala is a medium-sized creature that lives in trees feeding on leaves, a role that is filled elsewhere by monkeys. But the koala is scarcely monkey-like in appearance and its slow-moving plodding character is a long way from that of the intelligent and quick-reacting monkeys. The numbat is an ant-eater. It has the long sticky tongue that all ant-eaters use to collect their food, but its adaptations are not nearly so extreme as those of, for example, the great ant-eater of South America which has developed a long curving tube for a snout and lost all its teeth. The numbat's jaws are not nearly so elongated and it still has all its teeth.

In the temperate woodlands of Tasmania lives another creature which is also uniquely and quintessentially Australasian, the boodie. It is one of a small group of marsupials called collectively, rat-kangaroos. Very shy, strictly nocturnal, it feeds on all kinds of foods, including meat, and it has a pair of small pointed canine teeth to help it do so. It makes its nest in a burrow, industriously collecting material for it in a most ingenious way. It picks up a few straws in its mouth, stacks them in a bundle on the ground and then pushes them back over its long tail with its hind legs. The tail then

The koala – a fussy feeder

Koalas feed entirely on eucalyptus leaves, but of the 350 different species of the tree that grow in Australia they will accept leaves from only 20 and greatly prefer just five. The female breeds every other year. She produces one, very rarely two, at a time and carries it on her back for a whole year (right).

A marsupial ant-eater

The numbat is the size of a rat and like many so-called ant-eaters it eats termites, not ants. Most small marsupials sleep during the day but the numbat trots about boldly searching for termite colonies. The female has no pouch, but her teats are surrounded by bristly hair which may give her young some slight protection.

A TAIL FOR CARRYING BUILDING MATERIAL

The boodie is a small, shy Australian marsupial, one of a group called rat-kangaroos. To build its nest, the boodie gathers a bundle of grass and binds it together with its tail. It then hops, like a kangaroo, to its burrow with the load.

curls up tightly so that the straw is effectively baled and the boodie moves away. To do so, it hops. Boodies move about entirely on their back legs, which have very long feet. If you had to design a creature to serve as a primitive ancestor of the most famous Australian animal of all, the kangaroo, it might well look like the shy, forest-living, omnivorous, hopping boodie.

The mystery of why the kangaroo hops

The development of the kangaroo clan was accelerated by Australia's continuing drift northwards and the consequent drying and warming of its climate. This caused the forest that had covered much of the land to thin and be replaced by more open country and grassland. Grass is good food, but to move out of the forest and graze in the open is to be exposed to attack by hunting animals. So any grass-eaters that colonised the plains would have to be able to move fast. The kangaroos achieved that with a greatly exaggerated version of the boodie method. They hopped – and prodigiously.

No one knows why kangaroos use this method rather than running on all fours, as virtually all herbivorous plain-living creatures do elsewhere in the world. Maybe the tendency to an upright stance was already there in their ancestors, as it is in the boodie, though such a reply only puts the question back a stage. Maybe hopping is connected with the problems of carrying large babies in a pouch which might be more conveniently done, particularly when moving at high speed over rough and rocky ground, with an upright torso. Whatever the reason, the kangaroos have brought the hop to a high pitch of efficiency. Their hind legs are enormously powerful, the long muscular tail is held out stiffly behind so that it acts as a counterbalance and the animal, in bursts, can reach speeds of 60 kph and clear fences nearly 3 metres high.

The second difficulty that grass-eaters must overcome is the wear and tear on their teeth. Grass is tough, particularly the kind that grows today in the parched land of central Australia. Breaking it down into pulp in the mouth is a very valuable aid to its digestion, but it is very wearing on the teeth. Grazers elsewhere have molars with open roots so that wear can be compensated by continuous growth throughout the animal's life. Kangaroo teeth have no such ability. Their roots are closed, so they use a different system of replacement. There are four pairs of cheek teeth on either side of the jaws. Only the front ones engage. As they are worn down to the roots, they fall out and those from the rear migrate forward to take their place. By the time the animal is fifteen or twenty years old, its last molars are in use. Eventually these too will be worn down and shed so that even if the venerable animal does not die for any other reason, it will eventually do so from starvation.

There are some forty different species in the kangaroo family. The smaller ones are usually called wallabies. The largest is the red kangaroo, which stands taller than a man and is the biggest of all living marsupials.

An Australian speciality

The tiny mouse-sized honey possum, or noolbenger, has specialised in feeding on nectar and pollen to a degree that can only be paralleled by honey-eating birds like hummingbirds. It licks up its food with a long hair-covered brush-tipped tongue, and feeds from the blossoms of banksia and bottle-brush in western Australia.

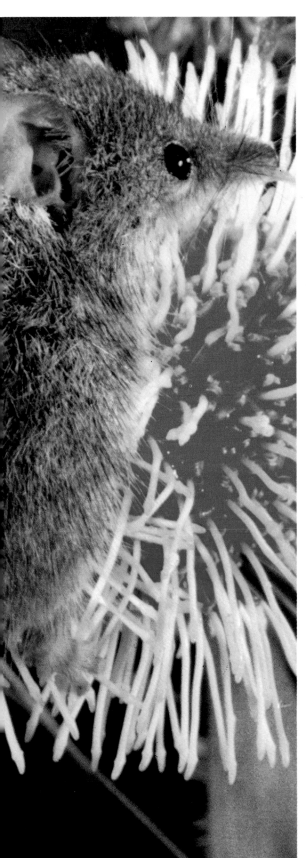

Kangaroos reproduce in much the same way as the opossums. The egg, which is still enclosed in the vestiges of a shell a few microns thick and has a small quantity of yolk within it, descends from the ovary into the uterus. There, lying free, it is fertilised and begins its development. If this is the first time that the female has mated, it does not stay there long. In the case of the red kangaroo it is only thirty-three days before the neonate emerges. Usually only one is born at a time. It is a blind, naked worm a few centimetres long. Its hind legs are mere buds. Its forelegs are better developed and with these it hauls its way through the thick fur of its mother's abdomen. She herself seems entirely oblivious of it.

The neonate's journey to the pouch takes about three minutes. Once there, it fastens on to one of four teats and starts to feed. Almost immediately, the mother's sexual cycle starts again. Another egg descends into the uterus and she becomes sexually receptive; she mates and the egg is fertilised. But then an extraordinary thing happens. The egg's development stops.

Meanwhile, the neonate in the pouch is growing prodigiously. The teat is a long one and has a slight swelling on the end so that if it is pulled out carelessly, the neonate's mouth may be torn and bleed slightly. But there is no truth in the story that mother and offspring become fused together, or that milk is pumped into the young under pressure.

After 190 days, the baby is sufficiently large and independent to make its first foray out of the pouch. From then on it spends increasing time in the outside world and eventually, after 235 days, it leaves the pouch for the last time.

If there is a drought at this time, as happens so often in central Australia, the fertilised egg in the uterus still remains dormant. But if there has been rain and there is good pasture, then the egg now restarts its development. Thirty-three days later, another bean-sized neonate will wriggle out of the mother's cloaca and make its laborious and risky way up to the pouch. The female will then immediately mate again. But the first-born does not give up its milk supply so easily. It returns regularly to feed from its own teat. What is more, the milk with which it is now supplied is a different mixture from that it first received. So now the female has three young dependent on her. One active young-at-foot which grazes but comes back to suckle; a second, the tiny neonate, sucking at her teat in the pouch; and a third, the fertilised but undeveloped egg, waiting its moment within her uterus.

It is a commonly held notion that the marsupials are backward creatures, scarcely much of an improvement on those primitive egg-layers, the platypus and echidna. That is a long way from the truth. The marsupial method of reproduction must certainly have appeared very early in mammalian history, but the kangaroos have refined it marvellously. No other creature anywhere can compare with the female kangaroo who, for much of her adult life, supports a family of three in varying stages of development.

The mammalian body is a very complicated machine that takes a long time to develop. Even as an embryo it is warm-blooded and burns up fuel very quickly. Both these characters demand that the developing young should be supplied with considerable quantities of food. All mammals have found methods of providing far more than could ever be packed within the confines of a shelled egg. We do not know whether the early mammals in the northern supercontinent ever passed through a marsupial stage. It could be that they sprang from a branch of the mammal-like reptiles that never acquired pouches. Certainly, it is extremely unlikely that their ancestors ever brought the method to such sophisticated levels of efficiency as those achieved by the Australian marsupials today. But the northern, placental method has its own benefits.

The placenta allows the young to remain within the uterus for a very long time. It is a flat disc that becomes attached to the wall of the uterus and is connected by the umbilical cord to the foetus. The junction with the uterine wall is highly convoluted so that the surface area between the placenta and the maternal tissues is very great. It is here that interchange between mother and foetus takes place. Blood itself does not pass from mother to young, but oxygen from her lungs and nutrients derived from her food, both dissolved in her blood, diffuse across the junction and so enter the blood of the foetus. There is also traffic in the other direction. The waste products produced by the foetus are absorbed by the mother's blood and then excreted through her kidneys.

All this makes for great biochemical complications. But there are further ones. The mammalian sexual cycle involves the regular production of a new egg. This causes no problem to the marsupial, for in every species, the neonate emerges before the next egg is due to be produced. The placental foetus, however, stays in the uterus for very much longer. So the placenta secretes a hormone which suspends the mother's sexual cycle for as long as the placenta is in place so that no more eggs are produced to compete with the foetus in the uterus.

There is also another problem. The foetus' tissues are not the same, genetically, as the mother's. They contain elements from the father. So when it becomes connected to the mother's body, it risks immunological rejection in the same way as a transplant does. Just how the placenta prevents this from happening we still do not know in detail, but it seems that it is achieved by the production of other hormonal substances.

So, by these means, the babies of placental mammals can remain in the uterus until, if necessary, they are so well developed that they can be fully mobile as soon as they are born. Even after this, they are provided with milk for a further period until they have to gather food for themselves from the world around them.

The placental breeding technique spares the young the hazardous journey outside their mother's body at a very early stage that a marsupial neonate has to undertake, and allows their mother to supply their every want during the long period they remain within her. So whales and seals can carry their unborn young even as they swim for months through freezing seas. No marsupial with air-breathing neonates in a pouch could ever succeed in doing such a thing. It was this placental technique that, in the end, was to prove one of the crucial factors in the mammals' ultimate success in colonising the whole of the earth.

New uses for fore-legs

The kangaroos' specialisation in hopping releases their forearms for other uses. They use their hands for pulling down vegetation, and males also spar with them (above). On very hot days they lick the inner sides of their forearms, covering them with a lather of spittle. The evaporation cools the blood which passes through a maze of capillaries just beneath the skin.

A protected childhood

About five months after it arrived in the pouch, a young kangaroo sticks its head out for the first time. A few days later, it climbs out completely, but returns to feed when danger threatens. While it is away, the mother cleans out her pouch by licking it, sometimes holding it open with her front legs. The young leave for good after about seven and a half months.

10. THEME AND VARIATIONS

When the dinosaurs disappeared, tiny, furry warm-blooded creatures that had lived with them suddenly began to develop

Sit quiet and motionless in a forest in Borneo and you have a fair chance of being visited by a small, furry, long-tailed creature which runs four-footedly along the branches of the bushes and over the ground, inquisitively testing everything with its pointed nose. It looks and behaves rather like a squirrel. A sudden unexpected noise makes it freeze, its glittering button-sized eyes wide with alarm. Equally suddenly it jerks back into frantic activity, flicking its tail backwards and forwards as it moves. But if, when it finds something to eat, it does not nibble at it with its front teeth but opens its mouth wide and champs vigorously with huge relish, then you are watching something much more unusual than a squirrel and a creature of considerable significance – a tupaia.

If ever there were a creature that has been all things to all men, this is it. Local people in Borneo very understandably, regard it as a kind of squirrel; they use the word, *tupai*, which science has adopted, for all such animals. The first European scientists to catch a specimen, discovering that it lacked the gnawing teeth of a rodent and had numerous small spiky ones, called it a tree shrew. Other people believed that some details of its genitals indicated a relationship with marsupials. Half a century ago, a very eminent anatomist, analysed the structure of its skull in great detail, noted that the creature had a surprisingly large brain, and argued that it should be regarded as an ancestor of monkeys and apes and classified it with them.

The debate is not over yet. Currently the balance of opinion has swung away from viewing it as an ancestral monkey and favours placing it with the shrews, but the fact that elements of so many different kinds of mammals can be seen in it, suggests that it might well resemble the ancient creature from which all placental mammals are

---

A prototype mammal?

The tree shrews of South-east Asia may resemble ancient animals that lived at the same time as the dinosaurs and from which mammals have descended. They are all rat-sized, and eat insects and fruit. A male marks out his territory with urine and with a sticky, strong-smelling substance that exudes from a chest gland. He and his mate then defend their boundaries against all-comers.

253

descended. Certainly, judging from fossil skeletons, the first mammals that scampered about in the dinosaur-dominated forests must have looked very like it – small, long-tailed and pointed-nosed, and, by inference, furry, warm-blooded, active and insect-eating.

The reign of the reptiles had been a long one. They had come to power about 250 million years ago. They had browsed the forests and munched the lush vegetation of the swamps. Meat-eating forms had developed and preyed on the plant-eaters. Other species lived by scavenging carrion. The plesiosaurs and ichthyosaurs cruised the seas seeking fish; and pterosaurs glided through the skies. And then, 65 million years ago, all these creatures disappeared.

The forests of the world lay tranquil. No great beasts of any kind crashed their way through them. But in the undergrowth those small tupaia-like mammals, that had been there when the dinosaurs first appeared, still hunted for insects. That scene scarcely altered for hundreds of thousands of years. On a human time scale, such a period seems an eternity. Geologically it was only a moment. In the history of evolution, it was a phase packed with swift and dazzling invention, for during it the little insectivores produced descendants to fill all the niches vacated by the ruling reptiles and so founded all the great mammalian groups.

The hedgehogs, shrews and moles of Europe

Tupaia is only one of the primitive insect-eating mammals to have survived until today. There are others scattered around the world in odd corners. Many have misleading names that indicate how puzzled people have been about their true nature. In Malaysia, alongside tupaia, lives an unkempt irritable creature with a long nose bristling with whiskers and smelling powerfully of rotten garlic that is known, quite unaccountably, as a moon rat. In Africa there is the biggest of all which, because it swims, is called an otter shrew; and a whole group the size of rats which hop, have slender elegant legs and mobile thin trunks and which are known as elephant shrews. Cuba had a creature called a solenodon, though no one has seen a living specimen since 1909 and it may by now be extinct. Another solenodon species still flourishes in the neighbouring island of Haiti. And Madagascar has a whole group, some striped and hairy, some with spines on their backs, called tenrecs.

But all are not rare or restricted in distribution. That common inhabitant of the European countryside, the hedgehog, is also a primitive insectivore and is not so dissimilar from the rest if, in our mind's eye, we can discount its coat of spines. These are no more than modified hairs and are little indication of true ancestry. And there are also shrews. In many parts of the world they are very abundant indeed, scurrying through the leaf litter in hedgerows and woodlands seemingly always in a fever of excitement. Although they are only 8 cms from nose to tail they are very ferocious, attacking any small creature they encounter including one another. To sustain themselves, they have to eat great quantities of earthworms and insects every day. Among them is one of the smallest of all mammals, the pigmy shrew that is so minute that it can

The hedgehog – an ancient success
The hedgehog has a huge distribution, living in most parts of Europe, Africa and Asia. Its success may be due to its very effective defence of rolling into a prickly ball when threatened, and its ability to eat almost anything – worms and fruit, beetles, frogs, wasps, young mice and even snakes. It can also survive seasons when food disappears, either because of winter cold or a parched summer, by hiding and going into a state of suspended animation.

Burrowing for worms and insects

Moles in the darkness of their tunnels find their way

about with the help of whiskers that grow profusely over their snouts and tails. One species in North America also has a cluster of tentacles on the end of its nose (left) which it keeps in constant movement.

squeeze down tunnels no wider than a pencil. Shrews communicate with one another by shrill high-pitched squeaks. They also produce noises of a frequency that is far above the range of our ears, their eyesight is very poor and there is some indication that they use these ultra-sounds as a simple form of echo-location.

Several species of shrew have taken to water in search of their invertebrate food. In Europe, there are two near-relatives called the desmans – one lives in Russia and the other only in the Pyrenees – which use their long mobile noses as snorkels, turning them up so that they project above the surface of the water as their owners swim about busily searching for food.

The shrew group has produced a variant that seeks its prey entirely underground, the

mole. Judging from the structure of its paddle-shaped forelegs and powerful shoulders, it seems that the mole's ancestors were once water-living shrews and the mole has simply adapted the same sort of actions for moving along its tunnels. Fur, underground, might be thought to be something of a mechanical handicap, but many moles live in temperate areas and they need fur to keep warm. So it has become very short and without any particular grain so that it points in all directions and the animal can move forwards or backwards along its tight tunnels with equal ease. Eyes are of very little value underground. Even if there were any light to see by, they would easily clog with mud, so they are much reduced in size. Nonetheless, a mole must have some way of finding its prey and, rather like a tram, it has sense organs at each end. At the front, its main sensor is not its eyes but its nose which is an organ of both smell and touch, being covered with many sensory bristles. At the rear, it has a short stumpy tail also covered with bristles which make it aware of what is happening behind it. The star-nosed mole of America has an additional device, an elegant rosette of fleshy feelers around its nose which it can expand or retract. It may be simply a tactile organ or it may be a means of detecting changes in the chemical content of the air.

Mole tunnels are not simply passageways but traps. Earthworms, beetles, insect larvae, innocently burrowing their way through the soil, may suddenly break into a mole's tunnel. The mole, scurrying along its passages, harvests whatever turns up. Incessantly active, it manages to patrol every stretch of its extensive network at least once every three or four hours and consumes vast numbers of worms each day. On the rare occasions when so many worms collect in the tunnels that even a mole's appetite is sated, it gathers up the surplus, gives each of them a quick bite to immobilise them, and then stores them away in an underground larder. Some of these stores have been found with thousands of paralysed worms in them.

Long, sticky tongues for eating termites
A few insectivores specialised early in eating one particular kind of invertebrate, ants and termites. There is no doubt as to what is the best tool for this job – a long, sticky tongue. Many unrelated creatures, taking to this diet, have developed such an organ independently. The numbat, the marsupial ant-eater in Australia, has one. So has the echidna. Even ant-eating birds, woodpeckers and wrynecks, have developed one that fits inside a special compartment of the skull and in some extends round the eye-socket. But the most extreme version of such a tongue is that evolved by the early placental mammals.

In Africa and Asia, there are seven different kinds of pangolin, medium-sized creatures a metre or so long with short legs and long stout prehensile tails. The biggest of them has a tongue that can extend 40 cms beyond its mouth. The sheath that houses it extends right down the front of the animal's chest and is actually connected with its pelvis. The pangolin has lost all its teeth and its lower jaw is reduced to twin slivers of bone. The ants and termites collected by the mucus on the tongue are swallowed and then mashed by the muscular movements of the stomach which is horny and sometimes

An armoured ant-eater and her baby
The scales of the pangolin are not formed from amalgamated tufts of hair, but are constructed from horn, and each is produced by a separate flap of skin. As they wear out they are replaced, one by one, so that the pangolin has the same number throughout its life. It has no scales on its belly, neck or the inside of its legs, so when it is disturbed (above) it rolls up and clasps itself together with its long muscular tail with which, at other times, it grips onto branches. The pangolin has no teeth, so the ants and termites it licks up reach its stomach more or less intact, but there they are mashed by small horny plates which line part of the stomach. Some species have three young, but most have only a single one which clings to its mother as she climbs through the trees (right).

contains pebbles to assist in the grinding process.

Without teeth and without any turn of speed, the pangolin has to be well protected. It has an armour of horny scales that overlap like shingles on a roof. At the slightest danger the animal tucks its head into its stomach and wraps itself into a ball with its muscular tail clasped tight around it. In my experience, there is no way in which a pangolin, once rolled, can be forced to unwind. If you want to see what it looks like, the only thing to do is to leave it and let it recover enough confidence to poke its head out nervously and then trundle away.

You might think that it needs protection, not only from predators but from the ants and termites on which it feeds. Its underside is naked except for a few sparse hairs and looks painfully vulnerable. The animal can shut its nostrils and ears with special muscles, but apart from attacks in these hyper-sensitive areas, it seems indifferent to insect bites. It may even welcome them, rather as a bird actively encourages ants to swarm through its feathers and for the same reason. The pangolin sometimes raises its armour and encourages ants to crawl in between its plates and onto its skin, so dealing with parasites that it cannot possibly scratch off itself. Then, according to one story, it shuts its plates with the ants still inside and trots down to the river for a swim so that they are all washed out and its toilet is completed.

South America has its own particular group of insect-eaters which became separated from the rest at a very early stage. Their ancestors were among those placental mammals that, sixty-three million years ago, migrated down from the north through Panama and mingled with the marsupials. However the land bridge did not, in this first instance, last for long. After a few million years, it became submerged beneath the sea. So once more the continent was cut off and its animals evolved in isolation. Eventually, contact was re-established and there was a second invasion from the north as a consequence of which many of the recently evolved South American creatures disappeared.

But not all. The least specialised of the survivors are the armadillos. Like the pangolins, they are protected by armour and it is this that gives them their Spanish-derived name. It consists of a broad shield over the shoulders and another over the pelvis, with a varying number of half-rings over the middle of the back to give a little flexibility.

Armadillos eat insects, other invertebrates, carrion, and any small creatures, like lizards, that they manage to catch. Their standard method of seeking food is to dig. They all have an excellent sense of smell and when they detect something edible in the ground, they suddenly start excavating with manic speed, scattering earth in plumes behind them, their nose jammed into the soil as though they are terrified of losing the scent and frantic to get a mouthful of food as soon as they possibly can. When you watch them, you wonder how they can possibly breathe. In fact they don't. They have the amazing ability to hold their breath for up to six minutes, even while digging. This talent makes credible one of the entertaining stories told about them by the local people in Paraguay. They say that when an armadillo comes to a river, it simply trots down the

A successful invader

The most widespread of armadillos is the nine-banded (below). It lives all over lowland South and Central America from Argentina to Mexico, and during the last century it extended its range north as far as Texas. It is a very variable creature. Though most individuals have nine bands of armour across their backs, some have eight and others have ten. The number of their teeth also varies. In one character it is unique. The females almost always give birth to identical quadruplets.

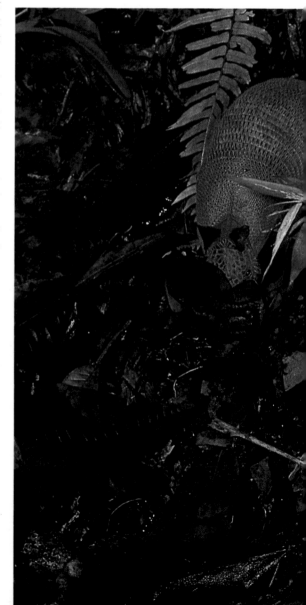

Reinforced armour
The armadillo's armour is reinforced beneath the skin by plates of bone. Some species can roll up into a complete ball but others, like the hairy armadillo (left), are so fat they bulge out, and their armour cannot close.

bank, into water and continues walking unperturbed along the river bed weighed down by its armour, to emerge dripping on the other side without having even faltered in its stride.

There are some twenty species of armadillo and once there were a lot more, including a monster with a single-piece domed shell as big as a small car. One such fossil shell has been found which, it seems, was used by early man as a tent. The biggest surviving species is the giant armadillo, the size of a pig, which lives in the forests of Brazil. Like all the group, it is very largely insectivorous and consumes great quantities of ants. In Paraguay, the little three-banded armadillo trots about on the tips of its claws like a clockwork toy – this is the one that can roll into a neatly fitting impregnable ball. Down in the pampas of Argentina there are tiny hairy ones that are mole-like and seldom come to the surface. All armadillos have teeth. The giant has about a hundred, which is almost a mammalian record, but they are small, simple and peg-like.

Theme and variations

The specialist ant-eaters of South America, however, like the pangolins of Africa, have lost their teeth entirely. There are three of them. The smallest, the pigmy ant-eater, lives entirely in trees and exclusively on termites. It is about the size of a squirrel with soft golden fur and curving jaws which form a short tube. A bigger version, the tamandua is cat-sized, has a prehensile tail and short coarse fur. It too is a tree-dweller but it often comes down to the ground. Out on the open plains, where termite hills stand as thick as tombstones in a graveyard, lives the biggest of the trio, the giant ant-eater. It

A cat-sized ant-eater
The tamandua, a South American ant-eater the size of a cat, varies in colour. Most are yellowish brown with dark markings but some are pale gold. The babies are either white or, like this one, almost entirely black.

The shyest ant-eater
The pigmy ant-eater is entirely nocturnal and spends all day curled up asleep on a branch high in the trees. If

anything disturbs it, its defence is to grasp a branch with its strongly gripping tail and rear up (below), waving its clawed fore-legs in the air in a short-sighted way, ready to slash at anything in range.

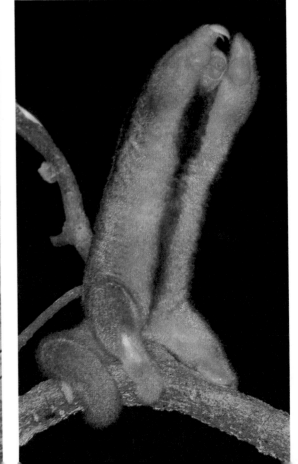

is 2 metres or so long. Its tail is huge, shaggy and flag-like and waves in the breeze as the animal shambles over the savannahs. Its forelegs are bowed, and its claws so long that it has to tuck them inwards and walk on the sides of its feet. With these claws it can tear open termite hills as though they were made of paper. Its toothless jaws form a tube even longer than its forelegs. When it feeds, its huge thong of a tongue flicks in and out of its tiny mouth with great rapidity and runs deep into the galleries of the excavated termite hill.

The biggest of the ant-eaters

The splendid heraldic-looking giant ant-eater is said to use its banner-shaped tail, fringed above and below with long coarse hair, as a broom to sweep up the termites it scatters when it rips open a nest of them. It certainly does use it as a kind of parasol when it lies sleeping out in the open during the day, bending it over its body and occasionally wafting it up and down. The animal makes no permanent nest but wanders widely, looking for termites, the females carrying their young pick-a-back.

All ant-eaters are fairly slow movers. Even a man can outrun the giant. Since they lack teeth as well, they appear fairly defenceless and it seems strange that they should be without the kind of armour which both the pangolins and armadillos are equipped. But the pigmy ant-eater and the tamandua favour tree-living ants and termites and spend most of their time up in the branches out of the way of most predators; and the giant ant-eater is less harmless than might at first appear. If you go to lasso one, it will turn and sweep blindly at you with its forelegs. If it were able to catch you with its huge hooked claws, there would be little chance of your breaking its embrace. There is a tale of the bodies of a jaguar and an ant-eater being found out on the savannahs, locked together. The ant-eater had been dreadfully torn by the jaguar's teeth, but its claws were sunk in the jaguar's back and even in death its clutch had not been broken.

THE GLIDERS: CREATURES THAT TOOK TO THE AIR WITHOUT WINGS TO FLAP

Several different groups of backboned animals have, at varying times, found it profitable to take to the air. The first did so at least 200 million years ago. Others developed their techniques comparatively recently.

The insects, the birds and the bats are the only living groups of animals to have achieved powered flight. By beating their wings, they can climb and swoop through the air, make long journeys against headwinds and, in some cases, even hover and fly backwards. It seems very likely that each group evolved the wing muscles and jointed bone structures needed for such feats by way of a simpler intermediate stage – gliding. This ability, in itself, could be of immediate advantage to creatures living in trees or on cliffs. It might enable them to escape from an enemy by unexpectedly diving into the air, and at the very least, it would be a labour-saving way of moving from one tree to another. It is no surprise, therefore, to discover that gliding has been developed quite independently, not only by the ancestors of birds, bats and insects, but also by several other kinds of animals at different times, and that several species use it today.

Two frogs, one living in Malaysia and the other in South America, can glide, and both use the same technique. Their broad webbed feet, so valuable to their relatives for swimming, have become even bigger, with toes so long that the membranes between them make each foot, in effect, a parachute. The frog, high on a tree, will suddenly leap into the air and glide on its spread-eagled feet to land, with a wet and adhesive flop, on the broad leaf of another tree, 6 or 7 metres away.

Several reptiles can also do the same trick, though they use very different means. The flying dragon of Southeast Asia – in spite of its fearsome-sounding name, only a little lizard about 15 centimetres long – has elongated

The 'flying' snake *The slender tree snake's ability to glide has only recently been established.*

'Flying' frogs and lizards *This frog from Costa Rica (above) glides with its feet membranes, and the lizard from Southeast Asia (left) uses flaps on its flanks.*

One of the first backboned flyers *This skeleton (below) of a thrush-sized pterodactyl from Bavaria shows clearly the nature of the strut that formed the leading edge of its wings – it was the fourth finger, greatly elongated. Other specimens show traces of the flying membrane between that finger and the flanks, and also clear traces of fur, indicating that the creature was warm-blooded.*

ribs. Normally, they lie close to its flanks, but by flexing special muscles, it can pull them forward so that the flap of skin that covers them forms a fan on each side of its body. It also lives in trees and a male, jealously guarding its territory, will glide down on to one of its branches immediately a rival tries to take it over.

Even more surprisingly, perhaps, there is a small snake in Borneo that can glide. It too draws its ribs forward. They are not extravagantly long, but the action has the effect of broadening its pencil-thin body and slightly cupping its underside. As it launches itself into the air from a branch, it bends its flattened body into a series of S-shaped curves, each coil almost touching those next to it, so that the whole snake, instead of being long and thin, becomes roughly plate-shaped. In this posture, it can not only glide for 20 metres or so, but it also has sufficient control of its flight to enable it to bank and float towards a particular tree.

Such creatures as these took to the air relatively recently in their evolutionary history. The first gliding reptiles of all appeared over 200 million years ago, at the time when the dinosaurs were beginning their great development. They were about the size of fruit bats and had membranes stretching between the sides of their bodies and the elongated fourth finger of each hand. Since they did not have large breast muscles, they were unable to do more than glide. Eventually, they gave rise to the pterodactyls that did have the ability to flap their wings, but they were also the ancestors of the most accomplished gliders the world has seen, the pteranodons.

Hunters that launched themselves from cliffs
Specimens unearthed at the end of the last century in Kansas were found to have had huge wings up to 7 metres across. Such immense creatures had to keep their weight to a minimum and they probably weighed as little as 10 kg. Their wing bones were tubular, with walls as thin as egg shells and so fragile that they could not have borne the strain of beating such vast sails, even if the animal had possessed the muscles to do so. It is thought that they lived on cliffs and took to the air by falling into it. They were then able to exploit the wind currents with such skill that they could soar over the sea, scooping up fish in their long jaws, and then glide back to their roosting ledges. The aeronautical technique by which they managed this has long been a source of puzzlement and stimulus to research, but in the last few years, the fossil bones of an even more mystifying member of the group have been found in Texas. Judging from the remains described so far, it had the almost unbelievable wing-span of over 15 metres. It was, without question, the largest known creature ever to have taken to the air, whether by gliding or by beating its wings. The deposits in which it was found were laid down on land, far away from any sea, so these gigantic pteranodons could not have fed on fish like those in Kansas. One suggestion is that they lived off the flesh of dead dinosaurs lying out on the plains, but if that is so, and if – as seems certain – they could not flap their immense wings, how did they get into the air again after their meals? No one, so far, has worked out the answer.

How mammals became air-borne

All these creatures collect crawling insects. But insects also fly. Put up a white screen in a tropical forest at night, illuminate it with a mercury vapour lamp which produces a light particularly attractive to insects, and within a few hours, the screen will be swarming with insects of amazing variety and in extraordinary numbers – huge moths shedding fluff from their wings, mantis with forearms at the ready in bogus piety, beetles moving their legs with the slow inevitability of robots, huge leaping crickets, chafers with bushy antennae, and so many mosquitoes and small flies that they often accumulate in a thick sludge over the lamp and almost blot out the light.

The insects first took to the air some 300 million years ago and had it to themselves until the arrival of the flying reptiles like the pterosaurs, some hundred million years later. Whether the reptiles flew at night we do not know, but it seems unlikely bearing in mind the reptilian problem of maintaining body temperature. Birds eventually succeeded them, but there is no reason to suppose that there were any more night-flying birds in the past than there are today – which is very few. So a great feast of nocturnal insects awaited any creature that could master the technique of flying in the dark. Yet another variation of the insectivore theme managed to do so.

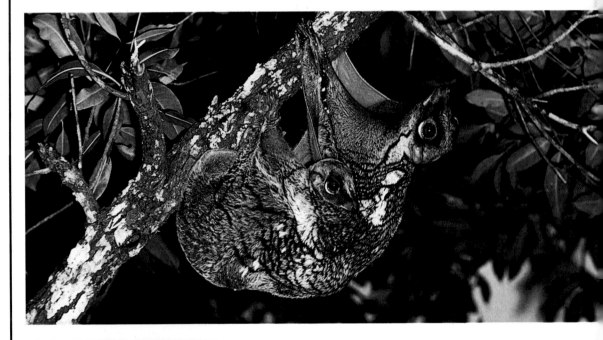

A superb and ancient glider
The colugo is a mystery creature. It is sometimes called a flying lemur, though its connections with the lemurs can only be remote. Other characteristics link it equally well to bats and to primitive insect eaters. At the end of a glide, it lands on a tree trunk head upwards, but when it sleeps, it hangs upside-down. The female above is cradling her baby.

263

We have some notion of how the mammals may have managed to get air-borne. In Malaysia and the Philippines there lives an animal so odd that zoology has had to give it an order all of its own. This is the colugo. It is about the size of a large rabbit but its entire body, from its neck to the end of its tail, is covered by a softly furred cloak of skin, delicately dappled in grey and cream. When the animal hangs beneath a branch or presses itself against a tree trunk, this skin makes it well-nigh invisible and when it extends its legs, the cloak becomes a gliding membrane. I was once taken to a patch of woodland in Malaysia where people said there were many of these strange creatures. I searched a likely looking tree with my binoculars, examining every bump on the trunk and branches with great care. Having convinced myself that it contained nothing, I turned away to scrutinise another, only to see out of the corner of my eye, a huge rectangular shape detach itself and glide silently away. I ran after it, but it landed low down on another trunk over a hundred yards away and by the time I got there, the animal was quite high and galloping upwards, its two front feet moving forward together and alternating with its hind, its cloak flapping around it like an old dressing gown.

The colugo's gliding technique has several parallels. The marsupial sugar glider planes through the air in just the same way. Two groups of squirrels have also independently acquired the talent. But the colugo has the biggest and most completely enveloping membrane and took to the habit early in mammalian history, for it is certainly a very primitive member of the group and seems to be a direct descendant of an insectivore ancestor. Having perfected a way of life, it has remained unchallenged – and unchanged. It cannot be regarded as a link with bats, for its anatomy is different in many fundamental respects, but it is an indication of a stage that some early insectivores may have passed through on their way to achieving flapping flight and becoming those truly accomplished aeronauts, the bats.

That development took place very early, for fossils of fully developed bats have been found that date back to fifty million years ago.

Bats adapt their bodies to life in the air
The bat's flying membrane stretches not just from the wrist, like the colugo, but along the extended second finger. The other two fingers form struts extending back to the trailing edge. Only the thumb remains free and small. This retains its nail and the bat uses it in its toilet and to help it clamber about its roost. A keel has developed on its chest bone which serves as an attachment for the muscles which flap the wings.

The bats have many of the modifications developed by birds in order to save body weight. The bones in the tail are thinned to mere straws to support the flying membrane or have been lost altogether. Though they have not lost their teeth, their heads are short and often snub-nosed and so avoid being nose-heavy in the air. They had one problem that birds did not face. Their mammalian ancestors had perfected the technique of nourishing their young internally by means of a placenta. The evolutionary clock can seldom be put back and no bat has reverted to egg-laying. The female bat must

therefore fly with the heavy load of her developing foetus within her. In consequence, it is not surprising to find that bat twins are a rarity and in almost every case it is usual for only one young to be born each season. This, in turn, means that if the population is to be maintained, the females must compensate by breeding over a long period, and indeed, bats are, for their size, surprisingly long-lived creatures, some having a life-expectancy of around twenty years.

Today, all bats fly at night and it is likely that this was always the case, since the birds had already laid claim to the day. To do so, however, the bats had to develop an efficient navigational system. It is based on ultra-sounds like those made by the shrews and almost certainly many other primitive insectivores. The bats use them for sonar, an extremely sophisticated method of echo-location. This is similar in principle to radar, but radar employs radio waves whereas sonar uses sound waves. These are of frequencies that lie a long way above the range of the human ear. Most of the sounds we hear have frequencies of around several hundred vibrations a second. Some of us, particularly when we are young, can with difficulty just distinguish sounds with a frequency of 20,000 vibrations a second. A bat, flying by sonar, uses sounds of between 50,000 and 200,000 vibrations a second. It sends out these sounds in short bursts, like clicks, twenty or thirty times every second and its hearing is so acute that from the echo each signal makes, the bat is able to judge the position not only of obstacles around it but of its prey which is also likely to be flying quite fast.

Most bats wait to receive the echo of one signal before emitting the next. The closer the bat is to an object, the shorter the time taken for the echo to come back, so the bat can increase the number of signals it sends the closer it gets to its prey and thus track it with increasing accuracy as it closes in for the kill.

Hunting success, however, can mean momentary blindness for if its mouth is filled by an insect, a bat cannot squeak in the normal way. Some species avoid this difficulty by squeaking through their noses and have developed a variety of grotesque nasal outgrowths which serve to concentrate the beam of the squeak and act like miniature megaphones. The echoes are picked up by the ears and these too are elaborate, extremely sensitive and capable, in many cases, of being twisted to detect a signal. So the face of many bats is dominated by sonar equipment – elaborate translucent ears, ribbed with cartilage and laced with an internal tracery of scarlet blood vessels; and on the nose, leaves, spikes and spears to direct the sounds. The combination is often more grotesque than any painted demon in a medieval manuscript. Each species has its own pattern. Why? Probably so that each can produce a unique call. Receptors matched to it alone filter out signals from other species.

The system, described in such terms, sounds simple. It seems less so when you encounter it in action. The Gomanton Caves in Borneo contain several million bats, belonging to eight different species. They have lived there for so long that in one

The social bats

Most bats are extraordinarily social. Some cave colonies may contain as many as 9 million individuals – almost certainly the greatest and most dense assemblies of mammals to be found anywhere. These small fruit bats have packed themselves onto the roof of a cave, but larger fruit bats live in trees where there is ample roosting space and even so hang cheek by jowl.

Theme and variations

chamber their droppings form a huge pyramidal dune that spreads across the cave floor and rises 30 metres to the roof. In order to see the bats, we once trudged our way up it. Its surface was covered by a moving, glistening carpet of cockroaches feeding on the guano and a heavy stench of ammonia rose from it. At the top close to the roof of the chamber, we found the bats roosting in narrow horizontal clefts in the rock. As we shone our torches on them, some detached themselves and flew past us, their wings brushing our faces. Others hung there, twisting their heads with frantic nervousness, to look at us with their black beads of eyes. Beyond we could see thousand upon thousand, packed together as thick and as uniform as heads of grain in a wheat field and swaying in their alarm as though a wind passed over them. Suddenly, they erupted in panic. Desperate to escape from the confines of their gallery to the main chamber behind us, they came rocketing out in a torrent. By the time we ourselves had retreated to the top of

The bats with a taste for nectar
Bats probably visited flowers first in order to hunt for the insects that went there seeking nectar and pollen. Subsequently, the bats themselves developed a taste for nectar, learned how to hover in order to collect it, and developed long tongues covered with hairs in order to sip deep in trumpet-shaped flowers like those of the agave (below).

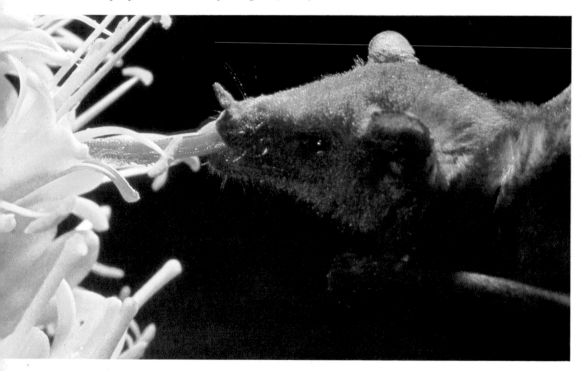

A cactus responds to a bat's needs
As bats brought benefit to some plants by transporting pollen, so the plants responded to the bats' needs. The saguaro cactus (right) has light-coloured flowers which are easily found in the dark and which open at night. They also project well above the dangerous spines, so the bats can not only sip from the flowers without risk of injury but even hang from them for a rest.

the guano dune the main chamber was a whirlpool of flying bats. Penned by fear of the unfamiliar daylight outside and terrified by our presence inside, they circled round in a vast eddy, filling the air with the beating of their skinny wings. We could just detect the lower components of their squeaks, like a cosmic rustling, but their sonar was beyond our ears. The heat from their bodies made the atmosphere, already hot and airless, even more suffocating. We were spattered by their droppings. There were certainly several hundred thousand, flying in a panic round and round beneath the ceiling, as thick as snow flakes driven by a gale. Yet flying at such speeds, they must all have been using their sonar. Why did their calls not interfere with one another, jamming the signals? How could they react with such swiftness that they did not collide? In such places, the dimensions of the problems of sonar navigation seem beyond comprehension.

When evening comes at Gomanton, the bats leave the cave travelling along regular and restricted paths along the rock ceiling flying nose to tail and half a dozen or so abreast so that they form one continuous flickering ribbon. They emerge from one corner of the cave mouth at the rate of thousands a minute, a stream of black bodies hurtling out over the forest canopy to begin the night's hunt. The dune of guano at the back of the cave is a testament to the scale of their success. A little simple arithmetic makes it clear that every night the bat colony must catch several tons of mosquitos and other tiny insects.

A few insects have developed systems to protect themselves from bats. In America, there are moths that have the ability to tune in to the frequency of the bat sonar. As soon as they hear a bat approaching, they drop to the ground. Other species go into a spiralling dive which the bats find hard to follow. Yet others manage to jam the signal or send back high-frequency sounds that convince the bat that they are inedible and to be avoided.

Not all bats feed on insects. Some have discovered that nectar and pollen are very nutritious, and refined their flying skills so that they can hover in front of flowers, just like humming birds, and gather nectar by probing deep into the blossoms with long thin tongues. Just as a great number of plants have evolved to exploit the services of insects as pollinators, so too some rely on bats. Some cacti, for example, only open their blossoms at night. These are large, robust and pallid, for in the darkness colour is valueless. Their scent, however, is heavy and strong and the petals project well above the armoury of spines on the stem so that the bats are able to visit without damaging their wing membranes.

The biggest of all bats live only on fruit. They are called flying foxes, not only because of their size – and some of them have a wing span of one and a half metres – but because their coats are reddish brown and their faces are very fox-like. They have large eyes but only small ears and lack any kind of nose-leaf, so it is clear that they are not sonar flyers. Whether this major difference between them and other insectivorous bats indicates that the two groups derive from separate branches of primitive insectivores is not yet agreed. Fruit bats live not in caves but in the tops of trees in communal roosts tens of thousands strong, hanging like huge black fruit,

A fishing bat

The bulldog bat of Mexico has unusual legs. They are particularly long and armed with huge hooked claws. The lower edge of each wing is attached to them not at the ankle, as in most bats, but at the knee. Thus the bat's legs, from the knee downwards, are entirely free. With the help of these legs, the bat goes fishing.

It flies slowly up and down stretches of calm water. Occasionally, it folds up its tail membrane, lowers its legs and, without catching its wings in the water, flies for a yard or so with its feet, toes outspread, trailing through the water to a depth of about an inch. If it gaffs a fish, it swings its catch out of the water and brings it up to its mouth. Sometimes it flies back to its roost to feed, but often it continues flying. It chews the fish in mid-air, stores the lumps in its cheek pouches, and then trolls for more.

The bulldog bat also feeds on insects, and these it undoubtedly catches with the help of echo-location. But does it use the same method in fishing? Ultra-sounds made in air are deflected almost totally by the surface of water so they can be of no help in finding fish at any depth. But they can detect ripples or any unevenness of the water surface, and it is noticeable that bulldog bats are quickly attracted to broken water. The small fish they usually catch are species that habitually swim at night near the surface in shoals that often cause considerable rippling. So it may well be that the bulldog bat's trawls are not entirely at random.

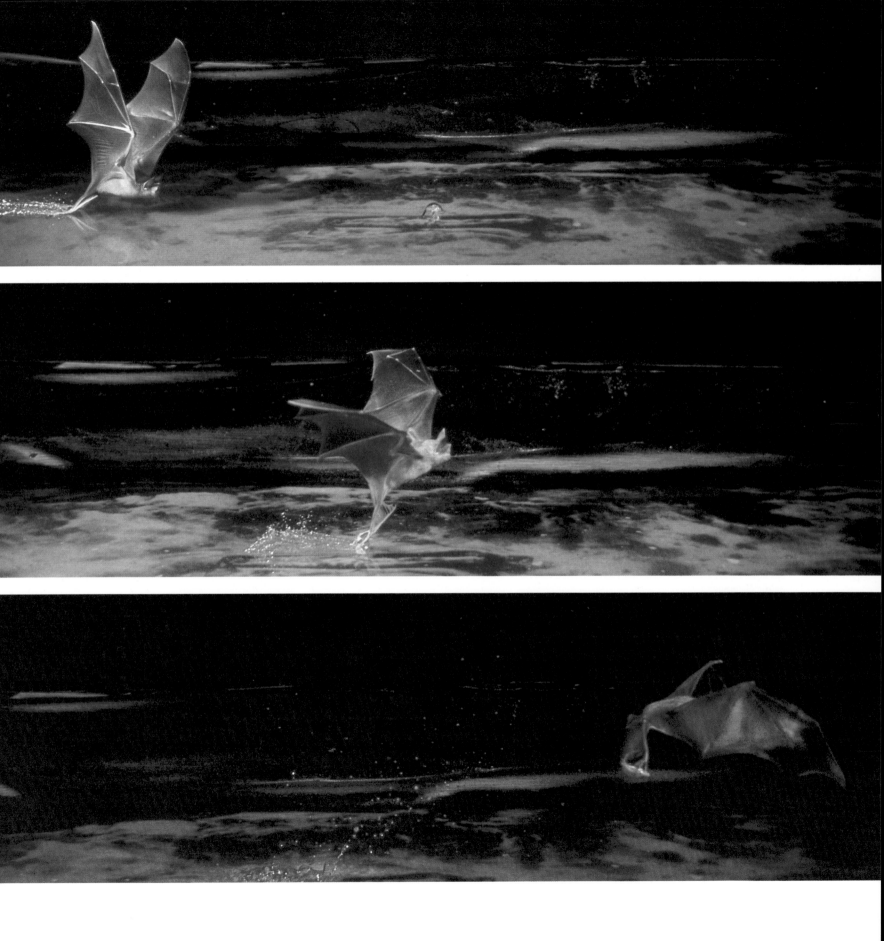

Theme and variations

A portrait gallery of bats

The face of a bat can give clues to its habits. The large eyes and small ears of a fruit bat indicate that it finds its way largely by sight. The elaborate movable ears of the long-eared bat make it plain that it depends to a considerable degree on sound, and the horse-shoe bat's semicircle of cartilage around its nostrils indicate that it transmits sounds through its nose. But other bat faces are more enigmatic. The wrinkle-faced bat is a fruit feeder – and no one yet knows the exact function of the grotesque structures on its face. The tomb bat and the mastiff bat, even though their faces are fairly uncomplicated, are in fact insect hunters that use sonar.

shrouded in their wings, squabbling noisily among themselves. Occasionally one will stretch a wing and carefully lick the elastic membrane, keeping it meticulously clean and in good flying order. If the day is hot, they may fan themselves with their half-spread wings so that the whole colony seems to shimmer. A sudden noise or a shake of the tree will produce a squall of angry shrieks and hundreds will take off with great flappings of wings, but they will soon resettle. In the evening, they set off in parties to feed. Their silhouette is quite unlike that of birds, for they lack a projecting tail and their flight is very different from the fluttering of insect-hunting bats. Their huge wings beat steadily as long skeins of them keep a level purposeful course across the evening sky. They may travel as far as 70 kilometres in their search for fruit.

Other bats have taken to feeding on meat. Some prey on roosting birds, some take frogs and small lizards, one is reported to feed on other bats. An American species even manages to fish. At dusk, it beats up and down over ponds, lakes, or even the sea. The tail membrane of most bats extends to the ankles. In the fishing bat, it is attached much higher up at the knee, so that the legs are quite free. The bat can therefore trail its feet in the water, keeping the membrane out of the way by folding up its tail. Its toes are large and armed with hook-shaped claws. When they strike a fish, the bat scoops it up into its mouth and kills it with a powerful crunch of its teeth.

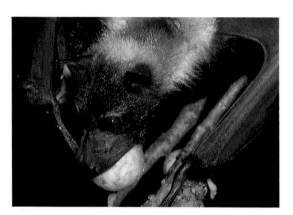
FRUIT BAT (FLYING FOX)

LONG–EARED BAT

HORSE-SHOE BAT

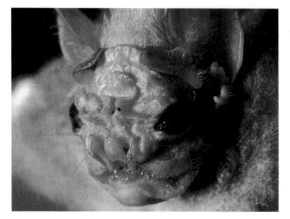
WRINKLE–FACED BAT

TOMB BAT

MASTIFF BAT

A bat catches a mouse

The false vampire, which lives in tropical America between Mexico and Brazil, was once unjustly suspected of sucking blood. Its tastes, however, are for flesh. Although it sometimes eats fruit and insects, the ground beneath its roosts is often littered with feathers and the tails of mice. It has the biggest wing-span of any bat in the Americas – 60 centimetres – and it is so powerful that it can catch mice and lizards, crushing their skull or neck with a single bite.

The vampire bat has become very specialised indeed. Its front teeth are modified into two triangular razors. It settles gently on a sleeping mammal, a cow or even a human being. Its saliva contains an anti-coagulant, so that the blood, when it appears, will continue to ooze for some time before a clot forms. The vampire then squats beside the wound lapping the blood. They fly by sonar and it is said that the reason that dogs, whose hearing is also tuned to very high frequencies, are so seldom attacked by them is that they can hear the vampires coming.

All in all there are nearly a thousand species of bats. They have made homes for themselves and found sufficient food in all but the very coldest parts of the world. The connection between them and the tupaia pattern is not difficult to credit when you look at them closely. They must be reckoned one of the most successful of the early insectivore variations.

Theme and variations

The ancestry of the whale

Whales and dolphins, of course, are also warm-blooded, milk-producing mammals and they too have a long ancestry, with fossils dating back to the beginning of the great radiation of the mammals fifty million years ago. But could these immense animals really be descended from a tiny creature like a tupaia? It is difficult to believe, and yet the logic of the deduction is undeniable. Their ancestors must have entered the sea at a time when the only mammals in existence were the little insectivores. But their anatomy is now so extremely adapted to swimming that it gives no clue as to how the move into the sea was made. It may be that the two main groups of whales have different ancestries, those with teeth having come from insectivores by way of primitive carnivores and the rest, the baleen whales, being descended more directly.

The major differences between the whales and the early mammals are attributable to adaptations for the swimming life. The forelimbs have become paddles. The rear limbs have been lost altogether, though there are a few small bones buried deep in the whale's body to prove that the whale's ancestors really did, at one time, have back legs. Fur, that hallmark of the mammals, depends for its effect as an insulator on air trapped between the hairs. So it is of little use to a creature that never comes to dry land, and the whales have lost that too, though once again there are relics, a few bristles on the snout to demonstrate that they once had a coat. Insulation, however, is still needed and whales have developed blubber, a thick layer of fat beneath the skin that prevents their body heat from escaping even in the coldest seas.

The mammals' dependency on air for breathing must be considered a real handicap in water, but the whale has minimised the problem by breathing even more efficiently than most land-livers. Man only clears about 15% of the air in his lungs with a normal breath. The whale, in one of its roaring, spouting exhalations, gets rid of about 90% of its spent air. As a result it only has to take a breath at very long intervals. It also has in its muscles a particularly high concentration of a substance called myoglobin, that enables it to store oxygen. It is this constituent that gives whale meat its characteristic dark colour. With the help of these techniques, the fin-back whale, for example, can dive to a depth of 500 metres and swim for forty minutes without drawing breath.

One group of whales has specialised in feeding on tiny shrimp-like crustaceans, krill, which swarm in vast clouds in the sea. Just as teeth are of no value to mammals feeding on ants, so they are no use to those eating krill. So these whales, like ant-eaters, have lost their teeth. Instead they have baleen, sheets of horn, feathered at the edges, that hang down like stiff, parallel curtains from the roof of the mouth. The whale takes a huge mouthful of water in the middle of the shoal of krill, half-shuts its jaws and then expels the water by pressing its tongue forward so that the krill remains and can be swallowed. Sometimes it gathers the krill by slowly cruising where it is thickest. It also can concentrate a dispersed shoal by diving beneath it and then spiralling up, expelling bubbles as it goes, so that the krill is driven towards the centre of the spiral. Then the whale itself, jaws pointing upwards, rises vertically in the centre and gathers them in one gulp.

A humpback leaps

Adult humpback whales may weigh 40 tons. Sometimes they will suddenly leap from the surface of the sea, landing on their backs or their sides with a gigantic splash and a booming noise like a cannon shot. Occasionally one will leap over and over again in the same place. Why they do so is not yet known. It may be a form of display, a way of responding to threat, for sometimes the approach of a boat seems to provoke it.

Ocean travellers

Humpback whales assemble every year in large numbers around the Hawaiian islands in order to breed. It is possible that these particularly warm waters help to rid the whales of parasites that collect on their skin. The whales do not, however, feed there. After the single young are born the whales vanish and appear again in the cold seas off Alaska where they feed on krill.

272

The exploring white whale

The beluga, or white whale (below), is born grey, but
when it is five years old and 5 metres long it has become
pure white. It normally lives in Arctic waters, but
seems to have an exploratory disposition for
occasionally it appears a long way up rivers.

How a humpback feeds on krill
Humpbacks often feed close to the surface, cruising slowly along taking in huge mouthfuls of water, thick with floating crustaceans, the krill. Then it partly shuts its jaws and pushes its immense tongue forward, expelling the water and leaving the krill caught on the mat of baleen plates.

On such a diet, the baleen whales have grown to an immense size. The blue whale, the biggest of all, grows to over 30 metres long and weighs as much as twenty-five bull elephants. There is a positive advantage to a whale in being large. Maintaining body temperature is easier the bigger you are and the lower the ratio between your volume and surface area. This phenomenon had affected the dinosaurs but their dimensions were limited by the mechanical strength of bone. Above a certain weight, limbs would simply break. The whales are less hampered. The function of their bones is largely to give rigidity. Support for their bodies comes from the water. Nor does a life spent gently cruising after krill demand great agility. So the baleen whales have developed into the largest living creatures of any kind that have ever lived on earth, four times heavier than the largest known dinosaur.

The toothed whales feed on different prey. The largest of them, the squid-eating sperm whale, only attains half the size of the blue whale. The smaller ones, dolphins, porpoises and killer whales, hunt both fish and squid and have become extremely fast swimmers, some reputedly being able to reach speeds of over 40 kph.

Moving at such speeds, navigation becomes critically important. Fish are helped by their lateral line system, but mammals lost that far back in their ancestry and the toothed whales have instead a system based on the sounds used by shrews and elaborated by bats, sonar. Dolphins produce the ultra-sound with larynx and maybe an organ in the front of the head, the melon. The frequencies they use are around 200,000 vibrations a second, which is comparable to those used by bats. With its aid, they can not only sense obstacles in their path, but identify from the quality of the echo, the nature of the objects ahead. This can be demonstrated easily enough, for dolphins flourish in oceanaria and eagerly cooperate in training. Blindfolded dolphins demonstrate that they can, without difficulty, pick out particular shapes of floating rings and will swiftly swim through the water, with blindfolds on their eyes, and exultantly collect on their snout the one shape that they know will bring a reward.

Dolphins produce a great variety of other noises quite apart from ultra-sounds and there has been considerable speculation as to whether these sounds constitute a language. Some workers have said that if only we were clever enough, we would be able to understand what they say and even exchange complex messages with them. So far, we have identified some twenty different sounds that dolphins make. Some seem to serve to keep a school together when they are travelling at speed. Some appear to be warning cries, and some call-signs so that each animal can be recognised at a distance by others. But no one yet has demonstrated that dolphins ever put these sounds together to form the equivalent of the two-word sentence that can justifiably be regarded as the beginning of true language. Chimpanzees can do so. But dolphins, as far as we can tell, cannot.

The great whales also have voices. Humpbacks, one of the baleen whales, congregate every spring in Hawaii to give birth to their young and to mate. Some of them also sing. Their song consists of a sequence of yelps, growls, high-pitched squeals and long-drawn-out rumbles. And the whales declaim these songs hour after hour in extended stately recitals. They contain unchanging sequences of notes that have been called themes. Each theme may be repeated over and over again – the number of times varies but the order of the themes in a song is always the same in any one season. Typically, a complete song lasts for about ten minutes, but some have been recorded that continue for half an hour; and whales may sing, repeating their songs, virtually continuously for over twenty-four hours. Each whale has its own characteristic song but it composes it from themes which it shares with the rest of the whale community in Hawaii.

The whales stay in Hawaiian waters for several months, calving, mating and singing. Sometimes they lie on the surface, one immense flipper held vertically in the air. Sometimes they beat the water with it. Occasionally, one will leap clear of the surface, all fifty tons in the air, the ridging of its underside plain to see, and fall back with a gigantic surge and thunderous crash. It will breach in this way again and again.

Then, within a few days, the deep blue bays and straits off the Hawaiian islands are empty. The whales have gone. Humpbacks appear a few weeks later off Alaska. It is very likely that these are the Hawaiian animals but more studies will have to be made before we can be certain that they are.

Next spring, they reappear in Hawaii and once more begin to sing. But this time they have new themes in their repertoire and have dropped many of the old ones. Sometimes the songs are so loud that the whole hull of your boat resonates and you can hear ethereal moans and cries coming mysteriously, as from nowhere. If you dive into the

The baleen-hung jaws of a minke whale
One group of whales, which includes the humpback, the minke and the biggest of all, the blue whale, have no teeth. The young have tiny rudiments but these are soon lost. In their place, hanging down from the edge of the upper jaw, they have as many as 400 triangular plates of a flexible horny material, the so-called whale-bone or baleen. This is not derived in any way from the true teeth but is akin to the transverse ridges that run across the palates of many mammals, such as a dog, and which help in the mastication of their food. The outer edges of the baleen plates are smooth and straight, but the inner edges are fringed with long fibres and it is these that mat together to form the continuous food-catching sieve.

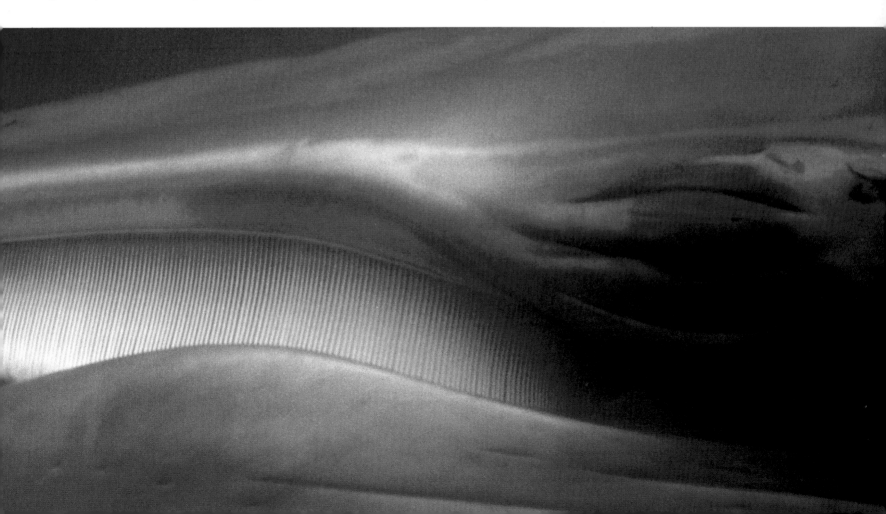

Theme and variations

peerlessly blue water and swim down, you may, with luck, see the singer hanging in the water below you, a cobalt shape in the sapphire depths. The sound penetrates your body, making the air in your sinuses vibrate in sympathy, as though you were sitting within the widest pipe of the largest cathedral organ, and the whole of your tissues are soaked in sound.

We still do not know why whales sing. Man can identify each individual whale by its song and if he can do so, then surely whales can do the same. Water transmits sound better than air so it may well be that sections of these songs, particularly those low vibrating notes, can be heard by other whales ten, twenty, even thirty miles away informing them of the whereabouts and activities of the whole whale community.

Ant-eaters, bats, moles and whales – to such extremes have the descendants of those early protean insectivores gone in the search for their invertebrate food. But there were other sources of nutriment to be tapped as well – plants. Some creatures developed that ate grass and moved out from the forest onto the plains to graze. They were followed by the flesh-eaters and in the open, the two interdependent communities evolved, side by side, each advance in hunting efficiency producing responses in defence from the hunted. A second group of creatures found their leaves up in the tree tops. Each group must have a chapter of its own; the first because they are so numerous; and the second, because of our own egocentricity – for those tree-dwellers were our ancestors.

The birth of a dolphin

A baby dolphin can swim perfectly from the moment it is born. Its mother nudges it upwards as soon as the umbilical cord breaks, so that it can take its first breath of air. Then it swims alongside her, within her slipstream. Dolphins navigate like bats, producing high-pitched sounds which bounce off obstacles ahead, enabling them to identify approaching objects with remarkable accuracy and speed.

FIN-FOOTED MAMMALS OF THE SEAS

Some mammals are so well adapted to swimming that even though they may have different ancestors they now closely resemble one another.

The first ancestral whales probably took to the sea about 50 million years ago. Considerably later – by probably as much as 25 million years, though this can only be a guess – some other early flesh-eating mammals made the same move. These late-comers became the fin-footed mammals – seals, sea-lions, fur seals and the walrus.

Like the whales, the fin-foots became considerably modified to suit their aquatic existence. Their limb bones are greatly shortened so that only their hands and feet project from their bodies. Their toes are joined together by a membrane, like a fin. Their nostrils, placed on top of the head so the animals can breathe with only a minimum of their body breaking water, are kept shut most of the time, but they are equipped with special muscles to open them when the animal wants to take a breath. Their eyes have developed a flat front surface, the shape best suited to producing a well-focused image under water. To conserve the warmth of their bodies, the fin-foots have all developed a thick layer of fat – the blubber – just below the skin. They have special modifications that enable them to dive and hold their breath for long periods. Their bodies contain a huge volume of blood, much more in proportion to their size than that of any land-living mammal, and as a consequence they are able to store abnormally large quantities of oxygen. Furthermore, when they dive, they constrict some major veins so that the circulation of oxygenated blood is largely confined to the heart and the brain. At the same time, the heartbeat drops from about 100 a minute to about 10. So the animal is able to keep its crucial organs supplied with oxygen, while starving the rest of its body which is more tolerant of such deprivation. The balance is restored when it next takes a breath.

A time of danger

The fin-foots' adaptations, however, are not as complete as those of the whales , for they have not yet developed a way of giving birth at sea. Instead, they haul themselves up on beaches to pup. The time they spend out of water is a difficult period for them, for not only are they vulnerable to attack by land animals, but also they cannot find food there. It is to the female seal's advantage, therefore, for her young to grow fast and become independent as quickly as possible. The milk she supplies to her pup is extraordinarily rich, containing about 50 per cent fat, and the pup puts on weight at the rate of about a kilo a day. Since the mother does not feed during the period she is suckling, she is, in

A herd of walruses *Walruses gather together on beaches during the breeding season, and on a few small islands in the Bering Sea they form vast herds over 3,000 strong. They use their tusks as spikes with which to haul themselves over land, but the primary use of the tusks is for digging up shellfish from the sea floor.*

effect, simply converting her own blubber to milk and transferring it to her offspring. Within a few days of giving birth, the female mates again. But the time needed for the development of her young is significantly less than a full year so the fertilised egg at first remains within the mother's uterus without developing. It becomes implanted on the uterus wall several months later. Only then does it begin to grow. The young is therefore not born until the next breeding season, a full year later.

The obvious difference: ears

There are two quite separate groups of fin-foots which are almost certainly descended from different groups of carnivorous ancestors. The sea-lions, the fur seals and the walrus, all of which have external ears, are probably derived from bear-like creatures. The others, the true seals, of which there are over two dozen different kinds and which all lack ears, are thought to have come from otter-like ancestors. Though the presence or absence of an external ear is the customary way of distinguishing the two groups, there is a much more significant difference in the nature of the limbs. Sea-lions and their relatives are able to turn their hind legs forward and have front flippers long enough to act as props when they rear up. With these somewhat clumsy limbs, the sea-lion can waddle about very adequately on land. The seal's limbs, however, are of very little help to it on land. The front ones are so short that they cannot give much assistance, and the hind ones are of no use at all for they cannot be brought forward. Indeed, out of water, the hind limbs are usually held with the soles together, like a rudder. In consequence, a seal can only get about on land by an awkward humping movement of its whole body.

From polar waters to the equator

The two groups also swim differently. The sea-lion propels itself using its front flippers as oars. A seal, however, uses its front flippers almost entirely for steering and gets its main drive by beating the hind pair. Its swimming technique is, in fact, very like that of a fish.

The fin-foots are often thought of as being largely cold-water creatures and they certainly do flourish in their greatest numbers in polar water where there are huge concentrations of fish. But some species live in warmer water. Monk seals are found in the Mediterranean and around Hawaii, and sea-lions breed on the Galapagos almost exactly on the equator. Some species are quite small – the little Lake Baikal seal, the only one that is exclusively freshwater, is only 1.5 metres long – but each group contains a giant. A full-grown walrus may weigh over a ton and the elephant seal, which is the biggest species of the entire group, grows to 6 metres in length and weighs about 3 tons.

Keeping warm at sea *The sea-lion (above) and the fur seal (left) belong to the same group of fin-foots, having external ears and flippers that can be used to some degree to help them get about on land. They both have a layer of fat, or blubber, beneath their skin, which helps them retain the warmth of their bodies, an essential requirement for a mammal. The fur seals have, in addition, a thick woolly under-fur with hair so fine that it mats together into a layer that is virtually impermeable to water. The sea-lions lack this under-fur. They have only a thin coat of relatively coarse glossy hair, although many of them live in the same cold waters as fur seals. Sea-lions acquired their name because the males of some species develop an impressive shaggy mane on their necks and shoulders. In some species, however, including the sea-lions from the Galapagos Islands pictured here, both sexes are sleek and have only thin coats of hair.*

Moving on ice *Most seals hump their way overland. The crab-eater, however, lives on ice floes so slippery that it has to wriggle its way along, rather like a snake.*

11. THE HUNTERS AND THE HUNTED

The ancient duels between flesh-eater and plant-eater result in new developments of speed and strategy

The forests of today are very much the same, in essence, as those that developed soon after the appearance of the flowering plants, fifty million years ago. Then as now, there were jungles in Asia, dank rain forests in Africa and South America, and cool verdant woods in Europe. Soft-stemmed herbs and ferns spread across the ground wherever there was enough light, trees, rising tall, extended their branches into many-tiered ceilings. Everywhere, leaves sprouted; season after season, century after century, they offered an ever-renewing, inexhaustible supply of food for any animal able to gather and digest them.

The dinosaurs had fed on them, smashing saplings in the forests of ash, elm and beech in North America, crashing through the palms and lianas of the tropics. But when, so unaccountably, they all disappeared, a calm settled over the forests of the world. Insects continued, unobtrusively, to claim their share, gnawing at the wood, scissoring the leaves into fragments. Lizards tore at fronds, and birds, as they acquired a taste for the newly evolving fruit, obliged the plants by distributing their seeds. But no large animals dined systematically from this larder of leaves in the wholesale way that the dinosaurs had done.

This comparative peace continued for thousands of years but eventually, the small warm-blooded furry animals that had been running at the feet of the dinosaurs, snapping up small invertebrates, began to acquire a taste for new foods. Just as some

The eternal duel

Flesh-eaters have preyed on grass-eaters since very early in the history of mammals, over 60 million years ago. As the herbivores sharpened their senses in order to detect danger, and improved their speed in escaping from an attack, so the flesh-eaters matched them in hunting strategy and in swiftness. Here, on the plains of East Africa, the fastest of all living hunters, a cheetah, in one short sprint has run down a wildebeest. As soon as its victim falls, the cheetah will rapidly change its grip and fasten its jaws on the throat so that the wildebeest is throttled within a minute or so. The cheetah can travel at more than 110 kph, but only in short bursts.

concentrated on capturing insects, so others turned their attentions to the leaves.

Eating plants is no easy business. It demands particular skills and structures just like any other specialist diet. For one thing, vegetable matter is not very nutritious. An animal has to eat great quantities in order to extract enough calories to sustain itself. Some dedicated vegetarians have to spend three-quarters of their waking hours stolidly gathering and chewing leaves and twigs. That process, in itself, may be dangerous, requiring that the creature stand out in the open, exposed to attack. One way for an animal to minimise that risk is to grab as much as possible, as quickly as possible, and run off with it to somewhere safe. That is the strategy of the giant West African rat. It emerges cautiously from its burrow at night and when it is sure that there is no danger, frantically loads its cheek pouches with anything that looks remotely edible. Seeds, nuts, fruits, roots, occasionally a snail or a beetle, all go in. The pouches are so large that they can hold two hundred or so such morsels. When both sides are crammed full and the rat can barely shut its mouth, its face so swollen that it looks as though it has a dreadful attack of mumps, it scurries back to its burrow. Below ground, it empties the whole collection in its larder and begins to sort through it, chewing the eatable pieces and putting to one side those objects, like little bits of wood and small pebbles, that seemed promising at the time but have proved to be disappointments.

The self-sharpening teeth that last a lifetime

Plant-eaters have to have particularly good teeth. Not only do they use them for very long periods but the material they have to deal with is often very tough. Rats, like other rodents – squirrels, mice, beavers, porcupines – cope with that problem by maintaining open roots to their front gnawing teeth, the incisors, so that they continue to grow throughout the animal's life compensating for wear. They are kept sharp by a simple but very effective self-stropping process. The main body of the rodent incisor is made of dentine, but its front surface is covered by a thick and often brightly coloured layer of enamel which is even harder. The cutting edge of the tooth thus becomes shaped like a chisel. As the top incisors grind over the lower ones the dentine is worn away more quickly and this exposes the blade of enamel at the front keeping a sharp chisel edge.

Once gnawed, ground and pulped, the food has to be digested. This, too, presents major problems. Cellulose, the material from which the cell walls of plants are built, is one of the most stable of all organic substances. No digestive juices produced by any mammal make any impression on it. But if the nutritious substances inside the cells are to be released, they have to be broken down in some way. Providing they are not too thick, this can be done mechanically to some extent by chewing. Some bacteria, however, have the rare ability to produce a ferment that dissolves cellulose and herbivores maintain cultures of them within their stomachs. The bacteria make a meal of the cellulose and the owner of the stomach can then absorb the cell contents. Even with bacterial help, adequate digestion of a thoroughly vegetarian meal can take a long time.

The rabbit provides for this in a straightforward if somewhat disconcerting way. Its

282

EARLY MAMMAL MODELS

With the extinction of the giant reptiles, the mammals, which until then had remained small and inconspicuous, developed spectacularly.

Every time a major development in the design of the animal body has appeared, allowing creatures to invade new environments, a multiplicity of new species has rapidly evolved. Some forms have proved to be effective and have expanded their numbers, while many others have disappeared.

This happened after the first backboned fish began to swim effectively, after the amphibians first crawled over land, and after the reptiles developed watertight skins. It also occurred 35 million years ago when the giant reptiles disappeared and mammals could invade new ecological niches. Then, for a short time, some extraordinary mammals roamed the earth.

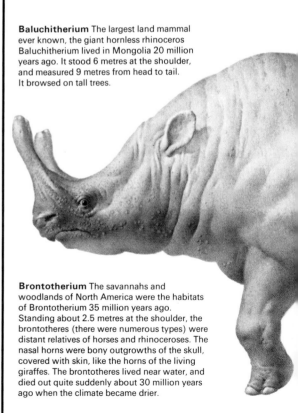

Baluchitherium The largest land mammal ever known, the giant hornless rhinoceros Baluchitherium lived in Mongolia 20 million years ago. It stood 6 metres at the shoulder, and measured 9 metres from head to tail. It browsed on tall trees.

Brontotherium The savannahs and woodlands of North America were the habitats of Brontotherium 35 million years ago. Standing about 2.5 metres at the shoulder, the brontotheres (there were numerous types) were distant relatives of horses and rhinoceroses. The nasal horns were bony outgrowths of the skull, covered with skin, like the horns of the living giraffes. The brontotheres lived near water, and died out quite suddenly about 30 million years ago when the climate became drier.

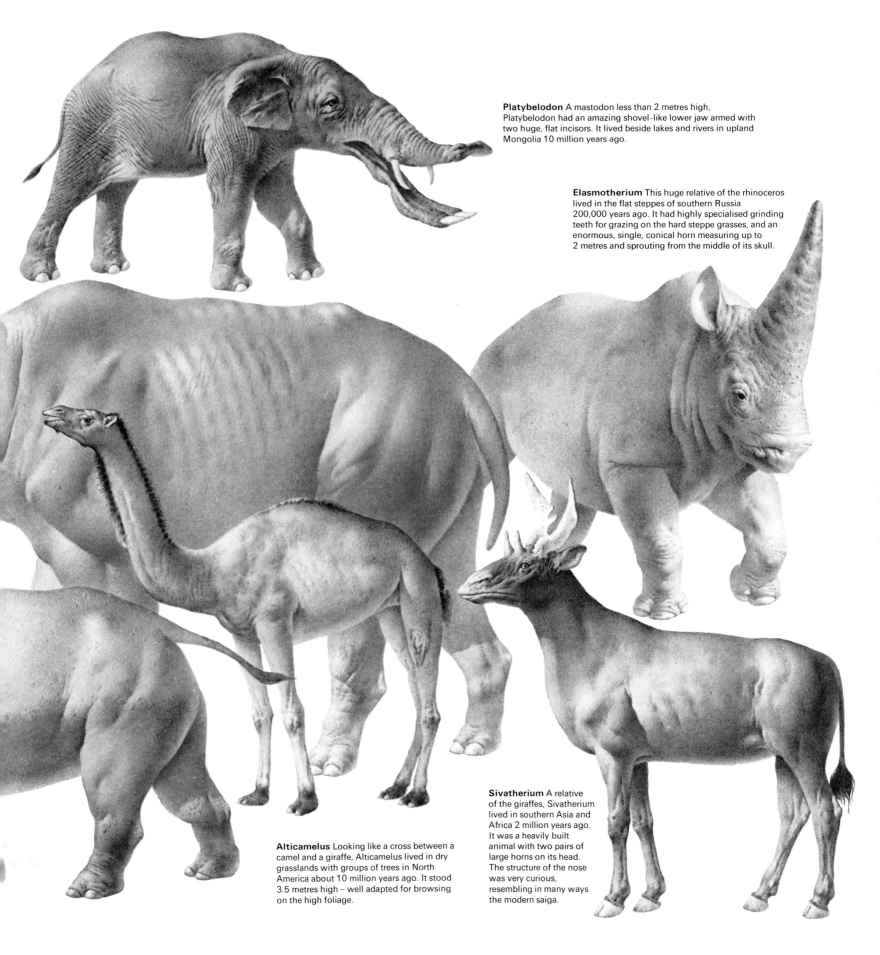

Platybelodon A mastodon less than 2 metres high, Platybelodon had an amazing shovel-like lower jaw armed with two huge, flat incisors. It lived beside lakes and rivers in upland Mongolia 10 million years ago.

Elasmotherium This huge relative of the rhinoceros lived in the flat steppes of southern Russia 200,000 years ago. It had highly specialised grinding teeth for grazing on the hard steppe grasses, and an enormous, single, conical horn measuring up to 2 metres and sprouting from the middle of its skull.

Alticamelus Looking like a cross between a camel and a giraffe, Alticamelus lived in dry grasslands with groups of trees in North America about 10 million years ago. It stood 3.5 metres high – well adapted for browsing on the high foliage.

Sivatherium A relative of the giraffes, Sivatherium lived in southern Asia and Africa 2 million years ago. It was a heavily built animal with two pairs of large horns on its head. The structure of the nose was very curious, resembling in many ways the modern saiga.

The hunters and the hunted

A winter kill

Winter brings an added urgency to a fox's hunt. Game is very scarce and a hare, once found, must not be allowed to escape. The hare, too, is weakened by lack of food and the deep snow hampers it badly. Though it zigzags desperately, it cannot escape. This one meal will now enable the fox to survive for another ten days.

meal of leaves, having been shredded by the incisors, ground with the molars and swallowed, goes down to the stomach where it is attacked by the micro-organisms and its own digestive juices. Eventually, it passes down into the gut, is moulded into soft pellets and excreted. This usually happens when the rabbit is resting in its burrow. As soon as the pellets emerge, the rabbit turns round and swallows them. Once more they go to the stomach and the last vestiges of nourishment are extracted. Only after this second processing are they deposited outside the burrow as the familiar dry pellets and abandoned.

Elephants have particularly acute problems, for they eat, in addition to leaves, a great deal of fibrous twigs and woody material. Apart from their tusks, their only teeth are molars at the back of the mouth, which form massive grinders. As they wear down, they are replaced every few years by new ones erupting from behind and migrating forward along the jaw. The molars pulp and crush with enormous power, but even so, the elephant's food is so woody it requires a very long period of digestion to extract anything of value from it. The elephant's stomach, however, is big enough to provide it. A meal taken by a human being normally passes through the body in about twenty-four

hours. An elephant's takes about two and a half days to make the same journey and for most of that time it is kept stewing in the digestive juices and bacterial broth of the stomach. Much earlier in history, some dinosaurs, eating ferns and cycads, had encountered the same problem and solved it in the same way – by becoming giants.

Elephant dung, even after all this protracted treatment, still contains a great deal of twigs, fibres and seeds that have remained virtually untouched. Some plants that have been stripped by elephants for millennia have reacted to the treatment by coating their seeds with rinds thick enough to withstand a prolonged soaking in the digestive juices. The paradoxical consequence has been that now, unless the rind is weakened by passing through an elephant, the seeds are unable to germinate at all.

The most elaborate apparatus for digesting cellulose is the familiar one used by antelope, deer, buffalo as well as domestic sheep and cows. They clip grass from their pasture with the lower incisors, pressing it against the tongue or the gums of the upper jaw, which has no teeth in the front. They then swallow it immediately and it goes down to the rumen, a chamber of the stomach which contains a particularly rich brew of bacteria. There it is churned back and forth for several hours, squeezed by a muscular bag, while the bacteria attack the cellulose. Eventually, the mash is brought up the throat, a mouthful at a time, to be chewed in a particularly thorough way by the molars: a ruminant's jaw can move not only up and down but backwards, forwards and sideways. This ruminating can be done, however, at leisure and in safety, when the animal has left the exposed feeding grounds and is relaxing in the shade during the heat of the day. Eventually, the mouthful is swallowed for the second time. It goes past the rumen and on to the stomach proper which has absorptive walls. Now at last the animal gains some benefit from all its labour.

Preparing for the leafless winter

Leaves have one further shortcoming as food. In temperate parts of the world, many disappear almost entirely for months at a time. The creatures dependent upon them must, therefore, make special preparations as winter approaches. Asiatic sheep turn their food into fat and store it in cushions around the base of their tails. Other species not only feed and fatten themselves as much as they can, but reduce the demands of the next few months to a minimum by hibernating.

The trigger for this reaction has not been precisely identified. It is certainly not simply a drop in the temperature as one might suppose, for an animal kept in a constantly warm room will nonetheless hibernate at the same time as its fellows in the autumnal chill outside. It may be that the stimulus comes from the fat reserves themselves. When the animal has filled itself with as much fat as it can hold, it might just as well go to sleep as keep on eating.

A dormouse in autumn is often almost spherical. It finds a hole, screws up its eyes, tucks its head into its stomach, wraps its soft furry tail around itself and allows the heat of its body to seep away slowly. Its heart beat slows considerably. Its breathing becomes so shallow and infrequent that it is difficult to detect at all. The muscles stiffen and the

THE WIDE-RANGING DEER FAMILY

The 40 species of deer alive today are found in habitats ranging from the tropical forests of Asia to the tundra of the Arctic.

The deer family arose more than 35 million years ago, probably in Asia, from small, forest-dwelling ancestors. The first deer lacked antlers but had enlarged upper canine tusks like those of the living musk deer of central Asia and the Chinese water deer. With the exception of these two species, the living deer are characterised by the presence of antlers in the males. The reindeer is unique in that both sexes have antlers.

Antlers differ from the horns of other ruminants, those hoofed animals which chew the cud, in that they are true bone, without a central core and horny sheath. They are grown and discarded every year – a process that must make an enormous demand on the animal. Antlers are used mainly in displays and as weapons during contests between the males for possession of the females. One of the advantages of shedding antlers every year may be that the males start each breeding season with an undamaged set – breakages are quite common during the rut.

Enormous antlers of the Irish elk
The early antlered deer were still small, with short antlers on elongated bony bases, as in the barking deer of Southeast Asia. Later forms tended to grow larger and more complex antlers on shorter, sturdier bases, culminating in the enormous Irish elk, whose antlers spanned 3 metres and weighed nearly 50 kilograms. The Irish elk and other similarly specialised forms died out within the last $2\frac{1}{2}$ million years. The surviving forms tend to be those that have best adapted to man's influence.

The deer spread from central Asia and colonised most of the climatic regions of Europe, Asia and the Americas.

Hog-deer of Asia *The hog-deer lives in the river valleys of northern India and Burma. It gets its name from the way it runs head down through the tall grass without the bounding action so characteristic of deer.*

The hunters and the hunted

Swamp deer of India *The swamp deer is well adapted to its life in the waterlogged grasslands along the rivers at the base of the Himalayan foothills. Its splayed hooves enable it to move through the mud and swamps with relative ease. Swamp deer live in herds and feed mainly on grass. This group (left) crosses a clearing in the tall grassland on a misty winter morning in Assam.*

Red deer of Scotland *The red deer was once a forest animal but has adapted to life on the open moorlands which man has created in the Highlands. This stag (below) roars during the rut, surrounded by his harem of does. Stags advertise their size and strength to each other by bouts of roaring. This display is a way of assessing an opponent, before deciding whether to do battle.*

Caribou of North America *The barren-ground caribou, the North American form of the reindeer, lives in vast herds of 20,000 or more in the Arctic tundra. Twice a year they travel 1,000 kilometres and more between their summer and winter haunts, running the gauntlet of wolves and human predators. This herd of caribou (above) gathers on a high snow field in summer to escape from smaller enemies – hordes of biting flies. In winter, caribou dig through the snow with their hooves to find food – hence their name, which means 'shoveller' in the language of the Micmac Indians.*

whole body feels as cold as stone. In this state of suspended animation, the body's fuel demands are so low that the fat store can provide enough to keep all the essential processes ticking over for months. Extreme cold, however, can wake an animal. If it is in danger of being frozen solid, then it stirs and begins to shiver violently, warming itself by burning fuel in its muscles. It may even, in such an emergency, squander some of its remaining reserves of fat by trotting about until the worst of the cold is past and it can go back to sleep again. Normally it is only the warmth of spring that brings the dormouse and other winter sleepers out of their holes. Their appetites are now huge and urgent, for during the winter, they may have lost as much as half of their body weight. But now starvation is over. The leaves once more are sprouting.

Life in the elevated world of the tree-tops

With such methods as these, a great variety of animals nourish themselves on the vegetable foods provided by the forests of the world. Up in the topmost branches, the squirrels scamper along the twigs, collecting bark and shoots, acorns and catkins. Some species have developed furry membranes between their hind and fore legs so that they can glide between the branches.

Up here too live the monkeys. Many species will take a wide variety of food – insects, eggs, nestlings and fruit – but others will only take the leaves of particular trees and have special complicated stomachs to deal with them. Life in their precarious elevated world has led all of them to become marvellously agile, with grasping manipulative hands and quick intelligences. This particular combination of talents eventually led to further developments of such consequence that they must be given a chapter to themselves. But their way is not the only one of winning a leaf-eating life above the ground. One of the first creatures to move up into the branches in South America was the sloth and it adopted a solution almost exactly the opposite to those of the monkeys.

There are two main kinds of sloth, the two-toed and the three-toed. Of these, the three-toed is considerably the more slothful. It hangs upside down from a branch suspended by hook-like claws at the ends of its long bony arms. It feeds on only one kind of leaf, Cecropia, which happily for the sloth grows in quantity and is easily found. No predators attack the sloth – few indeed can even reach it – and nothing competes with it for the Cecropia. Lulled by this security, it has sunk into an existence that is only just short of complete torpor. It spends eighteen out of twenty-four hours soundly asleep. It pays such little attention to its personal hygiene that green algae grow on its coarse hair and communities of a parasitic moth live in the depths of its coat producing caterpillars which graze on its mouldy hair. Its muscles are such that it is quite

A wolf pack hunts a moose in the snows of a Canadian winter

A single wolf has virtually no chance of bringing down a full-grown moose. Even a whole pack may not be able to do so, for a healthy adult moose will usually turn and face the wolves, kicking out powerfully and accurately with all four feet. After about five minutes of such resistance, the wolf pack usually gives up and goes off to look for easier prey. An aged or sickly moose, however, is more likely to try to run for safety and then the wolves have a better chance of getting hold of a flank of the fleeing animal. As soon as the animal is brought down, the wolves swarm all over it and it is swiftly killed.

incapable of moving at a speed of over a kilometre an hour even over the shortest distances and the swiftest movement it can make is a sweep of its hooked arm. It is virtually dumb and its hearing is so poor that you can let off a gun within inches of it and its only response will be to turn slowly and blink. Even its sense of smell, though it is better than ours, is very much less acute than that of most mammals. And it sleeps and feeds entirely alone.

But it has to have some kind of social life. With such blurred and blunted senses, how does one sloth find another in order to breed? There is one clue. The sloth's digestion works just about as slowly as the rest of its bodily processes and it only defecates and urinates once a week. But most surprisingly, to do so it descends to the ground and it habitually uses the same place. This is the one moment in its life when it is exposed to real danger. A jaguar could easily catch it here. There must be some important reason for it to take such apparently unnecessary risks. Its dung and urine have extremely pungent smells, and the sense of smell is the only one of the sloth's faculties that is not seriously blurred. So a sloth midden is the one place in the forest that another sloth could easily find – and the one place, too, where it stands a chance of meeting another sloth, say once a week or so. Maybe a sloth's midden is also its trysting place, and there is certainly no other easy way of compiling one, except on the ground. We cannot, however, be sure, for no student of animal behaviour has yet been brave enough to contemplate the days and nights of stupefying inactivity that would have to be endured by anyone who wants to find out more about the sloth's private life.

The solitary hunters and their solitary prey
The forest floor is not rich in vegetation. In some areas the shade is so dense that there is nothing but a deep, springy layer of rotting leaves with an occasional fungus pushing up from among them. Elsewhere, if the canopy is thinner, there may be small bushes, a few herbs on the ground and some spindly saplings. In Africa and Asia, such plants provide food for miniature antelope – the mouse-deer and the duiker. About the size of dogs, they are extremely shy, but to see one, after long hours of waiting, come silently stepping towards you through the dappled shadows, fastidiously nibbling a carefully chosen leaf, is a revelation of forest life never to be forgotten. Both animals have very ancient histories, for primitive ruminants very like them were among the first leaf-eating specialists to wander through those forests of fifty million years ago.

In South America, their role is played not by hoofed animals but by rodents, the paca and agouti. They have the same sort of shape and size and similarly solitary habits and dispositions. If anything, they are even more nervous and shy. The slightest suspicion of danger or whiff of an unfamiliar scent and they freeze, staring, panic-stricken, with large lustrous eyes. The snap of a twig will then send them careering headlong through the forest.

Browsing on the taller shrubs and saplings requires greater stature and every forest has a small population of creatures, ranging in size from ponies to horses, that do so. They are so secretive, silent, and few in number that they are hardly ever seen – in

THE OMNIVOROUS BEARS

A family of unspecialised mammals, bears spread from the jungles of the equator to the ice fields of the North Pole

Although bears are classified as carnivores, they have a very wide taste in food. Most will eat small mammals, fish, insects and carrion, but they also relish fruit and berries, leaves, roots and honey.

Their teeth reflect this omnivorous diet. Although one tooth on either side of the upper jaw is enlarged and pointed, it is not nearly as well developed as that of a true meat-eating animal like a lion. All bear molars, unlike those of any other carnivore, have broad flat crowns, suited to grinding up vegetable matter.

The bears' closest relatives are dogs. Fossils of extinct species have been discovered that are intermediate between the two groups and could easily be regarded either as large dogs or small bears. Even today, the two groups overlap in size – the Malayan sun bear is smaller than a timber wolf. No bears, however, have tails that are bigger than a stump.

The different kinds of bears
Bears are so variable in size and colour that at one time it was believed that there were a great number of distinct kinds in North America alone. Now it is recognised that there are only seven true species in the world. All, except the spectacled bear of the Andes, live in the northern hemisphere. There are none in Africa or Australia. (The koala of Australia is an unrelated marsupial.) Those bears that live in cold climates spend the winter sleeping in caves or dens that they excavate. There they live off their fat and there, too, the young are born, naked and little bigger than rats.

A bear from the Andes *The spectacled bear gets its name from the yellowish rings circling each eye. It is almost entirely vegetarian, living on leaves, fruit and nuts. It is an excellent climber and not only feeds high up in the tree tops but also builds a nest in the branches and sleeps there.*

The hunters and the hunted

The white bear of the north *Polar bears spend most of their lives away from land, hunting seals among the ice floes. Although they are excellent swimmers, with membranes between their toes, they do not hunt in the water; they catch seals on the ice, stealthily crawling up to them and killing them with a blow of their huge paws. In summer they make long journeys over land and then they may eat not only rodents, such as lemmings, but also berries and leaves.*

A grizzly shares a meal with a puma *Brown bears of varying size and colour live in many parts of the northern hemisphere, from Europe through Asia to North America, but all are regarded as belonging to the same species. The grizzly is a giant form. In spite of its huge size, it can run as fast as a horse over short distances and on occasions has attacked men. However, its habit of eating carrion has led to it being blamed for kills for which it was not in fact responsible.*

Malaya and South America, the tapirs, which are nocturnal; in parts of Southeast Asia, the Sumatran rhinoceros, with a slightly hairy hide, the smallest of all its kind and now sadly exceedingly rare; and in the Congo, the okapi, a short-necked primitive cousin of the giraffe, the largest of these creatures but so shy that it was the last big mammal to be discovered by science and was not seen alive by any European before the beginning of this century.

All these ground-living forest dwellers, large and small, are solitary creatures. The reason is not hard to find. The shaded forest floor seldom produces sufficient leaves to sustain a large group in one area for any length of time and in any case, if several animals are to maintain a relationship, they require some kind of communication. It is not possible to see far in the forest and signalling by sound would attract the attention of hunters. So the mouse-deer and the agouti and the tapir live in pairs or by themselves. They maintain territories which they mark with dung or secretions of a gland close to the eye and rely for their defence on concealment, melting away into the undergrowth of a territory that they know well to take refuge in secret hidden retreats.

The hunters that seek them are also solitary. The jaguar stalks the tapir, the leopard pounces on the duiker. A wandering bear will eat most things and will certainly tackle a mouse-deer if it gets a chance. The smallest of the hunters – genets, jungle cats, civets, and weasels – pursue rats and mice as well as birds and reptiles.

Of all the hunters, the cats are the most specialised for meat-eating. Their claws are kept sharp by being retracted into sheaths. When they attack, they hook their victim with them and then deliver a piercing bite in the neck that severs the spinal cord and brings a swift death.

The long dagger-like tooth on either side of the mouth, just behind the front teeth, typical of a meat eater, is used to slash open the hide of the prey. The jagged ones farther back in the jaw shear bones. They are all the tools of butchery. None of the dogs or cats can really chew. Most simply bolt their food in gobbets. Flesh is far easier to digest than leaves and twigs and the hunter's stomach needs little help.

These lonely nocturnal duels of ambush and detection, flight and pounce, follow the ancient tactics that were established between the plant-eater and the beast of prey in those very first forests. But some twenty-five million years ago new and very different techniques developed. A change in the world's climate and its vegetation drew these protagonists out of the shadows and into the open. Grasslands appeared.

An inverted life

The three-toed sloth is so extremely adapted to hanging upside down among the branches of trees that even the hair of its coat is parted, not along its spine like other animals, but along its belly.

A solitary hunter

The tiger usually hunts alone during the night or early evening. Its usual prey is deer, wild pig or cattle. Since it is not outstandingly swift, it needs to get close to its prey undetected, so it stalks silently through cover or waits in ambush beside an animal trail or a waterhole. Then, with a few bounds and a final spring, it leaps on its prey and seizes it by the throat with its immensely powerful jaws. After the kill, it often eats part of its victim and conceals the rest of the carcass so that it can be eaten later the following day or night.

The dangers of feeding on the grasslands

Grass may look to be a simple almost primitive plant, little more than leaves with roots. In fact, it is a highly advanced one, bearing tiny, unobtrusive flowers which rely not on insects to distribute their pollen but the wind that blows so freely and widely across the open spaces where it grows. It produces horizontal stems running close to the surface or just below it. When fire sweeps across the plains, consuming the old dry leaves, the flames pass quickly so that these stems and the root stocks are unharmed and they produce new sprouts almost immediately. They can do this because grass leaves grow, not from the tip as do those of bushes and trees, but from the base. This is also of enormous benefit to the grazing animals for it means that even though the leaves have been cropped, they will continue to grow unchecked and very soon produce another meal.

The grass itself benefits from the presence of the herds for they trample and eat the seedlings of bushes or trees that might take root on the plain and that would, were they to grow tall, rob the grass of light and eventually displace it. It seems likely therefore that the spread of the grasslands and the evolution of grazing animals proceeded together, step by step.

The plains attracted not only grazers. With no kind of cover in which to hide, they made tempting targets for beasts of prey as they too moved out of the forests in search of meals. Only the largest of the vegetarians, the elephants and rhinoceros, had nothing to fear. In the forest, they had needed to be able to move through the trees with ease and silence and this kept them to a certain size, but there was no such limitation out here and they grew still bigger. Their great bulk, together with their tough skin, put them beyond the power of any carnivore. But for smaller creatures, the plains, so full of food, were also beset with danger.

Some sought safety in burrows. Grasslands are marvellous sites for creatures with a taste for tunnelling. The ground is free from the knottings and intertwinings of tree roots. So here they can construct extended tunnel systems without hindrance and many species have taken spectacular advantage of the opportunity.

The underground world beneath the grass

One of the most dedicated and specialised of all these burrowers is a bizarre rodent, the naked mole-rat of East Africa. It eats not the leaves of grass but its roots, together with odd bulbs and tubers. Mole-rats live in families and excavate elaborate underground quarters with special dormitories, nurseries, larders and lavatories. Life spent entirely underground in the warm, dry earth of the African plains has changed them dramatically. They have lost the use of their eyes and shed all their fur. Blind, naked, their sausage-shaped bodies covered with grey wrinkled skin, their appearance is not improved by the most grotesque incisor teeth. These project clear of the head in a bony

The giant of the grassland

A bull African elephant is the largest living land animal, standing as much as 3.5 metres tall and weighing 5.5 tons. Its skin is so tough it is largely proof against any talons or fangs. The calf, however, is very vulnerable and its mother, helped by her companions, protects it with the greatest solicitude, charging any creature that threatens to interfere with it.

semicircle in front of the face. They are used not only for feeding but as burrowing tools. Gnawing one's way through earth could clearly be a distasteful business, but the mole-rat avoids mouthfuls of soil with a technique used by many other gnawers. It puckers its lips behind those extravagantly protruding teeth and so keeps its mouth tight shut while its teeth busily excavate.

When they dig, they work in teams. The one at the front gnaws with feverish speed, throwing the dislodged soil behind it and straight into the face of the second member of the team. Since it, in any case, is blind, this does not seem to worry it unduly and it simply hurls the soil back between its legs at the face of the next in the queue until at length the last member of the line receives it and throws it vigorously out of the end of the tunnel and onto the surface. A patch of ground colonised by mole-rats is studded by conical tips of this waste with plumes of sand spouting from holes in front of them like miniature volcanoes.

Few, if any, predators are able to make a meal of a mole-rat. It can dig faster than any cat or dog and it has no need ever to come to the surface. But those burrowers that eat not the roots of grass but its leaves have to emerge from their holes to feed at some time or other and then they can be in considerable danger. The plains of North America are colonised by rodents the size of small rabbits called prairie dogs. They not only graze above ground but do so during the day when coyotes, bobcats, ferrets and hawks are about, all creatures that are only too glad to dine off prairie dog if given the chance. Prairie dogs have accordingly developed defences which depend upon a highly organised social system.

They live in huge concentrations called towns which may contain as many as a thousand animals. Each town is divided up into a number of communities called coteries of about thirty individuals, all of whom know one another well. Many have interconnecting burrows. The coteries always have some members on sentry duty, sitting upright on the mound of excavated earth beside the burrow entrance where they can get the best view of what is going on. If one spots an enemy, it lets out a series of whistling barks. Different kinds of predators elicit different calls so that all know not only that there is danger but what the danger is. The call is repeated by others nearby and so spreads through the town, putting everyone on guard. The inhabitants do not immediately take to flight but take up strategic positions close to their holes. From there, standing on their hind legs, they stare at the intruder, watching its every move. So as a coyote trots through the town, the alarm spreads from coterie to coterie and the intruder is met with fixed glares from the citizens who let it come tantalisingly close before they duck into their burrows.

The social life of the prairie dog is not limited to defence. The adults, sitting outside their burrows, proclaim their ownership by giving yet another kind of whistle, accompanied by an engaging little leap in the air. During the breeding season, the coterie members keep very much to themselves and defend their boundaries against any intruders. When this tense time is over, they become more relaxed. Citizens move about the town, wandering into one another's areas. If a stranger approaches a resident,

THE RHINOCEROS FAMILY

A group of vegetarians which, like the elephant, find their defence in tough skin, sheer bulk and a readiness to charge at any provocation.

The first rhinoceroses appeared some 50 million years ago. They were small plant-eating creatures, rather horse-like, with comparatively slender legs. They probably had a hairy hide and lacked horns on their noses. Many different forms of them soon evolved. One, Indricotherium, grew to an enormous size, standing 5 metres tall and 7 metres long. Another, the woolly rhinoceros, flourished during the glacial period and was drawn accurately and vividly on cave walls by the Stone Age men who hunted it.

The survivors
Today, the fortunes of the family have faded and it is reduced to five species, most of which are now close to extinction. The most primitive of them is a small hair-covered creature with two horns, living in a few restricted localities in the jungles of Southeast Asia. There are probably not more than 150 individuals alive, and it seems very doubtful if this species of rhino can survive for much longer.

Two bigger rhinos also live in Asia, the Indian and the Javan. Both are clad in heavy hide which forms overlapping plates joined by pleats, like a suit of medieval armour.

The remaining two species of rhinoceros live in Africa. The square-lipped or white rhinoceros is the biggest of them all, and second only in size among land-living mammals to the elephant; the black rhinoceros is somewhat smaller and is the only one of the five species that still exists in any number.

An unusual group *Black rhino calves stay with their mothers, but adults are solitary creatures, wandering over a wide range and only occasionally coming together into groups.*

A rare baby rhino The Indian rhinoceros breeds only infrequently. The female's gestation period is about 16 months, and she bears a single baby at a time, which she suckles for a year and possibly two. In consequence, she is unlikely to produce a baby more than once in three years. The infant stays with its mother until it is sufficiently large to defend itself from tigers. Rhinos are predominantly solitary creatures, rarely forming groups larger than a mother and her calf.

Skin care, and keeping cool Indian rhinos seldom stray far from water (below). They feed on grass, shrubs and aquatic plants, but much of their time, especially during the summer, is spent lounging in rivers or muddy wallows. This may be necessary to keep their hide in good condition. It probably also helps to keep the animals cool, and protects them from the attacks of the biting insects that swarm over the swamps.

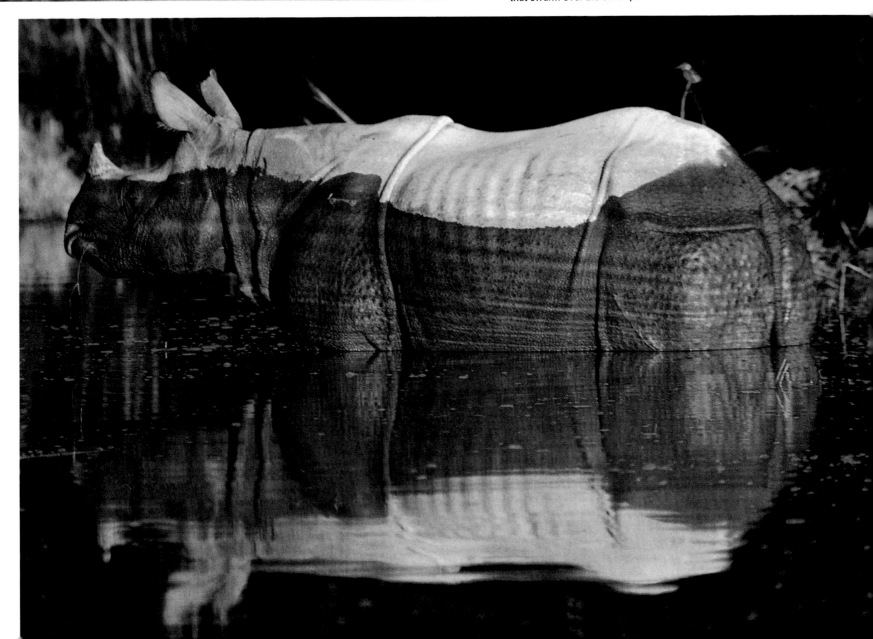

The hunters and the hunted

Town dwellers

Prairie dog coteries consist of a male, four or five females and the young from the two previous years. At breeding time the male chases away strangers, but at other times neighbours visit one another's burrows.

ADULTS GRAZING

A GROUP OF YOUNGSTERS (ABOVE)

ADULTS GREETING ONE ANOTHER (LEFT)

the animals cautiously exchange a rather reserved kiss and then inspect one another's anal glands to see if they are actually acquainted. If they are not, then they separate and the visitor eventually departs. But if they discover that they are members of the same coterie, then they kiss open-mouthed, gently groom one another and often move off to graze side by side.

The prairie dogs tend the vegetation within the town with great care. Their grazing is so intense that many of the plants they favour become eaten out. The animals then move to a different part of their territory and let the old pasture lie fallow for some time to recover. They also cultivate selectively. They do not like sage, one of the commoner and more robust plants on the plains. If a seedling of one takes root or if there is one growing in a newly colonised patch of territory, they do not simply ignore it but deliberately cut it down and so allow more room for the plants they prefer.

Further south, on the pampas of Argentina, the role of the prairie dog is taken by a guinea pig the size of a spaniel called the viscacha. It, too, lives in dense communities but it grazes only at dusk and at dawn. Like many creatures that are active in the twilight, they have prominent recognition marks, broad horizontal black and white stripes across the face. They build cairns over their burrows. If they find any sizeable stone during their excavations they laboriously drag it up to the surface and dump it in the pile on the top. What is more, like good farmers, they enthusiastically do the same with any large object they happen to find in their pastures. So if you drop something on the pampas near a viscacha colony, the place to look for it is not where it may have fallen but on top of the viscacha's monument.

The viscacha is another descendant of that battalion of placental mammals which migrated south from North America across the Panama land-bridge when it first formed and which, when it broke, were marooned in South America. Just as the forests were colonised by ant-eaters, armadillos and unique kinds of monkeys, so the grasslands were invaded by other placentals. Some of them developed into very strange creatures indeed. Two have already been mentioned – the giant ant-eater and the extinct armadillo with a shell 2 metres high. There were also many grass- and leaf-eaters. The viscacha is not the only survivor of this group; there are also small rabbit-coloured guinea pigs. But once there were herbivores that grew to a great size. One looked like a camel and stood as tall as an elephant. Another, a relation of the sloth, was even bigger, about 7 metres high, and lumbered about on the ground, feeding on bushes and trees.

A discovery that caused a sensation

When the Panama bridge was re-established, creatures from the north again spread south and many of these bizarre forms disappeared. Both the giant camel and the sloth died out. There was, therefore, a sensation when, at the end of the last century, it was reported that a German settler in Patagonia, right at the farthestmost tip of the continent, had found recent signs of the ground sloths. He had been exploring a cave on his estancia and had found at the back of it, behind an odd line of boulders that seemed

298

A baffled hunter

A coyote stands at the deserted entrance of a prairie dog's tunnel, while the owner crouches in safety below ground, having been warned of the coyote's approach by its neighbours' alarm calls. In the distance, three other inhabitants of the town sit watching the coyote, ready to whistle further alarms if it comes their way.

to divide the cave into two, a pile of huge bones, pieces of skin covered with shaggy brown hair with curious bony nodules embedded in it and lumps of fresh-looking dung. He hung a piece of the skin on a post to serve as a boundary marker and there, a few years later, a Swedish traveller noticed it. Eventually specimens reached the Natural History Museum in London, where they were pronounced to be the remains of a ground sloth. They seemed so fresh that some believed that the animals might indeed be still alive. The line of boulders looked quite like the foundations of a man-made wall. Grass stems in the dung had clean edges to them as though they had been cut rather than dragged up by the roots. Perhaps, some suggested, the Indians had driven these

monsters into the cave and had kept them penned there behind a wall, feeding them with bales of grass like semi-domesticated animals.

For a long time there was neither confirmation nor refutation of these romantic speculations. Now, sadly, they have been dispelled. When you go to the cave, you discover that it is vast and the line of huge boulders at the back, that might seem on a diagram to form the basis of a wall, are almost certainly nothing more than a collapsed part of the ceiling. The atmosphere of the cave is both very dry and extremely cold so the dung owes its fresh look to the fact that it was, in effect, freeze-dried. Today, the bleak country around is sufficiently well travelled for there to be no chance of creatures twice the size of cows to be wandering about unnoticed. Nonetheless, we now know that Indians reached this part of South America between eight and ten thousand years ago and the datings of the ground sloth remains show that the animals were alive only five thousand years ago. So at least some human beings saw these shambling and marvellous giants.

The horse is born on the North American plains
At the time that the sloths were evolving in the south, on the other side of the Panama strait in North America, another different group of grass-eaters were developing on the prairies. Their ancestors were forest-living creatures, not unlike tapirs but the size of mouse-deer. Their molar teeth were rounded and suited to forest browsing. On the plains, in order to escape their enemies, they began to run faster and faster. The first forms had four toes on the front legs and three on the hind. The longer the limbs, the better they serve as levers and, properly muscled, the faster they can propel their owners. As time passed these grazers lengthened their legs by rising off the ground onto their toes. Eventually, the side toes dwindled and the animal, an early horse the size of a dog, was running on a single elongated middle toe. The ankle bones thus became placed halfway up its legs, the side toes were reduced to internal vestiges called the splint bones, and the nail thickened to form the protective shock-absorbent hooves.

These changes in the limbs were accompanied by others. The grasses of the plains were becoming tougher to chew. They had started to produce in their leaves tiny sharp crystals of silica which wore teeth badly. So the proto-horses changed their rounded molars into bigger and bigger grinders with hard ridges of dentine in them. One of the problems of the grazing life is that an animal, with its head on the ground for such long periods, cannot keep a good lookout for predators. The higher the eyes can be placed on the head the better. This requirement, together with the necessity to provide room for the enlarged molars, resulted in a considerable elongation of the skull. So the early horses evolved into the forms we know today. They spread across the plains of America and eventually, at a time when the Bering Strait was dry, into Europe. From there they spread south and colonised the plains of Africa. Later, they died out in their original American home and only reappeared there some three hundred years ago when they were shipped across by the Spanish conquistadors. But in Europe and Africa, they flourished as horses, donkeys and zebras.

BIZARRE MAMMALS OF SOUTH AMERICA

This reconstruction of life on the Argentinian pampas 2 million years ago shows some of the unusual grazing animals that had evolved in isolation while South America was an island.

When the land-bridge between North and South America disappeared about 60 million years ago, an extraordinary group of mammals evolved in isolation on the island-continent of South America. Large birds were the dominant predators in the absence of large predatory mammals. When the land-bridge returned about 3–4 million years ago, new creatures crossed over from the north, and many of the old types eventually died out. Among the carnivores that arrived to prey on the grazing animals were sabre-tooth tigers.

One of the largest of the grazing animals was Toxodon, standing almost 2 metres high. But even this great size did not protect it from attack by tigers. The giant ground sloth, Megatherium, could reach more than 4 metres into trees to feed on the leaves. A group of camel-like Macrauchenia, with their long snouts, can be seen in the background. The giant armadillo-like Daedicurus had a club-like tail which probably served as a weapon – many Daedicurus fossils have been found bearing the marks of blows from tail-clubs.

The spectacular herds of African grazers

The zebras share the African plains with other running grazers which, during the same period, had been evolving along lines of their own. They were the descendants of the miniature forest antelopes, so like the mouse-deer and duikers. They had already elongated their legs for running within the forest though in a slightly different way from that of the horses, retaining not one toe on the ground but two. Now, out on the plains, their legs grew even longer and they became the cloven-hoofed grazers – antelope, gazelle and deer. Today they flourish in such numbers that they constitute some of the most spectacular assemblages of wildlife to be seen anywhere in the world.

On the edges of the plains in the open bush, where there is still a little cover to be had, the antelope – dik-dik and duikers – remain very like their forest-dwelling relations, small, browsing on shrubs and living alone or in pairs on territories that they mark and defend. Farther out in the open, where concealment is no longer possible, the antelope seek safety in numbers, gathering together in large herds. They lift their heads regularly from grazing to look around, and with so many sharp eyes and sensitive nostrils on the alert, it is virtually impossible for a hunter to take the herd by surprise. If an attack does eventually come, then the fleeing herd bewilders the hunter with a multiplicity of possible targets. A herd of impala explodes into hundreds of individuals, all running in different directions and leaping spectacularly into the air with soaring bounds three metres high.

Keeping together in such numbers makes great demands on the pasture and the herds have therefore to move regularly over great areas. Wildebeest seem able to detect a shower of rain falling as far away as 50 kilometres and will move off to find it and crop the newly springing grass. But this nomadic habit complicates the social arrangements for breeding that in the forest, based on a single pair, had been so simple. For some – the impala, springbok and gazelles – territory remains nonetheless the basis of their arrangements. Males and females form separate herds. A few dominant bucks will leave the bachelor herd to establish individual territories for themselves. Each marks the boundary of its land, defends it against other males and tries to attract females into it and mate with them. This however is a very demanding business and most of the bucks who undertake it are exhausted and badly out of condition after three months or so. Eventually, they are forced to yield to stronger, more rested rivals and they go back to join the bachelor herd.

The eland, the largest of the antelopes, and the plains zebra are among the few that have finally broken the bond with territoriality altogether. They form herds in which both sexes are always present and the males settle their problems over females by battling between themselves wherever the herd happens to be.

The oryx represents the most extreme form of this independence from territoriality, for it lives in the deserts and semi-deserts of Africa, and even though it can survive on the poorest grazing and can go for days without drinking any water it none the less has to follow a nomadic existence to find enough food to keep alive. It travels in herds, often 60 or 70 strong.

302

The discipline of the herd
Wildebeest live in huge herds, often several thousand strong. When they move, either on their long journeys to find water and fresh pasture at the beginning of the dry season, or on their daily treks down from a grazing area to a watering place, they often plod patiently behind one another in long single files (below).

The unending search for water

Some years, all the grazing animals that have spent the rainy season out on the Serengeti plains react simultaneously to the need to find food and water, and set off together in one vast migration. Zebras (left) join the columns of wildebeest and the herds of other antelope in a single mass movement that may involve a million animals.

The hunters and the hunted

Hunting tactics of the plains predators

In order to catch the grazers, the predators on the plain have had to improve greatly their own running techniques. They have not taken to moving on the tips of a reduced number of toes perhaps because they have always needed their toes, armed with claws, as offensive weapons. Their solution is different. They have effectively lengthened their limbs by making their spine extremely flexible. At full stretch, travelling at high speed, their hind and front legs overlap one another beneath the body just like those of a

A leopard, bloated after its meal, lies beside its larder

Leopards hunt all kinds of creatures. Small catches such as birds are eaten on the ground, but larger ones – gazelles and antelopes – are hauled up into a tree and wedged between the branches, where they are safe from other meat-eaters such as hyenas or lions. Even vultures, which habitually feed on the ground, find it difficult to tackle a carcass in a tree.

The apprehensive prey

The dik-dik (left) lives solitarily or in pairs in woodland, and relies on cover to conceal it from enemies. Impala (above), however, graze in the open. There they find safety by herding together for, even though one animal may have its head down feeding, others will be watching for danger.

The hunters and the hunted

An easy kill
A cheetah, running well below its top speed, pursues the fawn of a Thomson gazelle. There is little chance of escape. Having brought down such a fawn, a mother cheetah will sometimes carry it back to her cubs still alive, so that her youngsters may be able to practise their hunting skills.

galloping antelope.

The cheetah has a thin elongated body and is said to be the fastest runner on earth, capable of reaching speeds, in bursts, of over 110 kph. But this method is very energy-consuming. Great muscular effort is needed to keep the spine springing back and forth and the cheetah cannot maintain such speeds for more than a minute or so. Either it succeeds in outrunning its prey within a few hundred yards and makes a kill or it has to retire exhausted while the antelope, with their more rigid backs and long lever-legs,

continue to gallop off to a safer part of the plains.

Lions are nowhere near as fast as the cheetah. Their top speed is about 80 kph. A wildebeest can do about the same and keep it up for much longer. So lions have had to develop more complicated tactics. Sometimes they rely on stealth, creeping towards their victims, their bodies close to the ground, utilising every bit of cover. Sometimes, an individual works by itself. But on occasion, members of a pride will hunt as a team – and they are the only cats that do so. They set off in line abreast. As they approach a

group of their prey – antelope, zebra or wildebeest – those lions at the ends of the line move a little quicker so that they encircle the herd. Finally, these break cover, driving the prey towards the lions in the centre of the line. Such tactics often result in several of the team making kills and a hunt has been watched in which seven wildebeest were brought down.

A female selects the food for her family
A lioness runs alongside a stampeding herd of zebras, watching them intently as if selecting the weakest before making her final pounce. The males of the pride (left) seldom take part in such energetic work, but stroll up to the kill after it has been made and push their way between their females to claim a share.

A family dispute
Lion cubs follow their parents to a kill when they are only a few months old. The parents, however, will often dispute with the cubs for food, and in hard times the young may be left to starve. A lioness, who can breed quickly, has a better chance of passing on her genes to the next generation by staying well fed, rather than by risking her life for her cubs, who may die anyway.

Hyenas are even slower than lions. The best they can manage is about 65 kph and in consequence their hunting methods have to be even more subtle and dependent on teamwork. The females have separate dens where they rear their pups, but the pack as a whole works together and holds and defends a territory. They have a rich vocabulary of sound and gesture with which they communicate among themselves. They growl and whoop, grunt, yelp and whine and at times produce a most terrifying chorus of orgiastic laughs. In gesture, their tails are particularly eloquent. Normally they are carried pointing down. An erect tail indicates aggression; pointed forward over the back, social excitement; held between the legs tight under the belly, fear. By hunting in well-co-ordinated teams, they have become so successful that in parts of the African plains, they make the majority of kills and the lions merely use their bigger size to bully their way on to a carcass, the reverse of the popular conception of the relationship between these two species.

Hyenas usually hunt at night. Sometimes they set off in small groups of two or three and then a wildebeest is likely to be their quarry. They test the herds by charging them

The misjudged hyena

Hyenas, with their curious hobbling gait, were once thought to be no more than clumsy scavengers, coming to clear up after kills made by bigger predators like lions. In fact, they are among the most efficient hunters on the African plains and in some parts are responsible for the majority of kills. They adopt different strategies according to circumstances or their mood. Sometimes one will wander away from the pack and go hunting alone (above) for such quarry as flamingoes. Usually, however, they work as a highly co-ordinated team and then few creatures can escape them. Zebras (left) are among their favourite prey. In some areas hyenas live in clans, and defend hunting territories against intrusion by neighbouring clans.

311

and then slowing down to watch the fleeing animals closely, as if trying to detect any weakness among individuals. In the end, they appear to select one animal and begin to chase it doggedly, cantering after it, snapping at its heels until it is finally goaded into turning and facing its persecutors. When it does that, it is doomed. While it faces one hyena, the other lunges at its belly, sinks in its teeth and holds on. The wildebeest is now crippled. Soon it is disembowelled and dead.

Zebra are a more difficult prey. To hunt them, the hyenas unite to form a large team. They appear to decide that they will try for zebra even before they start. They assemble at a regularly used meeting ground in the evening, greeting each other with lavish care, smelling one another's mouths, necks and heads, standing head to tail and sniffing and licking genitals. The pack then moves off to hunt. They may stop along the boundary of their territory and refresh its markings with urine. Sometimes they stop and cluster round a patch of ground in a frenzy of excited sniffing. As far as can be seen, there is nothing to distinguish such a place from any other: the importance of the event comes from the activity which reaffirms the bonds between them all. When they are in groups like this, they will trot straight past herds of wildebeest, paying no attention to them. At last they sight a zebra and the hunt begins.

Zebras run in family groups of half a dozen or so, led by the dominant stallion. He it is who is likely to sound the alarm with a braying danger call. As the herd gallops away, he takes up the rear, placing himself between the pursuing hyenas and his mares and foals. The hyenas follow in a crescent behind. The stallion will swerve and attack the pack with powerful kicks and bites and even chase the leading hyena, who may be forced to drop back and allow others to make the running. But eventually one of the pack will get past the stallion and begin to snap at a mare or a foal. As the chase relentlessly continues, one gets a tooth-hold on a leg or the belly or the genitals and the animal is dragged down. While the rest of the terrified herd canters to safety, the hyenas leap on the fallen zebra, howling and whooping, ripping it to pieces. Within a quarter of an hour, the entire carcass – hide, guts and bones, everything except the skull – will have disappeared.

So the speed of the antelopes demanded the guile and teamwork of the hunters. That

A meal for infant hunters

Hunting dogs rival hyenas as efficient hunters. They live in packs up to 40 strong and may kill as often as twice a day, morning and afternoon. For much of the year, they roam widely over the African plains in search of prey – gazelles, wildebeest and zebras. They have even been seen attacking a solitary lion. During the breeding season, the range of the pack becomes more limited, for the females move into dens. These are usually old holes made by wart-hogs or aardvarks. Here the young are born. When the pups are about five weeks old they are weaned, and emerge from the burrows to explore. But they are still too small to keep up with the pack, so they stay behind in the den, often guarded by their mother or other dogs, when the pack goes off to hunt. The returning hunters regurgitate meat for the pups and the guards.

The beginning of a stalk
*Hunting dogs may select their prey from nearly
2 kilometres away. When they get to within 500 metres
of it, they begin to stalk, ears back, head lowered.
Eventually the victim will spot them and turn to run.
Then the chase begins.*

response came not only from members of the cat and dog family. Other kinds of animals also came out on to the grasslands to hunt. One group of them was particularly slow and poorly armed so that for them teamwork and communication were even more important. Eventually, they became the most wily, artful and communicative of all the hunters on the plains. To trace their history, we have to return to the forest, for it was there that they had their origins, searching for fruit and tender leaves in the tops of the trees.

The end of the chase
*Hunting dogs can run at about 50 kph for long distances. A gazelle is faster, but it has less stamina
and the dogs are relentless. Once the chase has begun the dogs seldom fail to catch up with their
quarry eventually. Here a Thomson gazelle makes a last despairing leap over its pursuer. But it
was in vain. The dog turned, and a few seconds later the gazelle was dead.*

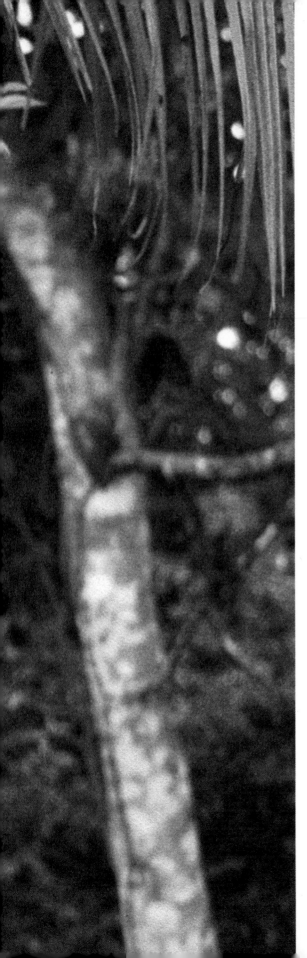

12. A LIFE IN THE TREES

*A sensitive nose and a turn of speed are not as valuable
in trees as good eyesight and grasping hands*

If you want to clamber about in trees, two abilities are extremely useful: a talent for judging distances, and a capacity for holding on to branches. A pair of forward-facing eyes that can both focus on the same object can provide the first; and hands with grasping fingers, the second. About two hundred living species have that pair of physical characteristics. They include monkeys, apes and ourselves and we, rather egotistically, call the whole group, the primates.

There is no doubt that the early insect-eating shrew-like mammals which were the ancestors of such diverse creatures as bats, whales and ant-eaters, also gave rise to the primates. Indeed, the tupaia, which serves as a reasonable model for those creatures, may itself be sufficiently close to the primates to be classified as one. It has two characteristics which weigh heavily with comparative anatomists when they consider the question. Its eye-sockets are completely encircled by bone; and its tongue is underlain by a cartilaginous sub-tongue. Whether these, together with several other more technical details, are enough to justify regarding it as a true primate is an argument for specialists. Most authorities agree, however, that the early ancestor of the group must have been a creature that looked very like a tupaia. But the tupaia does not yet have either of the primate hallmarks. Its hands have long separable fingers, but as the thumbs cannot be opposed to the fingers, it has not got a true grasp. Furthermore, each finger ends with a sharp claw, not a flat blunt nail. Its eyes are large and lustrous,

---

A runway through the jungle

A troop of squirrel monkeys make their way through the South American forest. Their long fingers enable them to grip the leaflets springing from either side of the slippery mid-rib of the palm frond. Their eyes, placed on the front of their heads, have overlapping fields of vision and so enable them to assess distance. The leader of the troop, looking forward intently, can therefore judge exactly how far it has to leap in order to reach the next tree. It was the perfection of these two talents of sight and grasp that enabled the first primates to become at home in the trees and that were, in the end, to provide the key to their further development.

A life in the trees

but they are placed on the sides of its long snout so that their fields only partly overlap. The animal, in fact, has not yet taken to climbing. One or two tupaia species, it is true, run along branches like squirrels, but most of them spend much of their time on or close to the ground in the forests of Southeast Asia where they live. With one exception they are all active during the day and when you watch them scuttling about through the

Sheltering and travelling on the forest floor
The ring-tailed lemur is as much at home on the ground as in the trees. The females with young (above) regularly settle down with their babies on the shaded forest floor during the heat of the day and indulge in bouts of relaxed grooming. When a troop moves through its territory, each member keeps its tail raised like a pennant, showing its companions just where it is.

318

undergrowth, it is easy to see that they rely very much on their sense of smell to guide them. They explore with their long noses, poking them into the leaf litter and under bark, sniffing beneath stones and into crevices.

Smell is also the basis of their social life. They mark their territories with little drops of urine and with scent from glands in their groin and neck. Their nose, which serves them so well, is very long with well-developed and extensive passages containing scent-receptors. It ends with two nostrils that are shaped like inverted commas and sur-rounded by bare moist skin like the muzzle of a dog. All in all, it has to be admitted that the tupaia seems at first sight to be a very unlikely creature to be related to a monkey. But there is a whole group of primates that share some of its characteristics and which are unmistakably monkey-like in other ways and these show how the transformation might have taken place. They are called the prosimians or 'pre-monkeys'.

The lemurs' battle of smells
Typical of them is the ring-tailed lemur of Madagascar. It is sometimes called the cat lemur, for it is cat-sized, with soft dove-grey fur, forward-facing lemon-yellow eyes and a long furry tail, handsomely ringed with black and white. One of its commonest calls even sounds like the miaow of a cat. But there the resemblance ends. It is not a hunter but, like many prosimians, largely vegetarian.

Ring-tails spend a lot of time on the ground in troops. Scent plays a very important part in their lives. Their nose is nowhere near as well developed as that of a tupaia, but it is still very fox-like in proportion and it too has a moist muzzle with bare skin around the nostrils. They have three kinds of scent glands. One pair on the inside of the wrist which opens through horny spurs; another high up on the chest, close to the armpits; and a third around the genitals. With these, the males and to a lesser extent the females, produce a barrage of signals. As the troop roisters through the forest, an animal will come to a particular sapling, smell it carefully, checking doubtless on which individual has been there before, then put its hands on the ground, hoist its rear as high as it can and rub its genitals several times on the bark. Often, within a minute or so, another individual will come along and repeat the performance. Males also grasp a sapling with both hands and swing their shoulders so that they twist from side to side. Their wrist spurs click against the bark, making deep scratches that are impregnated with their musk.

The male ring-tail uses scent not only as a signature but as a means of offence. When he prepares for battle with a rival, he vigorously folds his arms several times and rubs his wrists against his armpit glands. Then he brings his tail forward between his hind legs and in front of his chest and draws it several times between his wrist spurs so that it is loaded with scent. Thus armed, rivals face each other on all fours, lift their haunches high and thrash their splendid tails over their backs with the fur bristling, so that the smell is fanned forwards. Troops meeting on the frontier between their territories may do battle in this way for as long as an hour, hopping and skipping, squealing and yawning, and excitedly marking saplings with their wrist spurs.

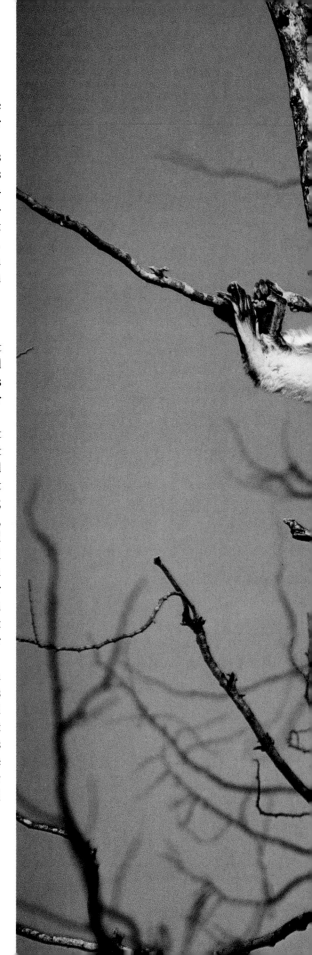

The ring-tail also spends a lot of its time in trees. Here, where it behaves in a much more monkey-like way, its primate characteristics show their usefulness. The eyes on the front of its head give it a binocular view. Its hands with their mobile fingers and opposable thumbs grasp branches, and fingers ending not in claws but in short nails that in no way interfere with its grip, are sufficiently dexterous to enable the animal to pluck fruit and leaves from the tips of branches. Although it is quite big, it can leap safely from tree to tree.

The ability to grip is put to good use by infant lemurs. Baby tupaias are deposited in a nest on the ground; their mother only visits them every two days perhaps to prevent attention being drawn to the vulnerable young. The baby lemur, however, is able to cling to its mother's fur and it does so as soon as it is born. So it travels with her wherever she goes and is provided with parental protection at all times. Ring-tails have one, occasionally two, babies at a time. Mothers often sit about in groups together, grooming and resting on the forest floor. The young will then scramble happily from one female to another; at times a particularly placid mother may have three or four youngsters clinging to her, while another female may lean over and affectionately lick the lot of them.

The ring-tails' limbs all have grasping digits and are all about the same length, so that when they run on the ground or along a branch, they do so on all fours. There are, however, over twenty different kinds of lemurs in Madagascar and most of them spend nearly all their time in trees. The sifaka, a beautiful creature with a pure-white fur a little larger than the ring-tail, has become a specialist in jumping. Its legs are considerably longer than its arms and enable it to leap four or five metres from one tree to another. The price it pays for this spectacular feat is the inability to run on all fours. On the few occasions that it does come down to the ground, the shortness of its arms leaves it with no alternative but to stand upright and it hops with both feet together, using much the same sort of action as it does when jumping from tree to tree.

Sifakas have scent glands beneath their chins: they mark their territory by rubbing them on an upright branch and then reinforce the effect by dribbling urine over the bark, wriggling their hips and slowly drawing themselves up the branch as they do so.

The most arboreal of all the lemurs – it hardly ever comes down to the ground – is a close relation of the sifaka, the indri. It is the biggest of all living lemurs with a head and body nearly a metre long. It is boldly marked with a variable black and white pattern and its tail is reduced to a tiny stump hidden in its fur. Its legs are even longer in proportion than those of a sifaka, the big toes are widely separated from the rest and about twice the length, so that each foot resembles a huge caliper with which the animal can grasp even thick trunks. It is the most magnificent jumper of all, launching itself with an explosive straightening of the hind legs and travelling through the air, torso upright, in soaring bounds which it can repeat again and again so that it seems to bounce

The long-legged leapers
Sifakas greatly relish the warmth of the sun. Morning and evening they climb to the tops of the trees and turn to face its rays, stretching out their arms to expose the sparsely furred inside surfaces in postures that lead the local people in Madagascar to maintain that these lemurs are worshippers of the sun.

its way from trunk to trunk through the forest.

Indris also use scent in marking the trees, though to a much lesser extent than the ring-tail – apparently smell does not play such a major part in their lives. Instead they have another way of proclaiming their ownership of territory. They sing. Every morning and evening, a family fills its patch of forest with an unearthly wailing chorus. Each individual joins in and draws breath in its own time, so that the sound continues unbroken for minutes on end. When they are alarmed, they lift their heads and trumpet a different hooting call which carries for great distances through the forest.

The indris' use of sound seems a very appropriate way of laying claim to an arboreal territory but of course, does have one disadvantage. It is extremely indiscreet. It gives away your presence and position to any predator that might be seeking you. Up in the branches, this does not trouble the indri. No natural enemy can reach it there and so it can sing with impunity.

Although the ring-tail, sifaka, indri and several other Madagascan lemurs are active during the day, their eyes have a reflecting layer behind the retina which increases the ability to see in very dim light. This is a characteristic of animals that move at night and strong evidence that these lemurs were nocturnal until quite recently. Many others of their relatives in Madagascar still are.

The gentle lemur, which is about the size of a rabbit, lives in holes in trees. It sits beside the entrance during the day, peering about myopically. When darkness comes, it becomes a little more lively, clambering around with a comic slow-motion deliberation which it seems unable to shake off no matter how dire the emergency. The smallest of the group is the mouse lemur, with a snub nose and large appealing eyes, that scampers through the thinnest twigs. The indri has a closely related nocturnal equivalent, the avahi, very similar in appearance and size except that its fur, instead of being black and white is grey and woolly. Oddest and most specialised of all is the aye-aye. Its body is about the size of that of an otter, it has black shaggy fur, a bushy tail and large membranous ears. One finger on each hand is enormously elongated and seemingly withered, so that it has become a bony articulated probe. With this the aye-aye extracts beetle larvae, its main food, from their holes in rotten wood.

Fifty million years ago, there were lemurs and other prosimians not only in Madagascar, but in Europe and North America. Around thirty million years ago, after the Mozambique Channel developed, separating Madagascar from the continent of Africa, more advanced primates evolved, which also lived in trees and fed on fruit and leaves and were thus in direct competition with the lemurs. They never reached Madagascar however. There, protected by the moat of the Indian Ocean, the lemurs continued to live unchallenged, producing the variety of forms that exist there today together with many recently extinct species – one the size of a chimpanzee – that we only know from fossils. Elsewhere, for the most part, they lost the competition with the monkeys. But not totally, for all living monkeys, with the single exception of the South American douracouli, are only active during the day. Those prosimians that were nocturnal did not have to cope with a head-on confrontation and some still survive.

322

A ferocious nocturnal hunter
The tarsier (right), hunts at night, scanning the forest with its huge eyes. This one's pupils, reacting to the light shining on them, have contracted to tiny points, but in darkness they open so wide that the iris becomes no more than a narrow ring around the rim of the eye. With such a wide aperture to its eye, the animal can distinguish its prey even in near-blackness. Tarsiers are almost entirely meat-eaters. This one has caught a cicada, but they will also pounce on small birds, lizards, rodents and even catch small fish.

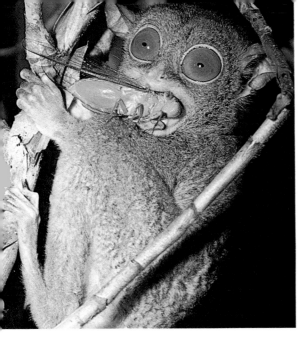

The prosimian with gigantic eyes

In Africa, there are several kinds of bush baby, very similar to mouse lemurs, as well as the potto and the more lissome angwantibo. These last two parallel the gentle lemurs and, like them, move with a grave deliberation. In Asia, there are two medium-sized nocturnal prosimians – a spindly creature, the slender loris from Ceylon, and the rather larger and plumper slow loris. Although all these creatures have quite large eyes, they still signpost their trees with scent and use it for route-finding in the dark. Their marks are made with urine, but since all of these animals are relatively small and live among twigs rather than tree trunks, this poses a problem of placement. A jet of urine might easily miss the intended spot, sprinkle another branch or simply fall uselessly to the ground. So they urinate on their hands and feet, rub them together and then enthusiastically plant pungent handprints throughout their territory.

One more prosimian lives in the forests of Southeast Asia, the tarsier. It is the size and shape of a small bush baby. It has a long near-naked tail tufted at the end, greatly

The lethargic loris

The slender loris (left) and the slow loris (above) both move with exaggerated slowness and seem physically unable to hurry, but, on occasion, they can suddenly lurch forward and deliver a swift and crunching bite.

elongated leaping legs and long-fingered grasping hands. But the briefest glimpse of its face is enough to show that it is a very different creature from the bush baby. It has gigantic glaring eyes. They are 150 times bigger in proportion to the rest of its body, than our own. Indeed, judged in that way, they are the biggest eyes owned by any animals anywhere. They bulge from their sockets and are fixed in them, so that the little creature cannot give a sidelong glance – as we can – or look out of the corner of its eye. Instead, if it wants to see something to one side, it has to turn its whole head, a manoeuvre that it performs with the same unsettling ease as the owl and for the same reason, swivelling its head through 180° to look directly backwards over its shoulder blades. In Borneo, the local people believe that it can turn its head, even more amazingly, through a complete circle and conclude that the attachment of head to body is therefore much less secure than in other animals. Being at one time enthusiastic headhunters, they thought that the sight of a tarsier in the forest was a sign that a head would be soon lost – a good omen if you were setting out on a headhunting raid but not so good if you had been planning to remain peaceably inside your longhouse.

As well as these spectacular eyes, the tarsier has paper-thin ears, like those of a bat, that can be twisted and crinkled so as to focus on a particular sound. With these two highly developed sensory organs it hunts at night for insects, small reptiles and even fledgling birds. It rests, usually with its torso upright, clinging to a vertical twig. A beetle, rustling clumsily through the leaves on the forest floor, will quickly attract its attention. The head makes a sudden swivel and a nod downwards. The mobile ears twist forward. The beetle blunders on. Then swiftly, in one leap, the tarsier springs downwards, grabs the beetle with both hands and sinks its teeth into it with an expression of ferocious relish, shutting its huge eyes with each crunch of its jaws.

It marks its territory with urine, but after watching it hunt, it is tempting to believe that vision is just as important to it as the sense of smell. A look at its nose not only confirms this but reveals that the animal is quite distinct from all other prosimians. For one thing, the eyes are so huge that there is little room in the front of the skull for the nose itself and the internal nasal passages are very much reduced in comparison with, say, a bush baby's. The nostrils are not comma-shaped nor are they surrounded by bare moist skin, as are the noses of lemurs and other prosimians. In this it resembles monkeys and apes and it is tempting therefore to see the tarsier as representing an ancestral form from which all the higher primates are descended. Indeed, this was once held to be the case. Today it is argued that this little creature is so specialised a leaper and nocturnal hunter that it could hardly have given rise directly to monkeys. Nonetheless, it is seen as a close relative of those early primates which, fifty million years ago, spread widely through the world displacing most of the prosimians and ultimately populating both the Old World and the New with monkeys.

Monkeys differ significantly from all the prosimians, except the tarsier, in that their world is dominated not by smell but by sight. Clearly it is very important for creatures of any size living in trees and, on occasion, jumping between them, to be able to see where they are going. So daylight suits them better than darkness and all monkeys,

The colourful monkeys

The monkeys' excellent eyesight provides them with colour vision so they can use colour to proclaim the identity of their species and to make immediately evident the difference between sexes. This they do to a spectacular degree with vividly coloured hair and special patches of pigmented bare skin. They are, in fact, the most colourful of mammals.

RED UAKARI, SOUTH AMERICA (ABOVE)   DE BRAZZA'S MONKEY, AFRICA (BELOW)

except for the douracouli, are active at that time. Their eyesight is better than that of prosimians. Not only do they see in depth, they have greatly improved colour perception. With this accuracy of vision they can judge the ripeness of distant fruit and the freshness of leaves. They can detect the presence in the trees of other creatures which, in a monochrome world, might be invisible. And they can use colour in their communications between one another: monkeys, because their colour-vision is so good, have themselves become the most highly coloured of all mammals.

In Africa there lives de Brazza's guenon which has a white beard, blue spectacles, orange forehead and black cap, the mandrill with a scarlet and blue face, and the vervet monkey, the males of which have startling blue genitals; in China, the snow monkey

DOUC LANGUR, S.E. ASIA (ABOVE)   MANDRILL, CENTRAL AFRICA (RIGHT)

GRIVET, CENTRAL AFRICA

BLACK HOWLER MONKEY, S. AMERICA

SPECTACLED LEAF-MONKEY, S.E. ASIA

RHESUS MACAQUE, INDIA

STUMP-TAILED MACAQUE, S.E. ASIA

DIANA MONKEY, WEST AFRICA

The unique night monkey

The douracouli is one of the most primitive of true monkeys. Alone of the whole group, it is active at night and has particularly large eyes which enable it to gather fruit in the darkness and even to catch insects.

TWO PATHS OF EVOLUTION

Monkeys of Africa and Asia have noses with downward-facing nostrils, while monkeys of South America have nostrils facing sideways – one of the differences indicating separate evolution.

Asian monkey   *South American monkey*

with a metallic golden coat and an ultramarine face; in the Amazon forests, the uakari with a scarlet naked face. These are among the most spectacularly costumed monkeys but a great number of other species also possess coloured fur and skin. With these adornments they advertise and threaten, proclaim their species and identify their sex.

They also use sound in a similarly extravagant way, for up in the trees, leaping acrobatically through the branches, they are beyond the reach of any predator except perhaps an eagle and need have little inhibition about revealing their presence. Howler monkeys in South America sit morning and evening, and sing in chorus. Their larynx is extraordinarily large and their throats swell into resonating balloons. The resulting chorus can be heard for several kilometres and is said to be the loudest noise produced by animals of any kind. But all monkeys have a varied repertoire of noises. There is no such thing as a dumb monkey.

The monkeys that became isolated by the sea

The monkeys that reached South America and became isolated there when the isthmus of Panama sank beneath the sea, have developed very much along their own lines. That they all are derived from one common stock is deduced from the number of anatomical features they have in common, including yet another detail of those revealing characteristics, the nostrils: all South American monkeys have flat noses with widely spaced nostrils opening to the side whereas monkeys in the rest of the world have thin noses with forward or downward pointing nostrils.

One South American group, the marmosets and tamarins, still use scent a great deal in communication even though they are active during the day. The males gnaw the bark of a branch and then soak it with urine. But they also have extremely elaborate adornments – moustaches, ear-tufts and wig-like crests – which they flaunt during their social encounters; and they threaten one another with high-pitched twittering calls. Their manner of rearing their young also, like their scent-marking, seems primitive, for it is reminiscent of lemurs. The infants readily move from adult to adult and often congregate on a particularly long-suffering and patient father.

Marmosets are the smallest of all true monkeys and seem to have moved from the basic monkey way of life to take up an existence that is more like that of a squirrel than a primate, eating nuts, catching insects and licking sap from bark gnawed by their special forward-pointing incisors. The pigmy marmoset has a body length of only ten centimetres. Since they are so small, they tend to run along branches rather than clamber between them and keep their foothold on the bark with claws. This might also appear to be a direct inheritance from their primitive insectivore ancestors but it seems to be a recent reversion, for the embryonic marmoset begins to develop monkey nails on its fingers and only at a later stage in its development do they change into claws.

The marmosets, however, are exceptional. Most monkeys are very much larger than they. Indeed, the primates, throughout their evolutionary history, show a tendency to increase in size. It is not easy to understand why this should be. Perhaps it is that in disputes between rival males, a bigger animal is likely, from sheer size and muscle and

The miniature marmosets

Tiniest members of the whole monkey tribe, marmosets are in some ways very squirrel-like. They scamper about in the branches, maintaining their foothold as much with their sharp nails as with their grasp. Many, like the golden lion marmoset (above) and the cottonhead tamarin (far left), are brilliantly coloured. The pigmy marmoset (left) is the smallest primate of all, weighing only 85 grams.

327

speed, to win the day and so pass on the tendency to grow large to its offspring. But greater weight makes increased demands on those grasping hands and the South American monkeys have developed a unique way of supplementing them. They have turned their tail into a fifth grasping limb. It is equipped with special muscles so that it can curl and twine, and at the end its inner surface has lost its hair and developed a ridged skin like that on its fingers. So powerful is it that a spider monkey can hang by its tail while gathering handfuls of fruit with both hands.

African monkeys, for some reason, have never developed their tail in such a way. They use it for other purposes. They extend it horizontally when they run along branches, as an assistance in balancing. When they jump, they swing it in such a way that it has some aerodynamic function, helping an individual to change its trajectory so that to some degree it can control where it lands. Even so, it is difficult to believe that the African monkey's tail is as useful to it as the prehensile tail of its South American cousins. Maybe the failure of the African monkeys to use their tail as a climbing aid has meant that, as they grew larger, they found life in the trees increasingly awkward and insecure and so began to spend more time on the ground. It is certainly a fact that there are no monkeys in the New World that are ground-living, whereas in the Old World there are many.

Down on the ground, the monkey tail seems to have less value. Baboons carry theirs with a droop halfway along the length, almost as though it is broken. Their close relatives, the drill and mandrill, have tails that are reduced to a tiny stump. And the same thing has happened in the macaque family.

The most successful monkey – the macaque

The macaque is one of the most successful and versatile of all primates. If you wanted to pick a monkey that was bright, adaptable, versatile, resilient, enterprising, tough and capable of surviving in extreme conditions and taking on all comers, the macaque would win hands down. There are about sixty different species and subspecies and between them they stretch halfway around the world, having been stopped only by the Atlantic Ocean at one end of their range and the Pacific at the other. One group lives on Gibraltar, the only non-human primate resident in the wild in Europe. Admittedly, it is questionable how wild they are. During the past two hundred years, the British garrison there has regularly imported more from North Africa every time the colony has become reduced in numbers. They were there before the British came, as long ago as Roman times, and it seems that even then men ferried them across the straits as pets. Nonetheless it is a tribute to the macaque that it has managed to survive on the Rock, one way or another, for so long. Another macaque species, the rhesus, is one of the commonest monkeys in India, often living around temples where it is held to be sacred. Farther east still, a species has become an able swimmer, paddling and diving in the

---

A leaf-eating specialist

One group of monkeys, which includes the langur of Asia (left) and the colobus of Africa, have specialised in eating leaves. Their molars have high ridges so that they can grind the leaves to pulp, and they have multi-chambered stomachs three times the size of those of other monkeys. After feeding, they spend long periods sitting quietly in the tree-tops, digesting their meal.

Monkeys with five hands

The spider monkey's tail has such a firm grasp that it becomes, in effect, a fifth limb (right). Its owner can hang from it, unsupported in any other way, pick up objects with it, carry things with it, and even use it to throw things. The young spider monkey travels on its mother's back, gripping onto her not just with its hands but by wrapping its tiny tail around the base of hers.

A cautious wade

Spider monkeys are so completely at home in the trees that they hardly ever come down to the ground. When they do, they are able to walk upright by using their versatile tails as balancers, as this one is doing (above), gingerly wading across a river.

mangrove swamps in search of crabs and other crustaceans. In Malaysia, the pig-tailed macaque is trained to climb palm trees and pick coconuts for its human masters; and the most northerly of all monkeys is a macaque, living in Japan where it has developed a long and shaggy coat to protect it from the rigours of very cold winters.

Nearly all macaques spend a great deal of time on the ground. Their hands and eyes, perfected in response to an arboreal life, have pre-adapted them for success in a terrestrial existence. They also have the advantage of a third faculty which has not yet been mentioned – an enlarged and more complex brain.

This was the necessary accompaniment of the other two developments. The separate manipulation of the fingers required additional control mechanisms. The combination of images from two eyes to produce a single picture required integrating circuits. If monkeys were to use their fingers in grasping and investigating small objects, then there had to be the most accurate coordination between hand and eye and this necessitated connections between the two relevant control areas in the brain. Only one section is less used – that concerned with the sense of smell. When the monkey brain is compared with that of a lemur, it can be seen that this part, the olfactory bulbs, has become greatly reduced in size and swamped by a huge expansion of the cerebral cortex, the section of the brain which deals with, among other things, the capacity to learn.

The Japanese macaques provide fascinating evidence of how capable monkeys have become at learning. Several troops of them have been studied by Japanese scientists. One lives in the high mountains of northern Japan where in winter the snow lies thick. Observers watched the monkeys extend their range into a part of the forest that none of them had explored before. It contained some hot volcanic springs. The monkeys investigated and found that the warm water could provide a delicious bath. A few tried it. Soon the habit spread. Now all the monkeys there take hot baths every winter. Their curiosity and the adaptability that allowed them to incorporate the new activity into their regular behaviour are typical of the enterprise of the macaques.

Another group demonstrated it in an even more dramatic way. They live on a small islet, Koshima, in southern Honshu, separated from the mainland by a narrow but turbulent tidal race so that the community is, to a very large extent, a closed one. In 1952 a group of scientists began to study it. The animals, at first, were wild and shy, so in order to entice them out into the open, the investigators began to feed them with sweet potatoes. In 1953 a young $3\frac{1}{2}$-year-old female whom the observers knew very well and had named Imo, picked up a sweet potato as she had done many hundred times before. As usual, it was covered with earth and sand, but Imo, for some reason took it down to a pool, dipped it in the water and rubbed off the dirt with her hand. How far this action was a consequence of logical thought it is impossible to say, but the fact was that, having done it once, she made a habit of it.

A month later, one of her companions began to do the same. Four months later, her

---

A warm bath on a cold winter's day
This troop of Japanese macaques quickly learned that the warm volcanic springs in their territory could provide relief from the chill of a snowstorm. Unhappily, however, there is no food to be found in the water, so eventually the monkeys have to clamber out, their thick fur sodden, and plod dripping through the snow in search of something to eat.

Salted potatoes

A Japanese macaque on Koshima Island washes her sweet potatoes in sea water. Originally, the monkeys developed the technique because the potatoes were dirty, but now the whole troop washes the potatoes as a matter of habit, even though the roots are already clean.

mother did so. The habit spread among the members of the group. Some began to use not just freshwater pools but sea water. Perhaps they found the salty taste more pleasant. Today washing sweet potatoes in the sea is a universal habit. The only individuals that never learned were those that were already old when Imo made her first experiment. They were too set in their ways to change.

But Imo was not finished with her innovations. The scientists also regularly threw down handfuls of unhusked rice on the beach and trod them into the sand, reasoning that it would take the monkeys so long to pick out the grains there would be plenty of time to observe them. They had reckoned without Imo. She grabbed handfuls of the rice, sand and all, scampered away to a rock pool and threw them into the water. The sand dropped to the bottom but the grain floated and she skimmed it off with her hand. Once again the habit spread and soon everyone was doing it.

This ability and readiness to learn from your companions results in a community having shared skills and knowledge, shared ways of doing things – in short, a culture. The word is normally used in the context of human societies, but here, among the macaques of Koshima, we can see the phenomenon beginning in a simple form.

Feeding the Koshima macaques has led to another development. They are tough aggressive little creatures, with powerful teeth which they do not hesitate to use on one another. They are now so familiar with human beings that they are no longer intimidated by them. When a man arrives with a sack of sweet potatoes, they have no hesitation in trying to snatch pieces. It is hardly practical to hand out roots one at a time, so the researchers simply tip them on the beach and retreat. The macaques fall upon the pile grabbing a root with one hand, stuffing another in the mouth, and run off, hobbling three-footed. A few, however, do better. They gather up several roots, clutch them to their chests with both arms and then manage to run, standing upright on their hind legs, across the beach to a defendable place in the rocks. If a daily sack of sweet potatoes were to be a permanent feature of their lives over many generations, it is easy to see that the major share of food would go to those that were genetically endowed with the requisite balance and leg proportions to enable them to perform this trick with ease. These would be better fed, and dominate the group. They would reproduce more successfully and their genes would become widespread in the group. So, over a few thousand years, macaques might become increasingly bipedal. Such a change, indeed, did happen in Africa. To trace its origins, we have to go back some thirty million years.

At that time, one group of lower primates were increasing in size. This brought a change in the way they moved through the trees. Instead of balancing on the top of a branch and running along it, they began to swing along beneath it. Swinging successfully involves physical changes. Arms lengthen, for the longer they are, the better they can reach; the tail can no longer play any part in balancing and so it disappears; and the

Sorting rice from sand

A mother macaque, presented with a mixture of rice and sand, uses a sorting method devised by a female of her troop several decades ago. She throws it into a pool. The sand sinks, leaving the rice floating on the surface so that she can skim it off with her hand. She learned the technique from her parents, and her babe, clinging to her throughout the first months of its life, watches her do so and thus, in its turn, inherits the knowledge.

musculature and skeleton of the body changes in order to support an abdomen that is no longer slung beneath a horizontal backbone but strapped to a vertical one as to a pillar. Those changes produced the first apes.

Today four main kinds survive: the orang utan and the gibbon in Asia, the gorilla and chimpanzee in Africa.

The orang utans and gibbons of Asia

The great red-haired orang of Borneo and Sumatra is the heaviest tree-dweller in existence. A male may stand over $1\frac{1}{2}$ metres tall, have arms with a spread of $2\frac{1}{2}$ metres and weigh a massive 200 kilos. The digits on all four limbs have powerful grips, so that the animal is best described as being four-handed and the ligaments of the hip joints are so long and loose that an orang, particularly when it is young, can stick its legs out at astonishing angles. Plainly, they are excellently adapted for the arboreal life.

At the same time, their size does seem to be something of a handicap to them. Branches break under their weight. Often they are unable to get fruit they relish because it is hanging far out on a branch that would never support them. Moving from tree to tree can also cause problems. There is little difficulty if substantial branches from each tree overlap, but that is not invariably the case. The orang deals with that problem either by reaching out until he can clasp a stout branch, or by rocking the tree that he is in until it bends over far enough for him to scramble across.

Ingenious though these techniques may be they can hardly be reckoned easy or swift. Indeed, sometimes an old male gets so large that he apparently finds the whole process too exhausting and whenever he wants to travel any distance, he comes down and lumbers across the forest floor. There is also evidence that the arboreal way of life is fraught with danger for the orang. A study of adult skeletons showed, rather pathetically, that 34 per cent had, at one time or another, broken their bones.

The males, as they grow old, develop immense pouches which hang down from the throat like gigantic double chins – not simply fat, but true pouches that can be inflated with air. They extend far down the chest across into the armpits and right over the back to the shoulder blades. Although they may have been used by ancestral orangs as resonators to amplify their voice like howler monkeys, the modern orang does not sing. His most impressive sound is his 'long call', a lengthy sequence of sighs and groans which continues for two or three minutes. To produce it, he partly inflates his throat pouch and the call ends with a number of short bubbling sighs as the pouch deflates. But he makes this call infrequently, and most of his vocalisations consist of grunts, squeaks, hoots, heavy sighs and a sucking noise made through pursed lips. It is a varied repertory but a quiet one that can only be heard fairly close by. The animal more often than not is alone, and during these monologues he gives the impression of a recluse, mumbling and grumbling to himself in an absent-minded way. Males take up this solitary life as soon as they leave their mothers, travelling and eating by themselves and only seeking company when they briefly come together with a female to mate.

Female orangs are about half the size of their mates but they too are solitary animals

A rubber-jointed climber

A young orang utan spends the first year of its life clinging to its mother. When it does at last begin to move away from her, it does so very cautiously, clinging nervously to the swaying branches and vines and seldom letting go with more than one limb at a time.

An orang utan family

Orang utans are the most solitary of all apes. Male and female only come together for mating. Immediately afterwards, the male leaves to resume his lonely wanderings. The female, however, will have the company of her young for several years.

THE HUMAN FACE OF THE ORANG UTAN – 'MAN OF THE FOREST'

Infant

Adult female

Adult male

The face of the orang utan – meaning 'man of the forest' in Malay – looks remarkably human, particularly in the young. But as they grow older many male orang utans develop enormous cheek flaps and heavy throat pouches, the purpose of which is not fully understood.

GIBBONS: TRAPEZE ARTISTS OF THE TROPICAL FORESTS

Gibbons, the smallest of the apes, travel through the tropical forests by swinging hand over hand, with their legs drawn up out of the way. Other apes can also swing through trees, but no others do so as often or as well as the gibbons, which can travel at up to 10 kph. Gibbons live most of their lives aloft. When they visit the ground they walk upright with their long arms outstretched or folded above the head, to keep them out of the way.

The variable gibbon

There are six species of gibbon. The lar (above) may be either buff or black. The so-called black gibbon is born fawn and becomes black at about 6 months, but the females revert to fawn when they mature.

and travel through the forest accompanied only by their young. This preference for solitude may well be connected with their size. Orangs are fruit-eaters, and being so big have to find considerable quantities of it every day to sustain themselves. Fruiting trees however are uncommon and widely scattered through the forest, at widely varying intervals. Some only bear fruit once every twenty-five years. Others do so almost continuously for about a century but on one branch at a time. Yet others have no regular pattern and are triggered irregularly by a particular change in the weather such as the sudden drop in temperature that precedes a heavy thunder storm. Even when they do produce fruit, it may only hang on the tree for a week or so before it becomes over-ripe, falls or is stolen. So the orangs have to make long journeys, continually searching, and may find it more profitable to keep their discoveries to themselves.

The gibbons, also fruit-eaters, of which there are two main kinds and several species, have followed a very different line of development. Increasing size may have been the stimulus that made apes start to swing beneath branches but the ancestral gibbons subsequently exploited the new style of locomotion to the full by becoming smaller again. In the end they developed into even more accomplished acrobats than any balancing, branch-running monkey. A gibbon in motion in the tree tops is one of the most glorious sights the tropical forest has to offer. With a supple grace that is breathtaking, it hurls itself nine or ten metres across space, grabbing an isolated branch and swinging itself off again in another dazzling swoop through the air. The arms that enable it to do this are as long as its legs and torso combined, so long, in fact, that on the rare occasions that it comes down to the ground, they cannot be used as props or crutches, but have to be held above its head out of the way. Its versatile grasping primate hands have also become specialised at the cost of some of their manipulative abilities. Swinging at gibbon speed requires that the hands be used as hooks that can be latched swiftly on to a branch and then detached almost instantaneously. Thumbs get in the way, so they have moved down towards the wrist and become much reduced.

A life in the trees

*The gibbons are so perfectly at home in trees that they
almost never come down to the ground. They seldom
need to descend for water because they usually get all
the liquid they require from eating fruit or by licking
leaves and branches after a rainstorm. If that supply is
insufficient, they will clamber down a branch
overhanging a river, gingerly lean down to wet the back
of their hands and then suck the fur. They are probably
the fastest moving of all primates, and swinging from
their long arms they can hurl themselves across
12 metres of space to land safely in another tree. So
agile are they that they can even catch birds in mid-air.
Watching the grace and skill with which they move, it
is easy to imagine that they never make mistakes. In
fact, a survey of their skeletons in the museums of the
world has shown that a considerable proportion of them
have suffered broken bones at some time.*

SHORT THUMBS FOR TREE-SWINGING

Orang utan   *Gibbon*

Instead of running along
the branches of trees,
like monkeys, apes
swing from branch to
branch. This mode of
travel requires hands like
hooks, and so thumbs
have become shorter,
keeping them out of the
way.

As gibbons are small, there is usually enough fruit on a tree to satiate several of them, so it is practical for them to travel together and they live in tightly knit families. A pair is accompanied by up to four of their offspring of varying ages. Every morning, the family sings in chorus. The male starts with one or two isolated and tentative hoots, others join in, the group launches into an ecstatic song and finally the female takes over with a rising peal that gets faster and faster and higher and higher until it becomes a high trill of a tonal purity that no human soprano could ever challenge. The parallel with the indri of Madagascar is an obvious one. Because of their different ancestral histories, one creature uses its fore limbs as its major propellant, the other its hind. Otherwise, the tropical rain forest in different parts of the world has produced creatures that are remarkably similar – families of singing, vegetarian gymnasts.

The gorillas and chimpanzees of Africa
The two African apes, in great contrast to their Asian relations, are much more terrestrial in their habits. Gorillas live in central Africa, one form in the forests of the

The placid gorillas
A gorilla family sits peacefully grazing on wild celery and nettles in the misty rain forests of central Africa. Each group is ruled by a huge male (far left). Younger males (above) will remain with the group until they are sexually mature. Then they may either accept a subordinate role and become possible candidates for the leadership or go off to form their own group.

339

A life in the trees

Congo basin, another slightly larger one in the cool sodden moss-forests that cover the flanks of volcanoes on the borders of Rwanda and Zaire. Young gorillas often climb trees, but they do so rather gingerly and without the solemn universal-jointed confidence of orangs. This is hardly surprising. The gorilla foot cannot grasp in the way that an orang's can, so the arms have to provide the main means of hauling up the body. When gorillas descend, they do so feet-first, lowering themselves with their arms, sometimes sliding down, braking by pressing the soles of their feet flat on the trunk and showering moss, creepers and bark all around them.

The big adult males are so huge, weighing up to 275 kilos, that only the stoutest trees can support them. They climb rarely and do not have much reason to, for although the shape of their teeth and the nature of their digestive system suggest that they were once primarily fruit-eaters, like the orang, they now subsist very largely on vegetation that can be reached without climbing, such as nettles, bedstraw creeper and giant celery. Usually, they also sleep on the ground, making a bed among the flattened vegetation on which they have fed.

They live in family groups of a dozen or so, each being led by a great silver-backed patriarch, who has several adult females attached to him. They sit quietly grazing, ripping huge handfuls of stems from the ground with slow, irresistible sweeps of their immense hands, lolling among the dense nettles and celery, sometimes grooming one another. For the most part they sit in silence. Occasionally they exchange quiet grunts or gurgles and if an individual wanders away from the main group it makes a little belching sound every now and then so that the rest know where it is.

While the adults doze, the young play and wrestle and occasionally rear up on their hind legs to beat a quick tattoo on their chests, rehearsing the gesture the adults use in display.

The silver-back leads and protects his group. If he is frightened and angered by intruders he may roar defiance and even charge. A blow from his fist can smash a man's bones. Pestered by a younger rival, who may be trying to lure away one of the females of his group, he will even fight. But the bulk of his days are spent quietly and in peace.

Several groups of gorillas have been studied for many years and, through the patience and understanding of the scientists, have come to accept other people, provided they are properly introduced and behave in a proper fashion. Encountering a gorilla family and being allowed to sit with them is a moving experience. They are in many ways so like us. Their sight and sense of hearing and smell are closely similar to our own, so that they perceive the world in very much the same way as we do. Like us, they live in largely permanent family groups. Their life expectancy is about the same as ours and they move from childhood to maturity and from maturity to senility at very similar ages. We even share the same kind of gestural language and one that you must observe when you are with them. A stare is rude or, put in a less anthropocentric way, threatening – a challenge that invites reprisal. Keeping the head low and the eyes down is a way of expressing submission and friendliness.

The placid disposition of the gorilla is connected with its diet and what it has to do to

get it. It lives entirely on vegetation of which there is an infinite supply growing immediately to hand. As it is so big and powerful it has no real enemies and there is no need for it to be particularly nimble in either body or mind.

The other African ape, the chimpanzee, has a very different diet – and temperament. Whereas a gorilla may eat two dozen kinds of leaves and fruit, the chimpanzee samples two hundred or so and in addition, termites, ants, honey, birds' eggs, birds and even small mammals like monkeys. To do this, it has to be both agile and inquisitive.

Several groups of chimpanzees, living in the forests on the eastern shores of Lake Tanganyika, are being studied by a Japanese team and are now so accustomed to the presence of human beings that you can sit among them for hours at a time.

The size of their groups varies, but they are very much bigger than those of the gorilla and may contain as many as fifty animals.

Chimpanzees are adept climbers, sleeping and feeding in trees, but they habitually travel and rest on the ground, even in thick forest. There they move on all fours, their hands knuckle-down and their long stiffly-held arms keeping their shoulders high. Even when the group is settled and at ease on the ground, there is constant activity. Youngsters chase one another up trees and play tag and king-of-the-castle. One may practise bed-making, bending over branches in a tree-crown to build a platform, but it will probably tire of it before it is finished and scamper down and do something else.

The sexual bonds between individuals are variable. Some females and some males are monogamous. Other males will mate with many females, and the females them-selves, when their hind-quarters inflate into pink fleshy cushions and they become sexually receptive, often court and mate with numerous males. The tie between the young and their mothers is very close. Immediately after birth, the infant clings to its mother's hair with its tiny fists, though at first it is not strong enough to stay there for long without maternal support. It will remain close to its mother, riding on her back like

Climbing trees for security
Adult gorillas hardly ever climb trees, for they are too big to do so with ease and safety. Young ones, however, frequently do (left) and often sit like sentries keeping watch for intruders. Chimpanzees (above) are much smaller and they remain agile climbers throughout their lives. They nearly always seek a tree each evening in order to build a nest in its branches.

a jockey when the group travels, until it is about five years old. This close dependence, made possible by the baby's grasping hands, has a profound effect on chimpanzee society, for as a result the young learn a great deal from their mother and she is able to keep a close eye on them as they grow up, supervising what they do, pulling them back from danger, showing them from her own example how to behave.

There is a constant interplay between adults in a resting group. New arrivals will greet one another, proffering the back of their outstretched hand to be sniffed and touched with the lips. Elderly males, grey and balding with bright eyes and wrinkled faces, often sit away from the main activity. They may be as much as forty years old and they often give an expression of short-tempered irascibility. They are treated with considerable respect, the females rushing up to them smacking their lips and effusively hooting. All of the group, young and old, spend hours grooming one another, carefully sorting through the coarse black hair, scratching the skin with a fingernail to remove a parasite or a scale. So anxious are they to perform this service to one another and so pleasurable do they find it that sometimes a chain of five or six individuals may form, each absorbed in grooming another. It has become a truly social activity and a gesture of friendship.

One way or another, the group investigates everything around it. A log smelling odd is carefully sniffed and probed with a finger. A leaf may be plucked, scrutinised with the greatest care, explored with the lower lip and gravely handed to others for a similar examination; and then thrown away. The group may visit a termite hill. On the way there, an animal will break off a twig, trim it to a particular size and strip it of its leaves. On arriving at the termite hill it pokes the twig into one of the holes. When it pulls it out again, it is covered with soldier termites that have gripped it with their jaws in an attempt to defend the nest against the intrusion. The chimp draws the stem through its lips, taking off the insects and eating them with relish. Chimps not only use tools but make them.

The move made so long ago by the early primates from a ground-based scent-dominated often nocturnal existence, to a life in the trees, led to the development of grasping hands, long arms, stereoscopic colour vision and increased brain size. With the aid of these talents, the monkeys and apes have made a great success of their arboreal life. But those of them that subsequently returned to the ground, whether it was because of increasing body size or some other reason, found that these very talents could be deployed in their new situation in a manner that opened up fresh possibilities and led to further changes. The enlarged brain led to an increase in learning and the beginnings of a group culture; the manipulative hand and the coordinated eyes made possible the use and manufacture of tools. The primates that are practising these skills today, however, are in essence repeating a process that another branch of their family started soon after the ancestral apes first appeared in Africa twenty million years ago. It was this branch that eventually stood upright and developed their talents to such a degree that they came to dominate and exploit the world in a way that no animal had ever done before.

The dexterous hands of the chimpanzee

The chimpanzee did not become a specialised swinging gymnast like the gibbon, and so kept a thumb that could be opposed to its fingers and used not only to grasp but also to pick up small objects. Its hand has therefore remained a marvellously versatile tool for grooming others, for exploring its surroundings in general and for manipulating what it finds.

A MOTHER CLEANS HER INFANT (ABOVE)

HOLDING ON (BELOW)

A MEAL OF SUGAR CANE (ABOVE)

AN INFANT GROOMS ITS MOTHER (BELOW)

A SENIOR MALE GROOMS A FEMALE (RIGHT)

13. THE COMPULSIVE COMMUNICATORS

One species of animal suddenly exploded in numbers, and in a few short millennia overran the earth

Homo sapiens has suddenly become the most numerous of all large animals. Ten thousand years ago, there were about ten million individuals in the world. They were ingenious, communicative and resourceful, but they seemed, as a species, to be subject to the same laws and restrictions which govern the numbers of other animals. Then, about eight thousand years ago, their number began to increase rapidly. Two thousand years ago it had risen to three hundred million; and a thousand years ago, the species began to overrun the earth. Today, there are over four thousand million. By the turn of the century, on present trends, there will be over six thousand million. These extraordinary creatures have spread to all corners of the earth in an unprecedented way. They live on the ice of the Poles and in the tropical jungles on the equator. They have climbed the highest mountains where oxygen is cripplingly scarce and dived down with special breathing devices to walk on the bed of the sea. Some have even left the planet altogether and visited the moon.

Why did this happen? What power did man suddenly acquire that turned him into the most successful of all species? The story starts five million years ago on the plains of Africa. The grass- and scrub-covered landscape was then much as it is today. Some of the creatures that lived there were giant versions of modern species – a pig as big as a cow with tusks a metre long, an immense buffalo, and an elephant standing a third again as tall as the one that is found there now – but others were very like contemporary species – zebra, rhinoceros and giraffe. There were also ape-like creatures about the size

---

The key to the growth of knowledge
The bushmen of the Kalahari Desert are an ancient race of nomadic hunters who once roamed widely over southern Africa. Like Stone Age man, they painted elegant, vivid images of the animals they hunted on the rocks of their territory. It was early man's graphic talent, born of dextrous fingers, sharp vision and a soaring imagination, that ultimately enabled mankind to transcend the physical, biological ways of passing on the lessons of experience to future generations, and to do so independently of his body or even his presence, in writing.

An ice desert

The Eskimoes, an Asiatic people, manage to survive in the snow fields and ice-floes of the Arctic on a diet of almost nothing but meat.

Fatal moment

Birds have to come down to earth to lay their eggs; seals must put their noses above water to breathe. Both moments give the Eskimo hunter his patiently awaited chance to catch his food.

of chimpanzees. They were descendants of a forest-living ape that had been widespread through not only Africa but Europe and Asia about ten million years ago. The first fossils of the plains-living ape were discovered in southern Africa and it was accordingly named Australopithecus, Southern Ape, but now several more kinds have been discovered in Africa and a great deal of work is going on in an attempt to disentangle their genealogies. Every time a fresh piece of fossil evidence is unearthed, the debates are renewed with great intensity, for all researchers are agreed that among these creatures are the ancestors of modern man. As a group, they can be conveniently called ape-men.

They were not abundant and their fossilised bones are rare, but enough have been found to give a fairly clear idea of what they were like in life. Their hands and feet resembled those of their tree-climbing ancestors and were very good at grasping things with nails on the digits, not claws. The limbs were not particularly well suited to running and were certainly not nearly as effective for that purpose as those of either the antelopes or the carnivores. Their skulls also show clear signs of their forest-dwelling past. The eyes, as can be judged from the sockets, were well developed. Clearly sight was of great importance for these animals as it is for all monkeys and apes. By contrast their sense of smell must have been relatively poor, for the skulls have short nasal clefts. The teeth are small and rounded and not well suited to grinding grass or pulping fibrous twigs. Neither do they have shearing blades, like those of a carnivore. On what, therefore, did these creatures feed out on the plain? They may have grubbed up roots and gathered berries, nuts and fruit, but they also, in spite of the inadequacies of their anatomy, became hunters.

The structure of their hip bones shows that, right at the beginning of their colonisation of the plains, they began to stand upright. The tendency towards a vertical torso was already present among the tree-living primates that used their hands for plucking fruit and leaves. Many of these had also been able to stand up on their hind legs for short periods when they descended to the ground. For a life on the plains, however, a permanent upright posture must have been very useful. The ape-men were small, defenceless and slow, compared with the predators of the plains, so advance warning of the approach of enemies must have been of the greatest importance and the ability to stand upright and look around might make the difference between life and death. It would also have been of great value in hunting. All the predators on the plain – lions, hunting dogs, hyenas – gather a great deal of information from smell. They keep their noses to the ground. But for the ape-men, sight was the most important sense as it had been in the trees. There was more to be gained from getting the head high and looking into the distance than there was from sniffing a patch of dusty grass. The patas monkey, that spends almost all of its time in open grassland, adopts just such tactics, standing up on its hind legs whenever it is alarmed.

The upright stance is certainly not a way of achieving speed. If anything, it must have slowed down the ape-men. A highly-trained human athlete, probably the best two-legged runner there has ever been among primates, can barely maintain a speed of 25 kilometres an hour for any distance, whereas monkeys, galloping on all fours, can go twice as fast. But bipedalism did bring one further advantage. The ape-men had hands with a precise and powerful grip, developed by their ancestors in response to the demands of a tree-climbing life. If they stood upright, these hands could be ready at all times to compensate for the lack of teeth and claws. If the animals were threatened by enemies they could defend themselves by hurling stones and wielding sticks. Faced with a carcass, they might not be able to open it with their teeth as a lion could do, but they could cut it open using the sharp edge of a stone, held in the hand. They could even take one stone, strike it against another and so shape it. Stones deliberately struck in such a way have facets on them that are quite different from those on stones that have been chipped by rolling in streams or split by frost. They can thus be identified and many such have been found associated with the skeletons of ape-men. The animals had become tool-makers. So ape-men claimed a permanent place for themselves in the community of animals on the plains.

This state of affairs lasted for a very long time, probably as much as three million years. Slowly, generation after generation, the bodies of one line of ape-men became better adapted to the plains-living life. The feet became more suited to running, lost their ability to grasp and acquired a slight arch. The hips changed, the joint moved towards the centre of the pelvis to balance the upright torso, and the pelvis itself became more bowl-shaped and broader to provide a base for the strong muscles running between pelvis and spine that were needed to hold the belly in its new upright position. The spine developed a slight curve so that the weight of the upper part of the body was better centred. Most importantly, the skull changed. The jaw became smaller and the forehead more domed. The brain of the first ape-men had been about the same size as that of a gorilla, around 500 cubic centimetres. Now it was double the size. And the animal grew to a height of over a metre and a half. Science has given this creature a name that reflects its new stance and height – Homo erectus, Upright Man.

He was a much more skilled tool-maker than his predecessors. Some of the stones he chipped were carefully shaped with a tapering point at one end and a sharp edge on either side, and were of a size that fitted neatly into the hand. Evidence of one of his successful hunts has been unearthed at Olorgesailie in southwest Kenya. In one small area, lie the broken and dismembered skeletons of giant baboons of a species that is now extinct. At least fifty adult animals and a dozen young appear to have been slaughtered here. Among their remains are hundreds of chipped stones and several thousand rough cobbles. All are of rock that does not occur naturally within 30 kilometres of the site. The implications are several. The way the stones have been chipped and shaped establishes that the hunters were Upright Men. The fact that the stones come from a distant site suggests that the hunts were premeditated and that the hunters had armed themselves long before they found their prey. Baboons, even the smaller living species, are very formidable creatures with powerful fanged jaws. Few men today, without firearms, would be prepared to tackle them. The numbers killed at Olorgesailie suggest that such hunts were regular team operations demanding considerable skill. Upright Man was clearly, by now, a very formidable hunter indeed.

A partnership between man and dog

The Eskimoes domesticated wolves many centuries ago, probably by taking newly born pups and rearing them with their own families. Wild wolves live in packs and obey their leader. That is what the Eskimo hunter became to his husky dogs. At his command they pull his sledge. He, in return, provides food for them out on the ice-floes where it is so cold that meat freezes solid and has to be cut up with an axe.

The face becomes a means of communication

Did he use what we would recognise as a language to discuss his plans and carry out such attacks? Attempts have been made to deduce from his skull and neckbones the structure of the soft parts of his throat and the current view is that although he was capable of making noises considerably more complex than the grunts and screams of modern apes, his speech, if indeed we can call it that, was probably slow and clumsy.

However, he had another medium of communication at his disposal – gestures – and we can make some confident guesses as to what they were and what they meant. Human beings have more separate muscles in their face than any other animal. They make it possible to move the various elements – lips, cheeks, forehead, eyebrows – in a great variety of ways that no other creature can match. There is little doubt, therefore, that the face was the centre of Upright Man's gestural communication.

One of the most important pieces of information it transmits is identity. We take it for granted that all our faces are very different from one another, yet this is a very unusual characteristic among animals. If individuals are to cooperate in an organised team in which each has his own responsibilities, then it is crucial for those taking part to be able to distinguish one from another immediately. Many social animals, such as hyenas and wolves, do this by smell. Men's sense of smell, however, was much less informative than their sight, so their identities were proclaimed not by fragrant glandular secretions but by the shape of the face.

Since the features of the face are extremely mobile, they can also convey a great deal of information about changing moods and intentions. We still have little difficulty in understanding expressions of enthusiasm and delight, disgust, anger and amusement. But quite apart from such revelations of emotion, we also send precise messages with our faces – of agreement and dissent, of welcome and summons. Are the gestures we use today arbitrary ones that we have learned from our parents and share with the rest of the community simply because we have the same social background? Or are they deeply embedded in us and an inheritance from our prehistoric past? Some gestures, such as methods of counting or insulting, vary from society to society and are clearly learned. But others appear to be more universal and deep-seated. Did Upright Man, for example, nod agreement and shake his head in disapproval as we do? Clues to the answers can come from the gestures used by people from another society who have had no contact whatever with our own.

New Guinea is one of the last places in the world where such people might be found. Even there, very few can be considered to have escaped all influences of Western European man, for almost every part of the island has been explored, but ten years ago, one small patch of country remained unentered by outsiders in the forested mountains at the headwaters of the Sepik River. A pilot, flying over the area, had noticed in what everyone had assumed to be uninhabited territory, a few huts in clearings. The Australian administration, who at that time controlled the island, decided to discover who these unknown people were. A patrol was organised, led by a District Commissioner, and I was able to join it. A hundred men from the villages along the river were

recruited to carry stores and tents. At the last known village on one of the tributaries, the people, themselves little visited, told us that they knew that somebody lived in the mountains ahead, but no one there had ever met them, knew what language they spoke or even what they called themselves. The river people referred to them as the Biami.

After we had been marching through the mountains for two weeks, drenched by daily rains, living entirely on the food we carried with us, we found footprints. Two people were ahead of us and travelling fast. We followed them. When we broke camp in the mornings, we found their tracks in the forest nearby and knew that they had been sitting watching us the previous evening. That night we left gifts in the forest, but they were not touched. We called greetings in the language of the river people, but we did not know whether or not the Biami could understand it. In any case, there was no reply. This continued, night after night, until eventually we lost the trail. After three weeks, we had almost given up hope of making contact. Then one morning, we awoke to find seven men standing in the bush within a few yards of our tent. They were very small, and naked but for cane wrapped round their waist with sprigs of green leaves thrust through it in the front and at the back. Some had earrings and necklaces of animal bones. One carried a woven bag full of roots and fruit.

As we scrambled out of our tents, they stood their ground. It was an act of great trust and we tried to demonstrate as quickly and convincingly as possible that our intentions were friendly. The river men spoke to them, but the Biami understood nothing. We had to rely entirely on such gestures as we had in common, and it turned out that there were many of them.

We smiled – and the Biami smiled back. The gesture may seem an odd one as an indication of friendliness, for it draws attention to the teeth, the only natural weapon that a man has. But its essential element is not the teeth but the movement of the lips. In other primates, this is a gesture of appeasement, an indication by a young male chimpanzee, for example, to his dominant senior that he is not challenging authority. In the human species the gesture has become slightly modified by upturning the ends of the mouth and is used to convey welcome and pleasure. We can be sure that this expression has not been entirely learned from our parents and is part of our built-in repertoire of gesture because babies, born deaf and blind, will nonetheless smile when they are picked up to be fed.

We were anxious to extend our relationship with the Biami. We had brought goods for them – beads, salt, knives, cloth – but it seemed condescending and patronising simply to hand them out as gifts. We pointed to the net bag and raised our eyebrows questioningly. The Biami understood immediately and pulled out taro roots and some green bananas. We began to trade. Pointing at an object, touching fingers to indicate numbers, nodding our head in agreement, all these gestures were unambiguous. We all used our eyebrows a great deal. They are the most mobile features of the face. It is

A language of gesture
This New Guinea man had never met Europeans before. Even so, the meaning of his smiles and frowns was plain. But although he indicated numbers up to five with his fingers, he signalled eight with a tap on his elbow and eleven by touching his neck. These signs were not, like his smile, the inheritance of all mankind, but a tribal invention that had to be learned.

possible that they may serve to keep sweat from running in to the eyes but that does not explain their great mobility. Their main function must surely be as signalling devices. The Biami drew their eyebrows together to express disapproval. When they accompanied this by shaking the head, they made it unequivocally clear that they did not want the beads that we offered. By raising their eyebrows when they examined our knives, they expressed wonder. When I caught the glance of a man standing hesitantly at one side of the group and raised my eyebrows momentarily at the same time giving a slight backward jerk of my head, the Biami man did the same, a gesture that seemed to be a recognition and a happy acceptance of one another's presence.

This eyebrow flash is used all over the world. It works as well in a Fijian market as in a Japanese store, with Indians in the Brazilian jungle as in an English pub. Its precise meaning may vary from place to place but that such signals are so widespread and used by such disparate groups suggests very strongly that they are the common inheritance of humanity. They may well have been used by Upright Man as he planned his hunts, greeted friends, collaborated in the killing of prey and brought back the carcasses to the delight of his mate and children.

With this improved talent for communication and skill in making tools, Upright Man became more and more successful. His numbers increased and he began to spread. From southeastern Africa he moved into the Nile valley and northwards to the eastern shores of the Mediterranean. His remains have been found farther east in Java, and in China. Whether he migrated into Asia from Africa or whether these people were the descendants of an Asiatic ape-man is still a question which we do not have enough evidence to answer with confidence. Some of the African groups reached Europe. A few crossed over a land bridge that once connected Tunisia, Sicily and Italy. Others travelled eastwards round the Mediterranean and up north through the Balkans.

Upright Man was in Europe in some numbers about a million years ago. But about 600,000 years ago the climate changed. It started to get very cold. The shift was gradual and by no means steady and continuous. There were long periods when the weather ameliorated and the ice sheets advancing down from the north paused and temporarily retreated. But the overall trend was a great cooling. So much water locked up in the ice caps caused a lowering of the sea-level and the emergence of more land bridges, so that eventually men were able to spread into the Americas across the Bering Strait and down the island chains of Indonesia towards New Guinea and Australia.

The talent that separates man from the animals
In Europe, Upright Man must have felt the increasing cold very keenly. He had evolved in the warmth of the African plain and did not have the protection of thick fur, like the mammals that had lived in these cooler regions for a long period. Doubtless, many creatures, in such circumstances, would have retreated to warmer parts or simply died out. Man, being dexterous of hand and inventive of mind, did neither. He hunted the furred animals, stripped the skins from their dead bodies and used them himself. And he found shelter in caves.

The hunting artists
The earliest known representational designs ever made by man are those painted on the walls of caves in Western Europe. The oldest of them were made some 30,000 years ago. Nearly all represent the animals that were hunted – mammoths, wild cattle and horses. Some, like this bison (below) in the French cavern of Niaux, painted about 15,000 years ago, have arrow-like signs on them suggesting to some archaeologists that they were painted as part of hunting magic. The habit of painting on rock eventually spread all over the world. Five thousand years ago, when the Sahara Desert was fertile, men included their own portraits (right) among game such as giraffes and gazelles, but they also drew the cattle which, by this time, they were beginning to domesticate.

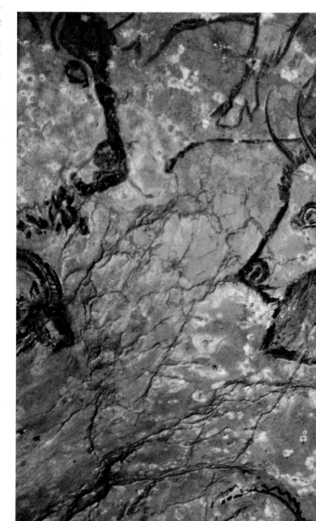

His living sites have been discovered in great numbers in southern France and Spain. Along the great limestone valleys of central France such as the Dordogne and in the foothills of the Pyrenees, the cliffs are riddled with caves and almost every one shows some sign of ancient habitation. From the objects that have been found in them, we know a great deal about these people. They used bone needles and sinew to sew clothes of skin and fur. They fished with carefully carved multi-barbed bone harpoons and hunted in the woods with spears tipped with stone blades. Blackened stones show that they had control of fire and they must have treasured it, for it gave them desperately needed warmth in the winter and enabled them to cook meat that their small teeth could not otherwise have chewed.

Their teeth, indeed, had become even smaller than those of their ancestors, but their cranium had expanded and was now as big as our own. Judging from casts taken from the inside of their skulls, that part of the brain that controls speech was fully developed, so it is reasonable to assume that these men now spoke a language that was fluent and complex. In short, as far as the skeletons alone are concerned, there is no significant difference between a man who lived in the caves of France 35,000 years ago and ourselves. Anthropologists, accordingly, have given these people the same name as they use, somewhat immodestly, for all modern humans – Homo sapiens, Wise Man.

THE ABORIGINES OF AUSTRALIA

This ancient race of hunter-gatherers live in a sun-scorched land where their extraordinary skills of observation and deduction enable them to survive with only the simplest tools. From them we can picture the way our forefathers lived 40,000 years ago.

The first true men living in Europe some 40,000 years ago left few material possessions behind them – blades and arrowheads of flint, bone fish hooks, crude grindstones and pestles. You might conclude, therefore, that their skills were elementary and their social lives of the simplest. The Aborigines of Australia show how unjustified such a deduction would be.

The Aborigines are a very ancient race. Superficially, they may seem to resemble Africans, but their black skin and gangling physique are direct adaptations to life in a tropical environment, and both groups almost certainly developed them independently. Other characteristics – their straight silky hair, often flaxen in their children, their

blood groups, the shape of their heads – indicate a different ancestry. Where they originated is still not known. It seems certain that they reached Australia from southern Asia by way of the island chain of Indonesia and that they arrived there over 20,000 and possibly as much as 30,000 years ago. At that time, all the rest of mankind was still, like them, finding its food by gathering fruits, leaves and roots and hunting wild animals.

Eventually, the Aborigines occupied the whole of Australia, from the tropical coral islands of the northern coast and the Barrier Reef, down to the grasslands and the cool dank eucalyptus forests of the south. Today, their numbers are greatly reduced and they have disappeared

from much of their former territories. Were it not for the written accounts of the early European settlers and the few collections of curios they made, the only evidence we would have of the extinct tribes would be a few stone tools and some bones – very much on a par, in fact, with the objects left behind by early man in Europe. But a few groups, living in the deserts of the interior, in land so riven and scorched by the sun that Europeans had no use for it, still survive to show us the richness and complexity of their ancient way of life.

Astonishing powers of deduction and memory

Their skill in hunting depends not so much on the sophistication of their weapons as on their extraordinary mental skills and physical endurance. Their powers of deduction and observation are astounding. A smudge in the sand can be sufficient to tell them not merely that some sort of animal passed that way, but just what it was, when it passed, whether it was fat or thin, what sex it was and what speed it was going. Their visual memory is so detailed and retentive that a man can recognise the individual footprints of other members of his group even if he has not seen them for years. The women, walking through the stony scrub, can recognise immediately the particular shape of a leaf that signals the existence, a metre deep in the sand, of a tuber full of water that could save a person's life, or the tiny differences in the body of an ant that mark it as the one which forcefeeds some of its workers with nectar and then stores them in underground galleries, living globules of the most delectable honey.

A drama from the beginning of the world
The myths of creation remain vivid in the minds of Aborigines, for the people re-enact them in long sequences of rituals that may take years to complete. Here, ancestral lizards, represented by men with lizards painted on their chests (left), are summoned for battle by the rainbow serpent, a painted wooden trumpet (above) which passes over them played by a devotee, sounding a deep, rasping drone.

So skilful are the Aborigines at gathering their food that except in the worst times, their lives are far from totally dominated by it. They have time for the maintenance of relationships among themselves that are far more complex than those of any people living in a modern city, so complex, in fact, that anthropologists still have great difficulty in working out the full ramifications and subtleties. Their imaginative lives, too, are extraordinarily rich, for they celebrate long cycles of rituals, some needing years for their completion, during which they describe, in chants and elaborate mime, the way in which the world was created, how all the individual creatures in it were formed and how man himself came into existence.

A variable people
All Aborigines are dark-skinned, but some are short and some tall, some have thick body hair and some almost none. Their noses may be wide-nostrilled or hooked, their hair reddish black or even flaxen. In fact, the Aborigines are no more uniform as a group than are Europeans.

The ancient weapons
Aborigines hunt with boomerangs and spears tipped with blades chipped from stone. They hurl a spear with the aid of a woomera, a length of wood with a peg which fits on to the butt.

The difference between the life of a skin-clad hunter leaving a cave with a spear over his shoulder to hunt mammoth, and a smartly dressed executive driving along a motorway in New York, London or Tokyo, to consult his computer print-out, is not due to any further physical development of body or brain during the long period that separates them, but to a completely new evolutionary factor.

Man has credited himself with several talents to distinguish him from all other animals. Once we thought that we were the only creatures to make and use tools. We now know that this is not so: chimpanzees do so and so do finches in the Galapagos that cut and trim long thorns to use as pins for extracting grubs from holes in wood. Even our complex spoken language seems less special the more we learn about the communications used by chimpanzees and dolphins. But we are the only creatures to have painted representational pictures and it is this talent which led to developments which ultimately transformed the life of mankind.

Its first flowering can be seen in those ancient European caves. The men who lived there ventured deep into the black holes that lead from the back of many of them, finding their way by the feeble flickering light of stone lamps filled with animal fat. There, in some of the most remote parts of the caverns, sometimes in passages and chambers that could only have been reached after hours of crawling, they painted designs on the walls. For pigments they used the red, brown and yellow ochres of iron, and black from charcoal and manganese ore. For brushes, they used sticks burred at the end, their fingers, and sometimes blew paint on to the rock, probably from the mouth. Sometimes the designs are engraved with a flint tool and there are a few examples of carving in the round, and modelling in clay. Their subjects were almost always the animals they hunted – mammoth, deer, horse, wild cattle, bison and rhinoceros. Often they are superimposed, one on top of the other. There are no landscapes and only very rarely human figures. In one or two caves, the people left a particularly evocative symbol of their visit, the image of their hands made by blowing paint over them so that the outline is left stencilled on the rock. Scattered among the animals, there are abstract designs – parallel lines, squares, grids and rows of dots, curves that some say represent the female genitalia, chevrons that might be arrows. These are the least spectacular of the designs but the most significant for what was to come.

Even now, we do not know why these people painted. Perhaps the designs were part of a religious ritual – if the chevrons surrounding a great bull represent arrows, then maybe they were drawn to bring success in hunting; if the cattle shown with swollen sides are intended to appear pregnant, then maybe they were made during increase rituals to ensure the fertility of the herds. Maybe their function was less complicated and the people painted simply because they enjoyed doing so, taking pleasure in art for art's sake. Perhaps it is a mistake to seek a single universal explanation. The most ancient of the paintings is thought to be about 30,000 years old, the youngest maybe 10,000. The interval between these two dates is about six times the length of the entire history of western civilisation, so there is no more reason to suppose that the same motives lay behind all these paintings than there is to believe that background music saturating a modern hotel serves the same function as a Gregorian chant. But whether they were directed at the gods, at young initiates or appreciative members of the community, they were certainly communications. And they still retain their power to communicate today. Even if we are baffled by their precise meaning, we cannot fail to respond to the perceptiveness and aesthetic sensitivity with which these artists captured the significant outlines of a mammoth, the cocked heads of a herd of antlered deer or the looming bulk of a bison.

Elsewhere in the world it is still possible to discover just what purposes rock painting can have to a hunting people. In Australia, the Aborigines still draw designs on rock that are, in many ways, very similar to the prehistoric designs of Europe. They are painted on cliffs and rock shelters, often in parts that are extremely difficult to reach; they are executed in mineral ochres; they are superimposed one on top of another; they include abstract geometrical designs and stencilled handprints; and very often, they represent creatures on which the aborigines rely for food – barramundi fish, turtles, lizards and kangaroo.

Some of these designs are repainted time and time again, in the belief that by keeping the image of the animals fresh on the rock they will continue to flourish in the surrounding bush. Elsewhere, men paint as an act of worship. The Walbiri people of the central desert believe that the world was created by a great spirit snake, the rainbow serpent, whose many-coloured trail appears in the sky after storms. The old men say that it lives in a hole at the base of a long sandstone cliff in the heart of the tribal territory. No man has ever seen the snake itself, though it sometimes leaves the marks of its passing in the sand. Many generations ago, the people painted the snake-god's image on the rock, a huge undulating curve in white ochre, outlined with red. Horseshoe shapes beside it, not unlike some of the geometric designs of prehistory, represent human beings who are descended from the snake. Beside them on the cliff are more symbols, parallel lines and concentric circles, dots and chevrons, that represent the footprints of ancestral animals, carpet snakes and spears.

These designs have been repainted regularly by generations of men. The process of doing so is, in itself, an act of worship, a communion with the snake god creator. The old Walbiri men went there regularly to chant the ancient myths and to meditate on their meaning. Relics of the snake, rounded stones engraved with abstract symbols, were kept in clefts in the rocks. The old men took them out reverently, anointed them with red ochre and kangaroo fat, and chanted. Young men used to be taken there to be initiated under the image of the snake, to be instructed in the meaning of the symbols, and to witness the reenactment of the legends in mime and song.

There is no reason to suppose that the Aborigines are any more closely related to the prehistoric cave dwellers of France than we are, but their way of life is still very close to that of the men of the Stone Age. Homo sapiens led such an existence, hunting animals and gathering fruits, seeds and roots everywhere in the world for many thousands of years. Such a life is hazardous and rough. Men, women and children are exposed to the pitiless sifting of an impersonal environment. The slow and the careless are likely to be

A forbidden sanctuary
The most sacred site on the land of the Walbiri people is this remote cliff. At one end (below), a cave runs into the rock. This, the men say, is the home of the most powerful of the creator spirits, the rainbow serpent. Above it, men have painted the snake's image and worshippers come to inscribe their own symbols beside it.

Cherishing the spirits
No one but fully initiated men may visit the snake rock. First, they must paint themselves (above). Then they may take out sacred stones, anoint them with ochre and fat, and so commune with the spirits (right).

Hunters of the tropical jungle

The Punan of Borneo are hunters who live in temporary shelters as they travel from place to place with their long wooden blow-pipes. Their darts are wrapped around the base with pith so that they fit the pipe exactly, and are tipped at the other end with poison. With this totally silent weapon, a Punan can bring down bird after bird without disturbing the flock.

killed by predators; the weak may starve; the old may fail to survive the torment of a drought. Those whose bodies were, by the chance of genetic variation, better suited to the conditions, had an advantage. They survived and reproduced, handing on that advantage to their children.

Skin colour and body shape adapt to climate

So the bodies of men responded to the impress of the world they lived in and made the most recent major physical changes to be incorporated in their genes. Those that lived in the tropics, like the Australian Aborigines and the Africans, had dark skins. Pigmentation may have been acquired several times, quite independently, so a black skin is not by itself an indication of a close relationship to another black skin. Its purpose is protection. The rays of the sun, in excess, can be very harmful. Beating on an unprotected fair skin, they can produce a cancer. Dark pigment, however, provides an effective shield.

Many people living in such environments, in Africa, India and Australia, also share another characteristic – thin, attenuated bodies. This shape provides a large area of skin surface in proportion to body weight, a greater expanse over which winds and evaporating sweat can cool the body.

In cold regions, the situation is reversed. The sun's rays, in moderate quantities, are important for health. Without them, the body cannot manufacture vitamin D, so in the north, where the sun is so often hidden, people like the Lapps of Scandinavia have fair skins. Eskimoes, living within the Arctic Circle, also have light-coloured skin and, in addition, a physique that is the opposite of the gangling tropical desert-dweller. They are short and squat, the shape with a low surface-to-weight ratio which retains heat.

Since such characters as these became fixed in the genes by natural selection, they remain apparent in individuals, generation after generation, no matter where they live, unless the processes similar to those that brought them into existence cause over many thousands of years further changes.

Communities who live by hunting and gathering still exist. The Aborigines and the African bushmen live in deserts. Other groups find all they need from the rain forests in Central Africa, and Malaysia. They all live in harmony with the natural world around them, altering it not at all and making do with what it immediately provides. Nowhere are they overwhelmingly numerous. Their expectation of life is short, their birthrate and the survival of their children are curbed by the scarcity of food and the hazards of their lives. Such has been the condition of man for almost all his existence. It is very close to the way Upright Man lived about a million years ago. And for about nine hundred and ninety thousand years afterwards, it was the life that he and his descendant, Homo sapiens, was to follow. Throughout that time, as far as we can judge, man's numbers increased by only about one tenth of one per cent each century.

Tribal splendour

The mammals and birds brought back by tribal hunters provide more than food. Man developed an appreciation of visual beauty very early in his history, as the Stone Age cave paintings vividly demonstrate, and tribal people all over the world, like this painted dancer from Xingu in central Brazil, continue to use feathers and fur from their prey to make themselves glorious.

HOW MAN MOULDED ANIMALS TO HIS OWN NEEDS

When primitive hunters first began selecting the most suitable animals for slaughter, they set man on the long evolutionary path that led to the domesticated herds of today. Some animals, such as sheep and cattle, were selected for food and clothing; others, particularly dogs, became man's working partners.

The first step towards domesticating animals may well have been taken about 10,000 years ago. Hunters realised that herds of grazing animals could be found regularly in particular places from where they could be driven into natural traps and easily slaughtered – down a rocky gorge or against the edge of a cliff or the margin of a lake. Such herds deserved to be cherished rather than exterminated, so the hunters would have done well to spare young and pregnant females and kill instead young males. In that way, they would ensure that there would still be animals to hunt the following year.

The discovery that the bones of sheep in some refuse tips of ancient settlements in Iraq are predominantly those of young males shows that such selective hunting was already being practised about 8500 BC. That was the first step towards selective breeding.

A modern nomadic people, the Lapps, illustrate very vividly the next stage in the process. Traditionally, these people are totally dependent on the herds of reindeer that move across the Arctic tundra. In the completely wild state, the young reindeer males fight between themselves and so move away from one another to collect their own

group of hinds and establish their own herds. But such small groups do not suit the Lapps. They greatly prefer herds several thousand strong which will keep them and their large families in meat, milk and clothing throughout the year. So the Lapp herdsmen prevent fights in the herd by lassoing the young males and castrating them in order that they will remain relatively docile and stay in the herd. But the Lapps take the process of selection a stage further. To that extent they parallel the early hunters weeding out young males. The males that they leave unmutilated are those that have the characteristics the Lapps particularly value – a strong, well-muscled body and a relatively unaggressive character. Those males can then pass on their traits to the calves and so the quality of the stock as a whole will be changed.

The Arctic tundra provides such poor grazing that the reindeer have to keep on the move to find enough vegetation to keep alive, and the Lapps have to follow them. But people living in a country with a richer pasturage would doubtless find it worth trying to prevent the herds from straying too far so that they themselves could lead a more settled life. The early hunters may have

therefore regarded a predisposition to stay in the same area as another very desirable characteristic in an animal, and selected for that as well. Some characteristics may have become perpetuated almost by accident. A vivid coat colour, for example, is a liability for creatures living in the wild, but not for those under the protection of man. So the piebald pattern, common among domestic creatures, may have become widespread simply because wild predators were prevented by man from pouncing on such conspicuous creatures and weeding them out.

Horses and dogs come under human control

By about 8,000 years ago, in many parts of the Middle East, sheep and goats, pigs and cattle had all been converted from wild timorous creatures into ones that habitually remained around man's settlements and were cared for by him. In the New World, the llama and the guinea pig were domesticated a little later, and about 5,000 years ago, in north-eastern Europe, man succeeded in taming the horse.

The origins of the domestic dog seem to have been slightly different from those of grazing animals. The dog

chose to associate itself with man, rather than the other way around. Morsels can be picked up around the camps of human hunters as well as from the kills of other powerful predators, and wolf-like dogs scavenged after human nomadic hunters from a very early date, just as jackals do around the kills of lions in Africa today.

In time, the association became habitual. Perhaps man's pleasure in keeping pets, which seems to be universal and deep-seated, was already present. Maybe women and children adopted orphan pups which grew up in human company and eventually adopted the dominant human male of the family as their leader just as, had they remained in the wild, they would have followed and obeyed the leader of their pack. Somehow, a hunting alliance between the two species was formed in which each partner contributed its own particular skills – a highly refined sense of smell and tracking abilities from the dog; weapons and planning and tactical skills from the man – and both shared in the spoils. And once again, by selecting and cherishing those individual dogs that suited them best, the human hunters began the selective breeding of their partners.

A domesticated survivor *The llama (left) is a South American camel that has been domesticated by the people of the Andes for centuries and no longer exists anywhere in the wild state.*

The beginnings of selective breeding by man
The Lapps (above) have for centuries followed the herds of reindeer that migrate across northern Scandinavia in search of grazing. Once a year they round them up, and castrate all the young males except those few they decide should continue to breed.

The revolution of the written word

Then, with dramatic swiftness, about eight thousand years ago, that began to change. In lands outside the forests and the deserts, the human population began to increase. The trigger may well have been a wild grass that grew then, as it still does, on the sandy hills and fertile river deltas of the Middle East. It bears numerous seeds, full of nourishment, that are easily plucked and winnowed from their husks. Doubtless man, as he hunted across the open lands, had gathered it and eaten it whenever he encountered it. But a change in his fortunes came when he realised that he need not rely on chance encounters with the wild plant. If he forbore to eat all the seeds that he gathered but planted them in a convenient place, he would no longer be forced to wander in search of the plant the following summer. He could settle down beside his plots and wait for the grain to sprout, stop being a gatherer and become a farmer, build himself permanent huts and live in villages. So he founded the first towns.

Uruk, in Syria, was built on what was then the marshy reed-covered delta of the Tigris and Euphrates Rivers. Now it is a desert. The town was a complex one. The people planted fields of grain around it and kept herds of goats and sheep. They made pottery, fragments of which still lie all over the site. And in the centre of the town, they constructed an artificial mountain out of baked mud-bricks, held together with plaited layers of reeds. The settled life led by the citizens of Uruk enabled them to make a further crucial advance in man's techniques of communication. People who travel perpetually have to keep their material possessions to a minimum. People who live in houses, however, can accumulate all kinds of objects. In the remains of one of the buildings at Uruk a small clay tablet, covered with incisions, was found. It is the earliest known piece of writing. No one yet knows exactly what it means. It appears to be a record of rations of food. The shapes seem to be based on the appearance of the objects they represent, but there is no attempt at naturalistic portrayals. The marks are simple diagrams that must have been recognised by people for whom they were intended.

When that tablet was baked, men turned the surge of evolution into a new course. Now an individual had a means of conveying information to others in a way that was independent of his presence or indeed of his continued existence. People elsewhere and generations unborn could now learn about his successes and his failures, his insights and his strokes of genius. If they had a mind to, they could sift through accumulations of humdrum facts and extract a seed of significance that could lead to wisdom.

Other communities elsewhere, in the valley of the Nile, the jungles of Central America and the plains of China, made similar innovations. The diagrammatic representations of objects became simplified and took on new meanings. By using them as puns, they could represent sounds. At the eastern end of the Mediterranean, people developed them into a comprehensive system with which they represented every sound they spoke by shapes cut in stone, scored on clay or drawn on paper.

The revolution caused by the sharing of experience and the spread of knowledge had begun. The Chinese, a thousand years ago, gave it further impetus by devising mechanical means of reproducing such marks in great numbers. In Europe, Gutenberg

The compulsive communicators

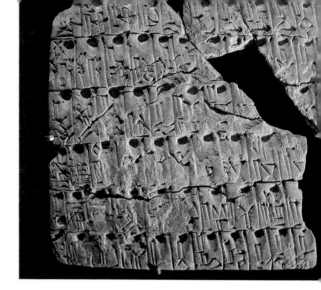

The early cities

About 5,000 years ago men began to build cities around the deltas of the Tigris and Euphrates Rivers in the Middle East, which were then rich farming land. Nearly all, like Nippur (below), had in their centre a ziggurat, an artificial mountain of mud bricks, that was their temple. Around its base clustered the houses of the people. Excavations have produced huge numbers of baked clay tablets, inscribed with symbols pressed in the once soft clay with a writing stick. The tablet on the right comes from Uruk and dates from about 2900 BC. Each line begins with a symbol meaning wood, so it may be some kind of dictionary, listing the different kinds of wood, or objects that can be made from wood.

independently though much later, developed the technique of printing from movable type. Today, our libraries, the descendants of those mud tablets, can be regarded as immense communal brains, memorising far more than any one human brain could hold. More than that, they can be seen as extra-corporeal DNA, adjuncts to our genetical inheritance as important and influential in determining the way we behave as the chromosomes in our tissues are in determining the physical shape of our bodies. It was this accumulated wisdom that eventually enabled us to devise ways of escaping the dictates of the environment. Our knowledge of agricultural techniques and mechanical devices, of medicine and engineering, of mathematics and space travel, all depend on stored experience. Cut off from our libraries and all they represent and marooned on a desert island, any one of us would be quickly reduced to the life of a hunter gatherer.

An awesome responsibility

Man's passion to communicate and to receive communications seems as central to his success as a species as the fin was to the fish or the feather to the birds. We do not limit ourselves to our own acquaintances or even our own generation. Archaeologists labour to decipher clay tablets rescued with painstaking care from Uruk and other ancient cities in the hope that some citizen long ago may have recorded a message of more significance than a boastful genealogy of a chief or a laundry list. In our own cities, dignitaries arrange for messages to be sent to future generations by burying writings in steel cylinders strong enough to survive even a nuclear catastrophe. And scientists, convinced that man's most refined language of all is that of mathematics, select a universal truth that they believe will be recognised through all eternity – a formula for the wavelength of light – and beam it towards other galaxies in the Milky Way to proclaim that here on earth, after three thousand million years of evolution, a creature has emerged that has for the first time devised its own way of accumulating and transferring experience across generations.

This last chapter has been devoted to only one species, ourselves. This may have given the impression that somehow man is the ultimate triumph of evolution, that all these millions of years of development have had no purpose other than to put him on earth. There is no evidence whatever to support such a view and no reason to suppose that our stay will be any more permanent than the dinosaurs'. The processes of evolution are still going on among plants and birds, insects and mammals. So it is more than likely that if men were to disappear from the earth, for whatever reason, there is a modest, unobtrusive creature somewhere that would develop into a new form and take our place.

But although denying that we have a special position in the natural world might seem becomingly modest in the eye of eternity, it might also be used as an excuse for evading our responsibilities. The fact is that no species has ever had such wholesale control over everything on earth, living or dead, as we now have. That lays upon us, whether we like it or not, an awesome responsibility. In our hands now lies not only our own future, but that of all other living creatures with whom we share the earth.

地球の生物

JAPANESE

Men invent scripts
Many different human societies have independently invented their own set of signs with which to record the sounds of their speech. Each, like the language it conveys, is the unique product of one culture and bears little resemblance to any other, even though it may be used to convey identical meanings. And electronic computers demand a version all their own.

חיים עלי אדמות

HEBREW

Жизнь на земле

RUSSIAN

زندگی در روی زمین

PERSIAN

Life on Earth

ROMAN

Ἡ Ζωή πάνω στήν Γῆ

GREEK

ชีวิตบนพิภพ

THAI

COMPUTER

Index

Index

Index

Index

Index

Acknowledgements

This book was written while a series of television programmes was being filmed on the same themes. In consequence, all those who worked on the films contributed both consciously and unconsciously to the book. Their names appear on the right, and I am grateful to them all without exception. I have special debts among them. Three, Maurice Fisher, Paul Morris and Lyndon Bird, were my companions during the bulk of my location filming. Their resilience and cheerfulness remained unquenched in even the most uncomfortable and trying circumstances, and when the sense of the words I spoke into their lenses and microphones became opaque, they compelled me, in the gentlest of ways, to clarify my thoughts. Each of the programmes, and thus each of the chapters, was in the particular charge of one of three producers, Christopher Parsons, Richard Brock and John Sparks. They were indefatigable in criticising the conventional assumptions of natural history and continuously searched for new, unfilmed examples to illustrate our points. I am much wiser for their generous conversations.

During our three years of travelling and filming, we were given the most generous assistance from experts of many kinds who took us to remote and little known sites to give us privileged views of creatures that they alone, as a result of their patient work over long periods, could provide. They include: in Africa, Peter Britton, Dian Fossey, Ian Redmond and Shigao Uehara; in Australia, Terry Dawson, Graham George, Dione Gilmour, Richard Jenkins, Peter Kupke, Frank Mugford, Phil Playford, Peter O'Reilly and Rod Wells; in Canada, David Sergeant; in Fiji, Ian Brown; in Japan, Mrs Ito; in Malaysia, Ken Scriven; in Panama, Ira Rubinoff; and in the United States, Don Beckmann, Bill Breed, Sylvia Earle, Carl Schuster, Steve Smith and Warren Zeiller.

I was further helped with the text by scientists who read individual chapters, among them: Robert Attenborough, Brian Gardner, Alice Grandison, Humphrey Greenwood, Leo Harrison Matthews and Vernon Reynolds. I am indebted to them for deflecting me from many errors. Peter Campbell, Robert Macdonald and Naomi Narod then laboured to turn the typescript into the original edition of the book with astounding speed and the greatest care.

This new enlarged edition was prepared at the suggestion of The Reader's Digest Association. Its London design and editorial team assembled the great number of photographs and drawings which appear in these pages and which have given a new dimension to the text. It is their skill, care and imagination that has brought about this spectacular metamorphosis and I am extremely grateful to them all.

LIFE ON EARTH
The television team

PRODUCERS
Richard Brock, Christopher Parsons
John Sparks

ASSISTANT PRODUCERS
Neil Cleminson, Keith Hopkins
Mike Salisbury

PRODUCER'S ASSISTANTS
Pamela Jackson, Jane Trethowan

CAMERAMEN
Maurice Fisher, Ray Henman
Martin Saunders

ASSISTANT CAMERAMEN
Jeremy Gould, Neil Matthews
Hugh Maynard, Paul Morris

SOUND
Lyndon Bird, Peter Copeland
Roger Long, Bob McDonnell

FILM EDITING
David Barrett, Alec Brown
Ron Martin

ORGANISERS
Derek Anderson, Rosanne Leigh

SPECIALIST CAMERAMEN
Densey Clyne, Walter Deas
Ron Eastman, Jim Frazier, Chris Fryman
Al Giddings, David Hughes
Rodger Jackman, Alasdair MacEwen
Hugh Miles, Sean Morris, David Parer
Peter Parks, Peter Scoones
David Thompson, Maurice Tibbles

Picture credits

The publishers wish to thank the following people for their help in preparing artwork for this edition of LIFE ON EARTH.

The Staff of the British Museum (Natural History), particularly members of the Department of Palaeontology, Botany and Entomology: The Staff of the University Herbarium and Botanic Gardens, Cambridge: Dr W. B. Amos, Department of Zoology, University of Cambridge: Dr Mahala Andrews, Royal Scottish Museum, Edinburgh: P. G. Barnes, Royal Horticultural Society: Dr D. E. G. Briggs, Department of Geology, Goldsmiths' College, University of London: Professor W. G. Chaloner, Department of Botany, Bedford College, University of London: Dr D. J. Chivers, Sub-department of Veterinary Anatomy, University of Cambridge: Dr T. R. Halliday, Department of Biology, Open University, Milton Keynes: Dr L. M. Hurxthal, University of Nairobi: Dr Roger Lubbock, Department of Zoology, University of Cambridge: Dr W. D. Ian Rolfe, Hunterian Museum, University of Glasgow: Dr P. A. Selden, Department of Geology, Goldsmiths' College, University of London: Dr K. R. Sporne, Department of Botany, University of Cambridge: A. J. Whitten, Sub-department of Veterinary Anatomy, University of Cambridge: Professor H. B. Whittington, Sedgwick Museum, University of Cambridge.

Photographs and artwork in this edition of LIFE ON EARTH came from the following people.

The credits for each page read from left to right in descending sequence. Where all photographs on one page come from the same source the credit is given once only.

Cover John Dominis/Life/© Time Inc. 1969. 1 Neville Fox-Davies. 2–3 Minoru Takedatsu/'Fox Family' Weatherhill/Heibonsha, Tokyo 1979. 4–5 David Doubilet. 6–7 Neville Fox-Davies. 8–9 © Horst Munzig/Susan Griggs.

1. THE INFINITE VARIETY

10–11 Gunter Ziesler. 12 Heather Angel. 13 Miguel Castro/Photo Researchers Inc.: Gunter Ziesler: Heather Angel. 14 From 'The World of Fossils' by Giovanni Pinna © Istituto Geografico De Agostini, Novara. 15 R. Levi-Setti: From 'The World of Fossils' by Giovanni Pinna © Istituto Geografico De Agostini, Novara. 16 Donald Baird: F. M. Carpenter: George Whiteley/Photo Researchers Inc. 17 Emil Muench/Ostman Agency. 18–19 Inez and George Hollis/Photo Researchers Inc. 22 Dr H. Canter-Lund. 23 David Attenborough. 24 Dr W. B. Amos. 25 Manfred Kage/Bruce Coleman Ltd. 26 Hermann Eisenbeiss. 27 Pat Morris: Peter D. Capen/Seaphot: F. van Santen/Tom Stack and Associates. 28 Oxford Scientific Films. 29 Oxford Scientific Films: Oxford Scientific Films: Peter David/Seaphot: Oxford Scientific Films: Oxford Scientific Films: Oxford Scientific Films: Neville Coleman/Bruce Coleman Ltd: Al Giddings/Sea Films Inc.: Oxford Scientific Films. 30 Runk/Schoenberger/Grant Heilman Photography © Oxford Scientific Films. 31 Heather Angel: Oxford Scientific Films: Oxford Scientific Films. 32 K. Kleeman/Seaphot. 32–33 David Attenborough. 33 David Attenborough. 34 Christian Petron/Seaphot: Douglas Faulkner. 35 Douglas Faulkner: Douglas Faulkner: Allan Power/Bruce Coleman Ltd. 36 Douglas Faulkner. 37 Nicholas de Vore/Bruce Coleman Ltd.

2. BUILDING BODIES

38–39 George Marler/Bruce Coleman Inc. 40–41 From 'The World of Fossils' by Giovanni Pinna © Istituto Geografico De Agostini, Novara. 41 Institute of Geological Sciences: R. Levi-Setti. 42 Christian Petron/Seaphot: *artist*, Norman Weaver. 43 Oxford Scientific Films: Isobel Bennett/Natural Science Photos. 44 Isobel Bennett/Natural Science Photos. 45 Universitets Zoologiske Museum, Denmark: Isobel Bennett/Natural Science Photos: William H. Amos/Bruce Coleman Inc.: A. van den Nieuwenhuizen: Isobel Bennett/Natural Science Photos. 46 D. P. Wilson/Eric and David Hosking: D. P. Wilson/Eric and David Hosking: Bill Wood/Bruce Coleman Ltd: Neville Coleman/Bruce Coleman Ltd: W. E. Harvey/Photo Researchers Inc. 47 Dr J. David George/Seaphot: Des Bartlett/Bruce Coleman Ltd: Nancy Sefton: W. E. Harvey/Photo Researchers Inc.: Oxford Scientific Films. 48 A. van den Nieuwenhuizen. 49 James H. Carmichael/Bruce Coleman Inc.: William H. Amos/Bruce Coleman Inc.: *artist*, Michael Woods. 50 John Fennell/Bruce Coleman Ltd. 51 Douglas Faulkner. 52 Kjell B. Sandved/Photo Researchers Inc.: Peter David/Seaphot: Lee E. Battaglia/Photo Researchers Inc. 53 Peter David/Seaphot. 54 *Artist*, Norman Weaver: Runk/Schoenberger/Grant Heilman Photography ©: David Doubilet: *artist*, Norman Weaver. 55 *Artist*, Norman Weaver: S. Summerhays/Biofotos: Kjell B. Sandved/Bruce Coleman Inc.: *artist*, Norman Weaver: Dr Armin Svoboda/Seaphot. 56 Oxford Scientific Films. 57 Jane Burton/Bruce Coleman Ltd: Dr Armin Svoboda/Seaphot. 58 Dick Clarke/Seaphot: Smithsonian Institution; photo numbers 18Fs, 52Fs, 37Fs. 59 Smithsonian Institution; 17Fs, 29Fs: S. Conway Morris 'Palaeontology' Volume 20 (3) 1977, Page 623. 60–61 *Artist*, Tom Adams. 62 Oxford Scientific Films: R. Levi-Setti, 'Trilobites; A Photographic Atlas': R. Levi-Setti: R. Levi-Setti, 'Trilobites; A Photographic Atlas'. 63 R. Levi-Setti, 'Trilobites; A Photographic Atlas'. 64–65 David Attenborough. 65 Oxford Scientific Films: Robert L. Dunne/Bruce Coleman Inc. 66 Oxford Scientific Films: Serge Pecolatto/Jacana: Oxford Scientific Films. 67 C. Newbert/Bruce Coleman Inc.: Shabica/Tom Stack and Associates: Anthony Mercieca/Photo Researchers Inc. 68 *Artist*, Norman Weaver. 69 Roger Perry: Oxford Scientific Films: David Attenborough.

3. THE FIRST FORESTS

70–71 Bill Ratcliffe. 72–73 David Attenborough. 73 Neville Fox-Davies. 74 Donald Baird. 74–75 *Artist*, Tom Adams. 76 Jane Burton/Bruce Coleman Ltd. 77 Jeff Foott/Bruce Coleman Inc.: *artist*, Michael Woods, after P. Weygoldt 'The Biology of Pseudo Scorpions' Harvard University Press. 78 Jane Burton/Bruce Coleman Ltd: John Markham/Bruce Coleman Ltd: John Markham/Bruce Coleman Ltd. 79 *Artist*, Norman Weaver: John Markham/Bruce Coleman Ltd. 80 *Artist*, Michael Woods, after W. S. Bristowe 'The World of Spiders' Collins 1958: Oxford Scientific Films. 81 Jane Burton/Bruce Coleman Ltd: James H. Carmichael, Jnr/Photo Researchers Inc. 82–83 C. B. and D. W. Frith/Bruce Coleman Ltd: *artist*, Norman Weaver. 84 Dr F. Sauer/Bavaria-Verlag. 85 Stephen Dalton/Bruce Coleman Ltd: F. M. Carpenter. 86 Heather Angel. 87 *Artist*, Harry Titcombe. 88–89 Bill Ratcliffe. 89 F. M. Carpenter. 90 Neville Fox-Davies. 91 Stephen Dalton/N.H.P.A.: *artist*, Norman Weaver. 92 David Barlow/Stephen Bolwell. 93 Hermann Eisenbeiss. 94 Eric Crichton/Bruce Coleman Ltd. 95 A. J. Deane/Bruce Coleman Inc.: G. E. Hyde: Oxford Scientific Films. 96 M. P. L. Fogden/Bruce Coleman Inc. 97 Bill Ratcliffe.

4. THE SWARMING HORDES

98–99 R. A. Preston-Mafham/Premaphotos Wildlife. 100 © David Scharf, 1977; all rights reserved, from 'Magnifications' Schocken Books Inc., NY. 101 © David Scharf, 1977; all rights reserved, from 'Magnifications' Schocken Books Inc., NY: Dr W. B. Amos: Dr W. B. Amos. 102–3 *Artist*, Peter Barrett. 104 Peter Ward/Bruce Coleman Inc.: N. Smythe/National Audubon Collection/Photo Researchers Inc.: David Overcash/Bruce Coleman Ltd. 105 M. P. L. Fogden/Bruce Coleman Inc.: Ed Ross: Mantis Wildlife Films. 106 C. K. Mylne: R. C. Hermes/National Audubon Collection/Photo Researchers Inc.: Kjell B. Sandved/Photo Researchers Inc.: M. P. L. Fogden/Bruce Coleman Inc.: Mantis Wildlife Films: Mantis Wildlife Films. 107 K. G. Preston-Mafham/Premaphotos Wildlife. 108 Mantis Wildlife Films. 109 Oxford Scientific Films. 110 Kjell B. Sandved/Photo Researchers Inc.: Oxford Scientific Films: Ed Ross: Mantis Wildlife Films: Oxford Scientific Films. 110–11 M. P. L. Fogden/Bruce Coleman Ltd. 112 Dr W. B. Amos. 113 © David Scharf, 1977; all rights reserved, from 'Magnifications' Schocken Books Inc., NY. 114 K. G. Preston-Mafham/N.H.P.A.: F. Collet/Photo Researchers Inc.: K. G. Preston-Mafham/Premaphotos Wildlife. 115 Gunter Ziesler/Bruce Coleman Ltd. 116 *Artist*, Michael Woods, after L. J. and M. Milne 'The social behaviour of burying beetles' Scientific American, 1976. 116–17 Glenn Prestwich. 117 Pat Morris/Ardea London: Peter Ward/Bruce Coleman Inc.: Klaus Paysan. 118–19 J. B. Free. 120 J. L. Mason/Ardea London: Stephen Dalton/N.H.P.A.: Stephen Dalton/N.H.P.A. 121 Ivan Polunin: Adrian Warren/Ardea London. 122 K. G. Preston-Mafham/Premaphotos Wildlife: Oxford Scientific Films. 123 M. P. L. Fogden/Bruce Coleman Ltd.

5. THE CONQUEST OF THE WATERS

124–5 Scott Johnson/N.H.P.A. 126–7 Dick Clarke/Seaphot: M. Laverack/Seaphot: Maurice Fisher. 128 Runk/Schoenberger/Grant Heilman Photography ©: Heather Angel: Tom Stack and Associates. 129 British Museum (Natural History). 130–1 *Artist*, Peter Barrett. 132 Runk/Schoenberger/Grant Heilman Photography ©. 133 Douglas Faulkner: Chris Newbert/Bruce Coleman Inc. 134–5 Tom McHugh/Steinhart Aquarium/Photo Researchers Inc. 135 Peter David/Seaphot. 136 Jane Burton/Bruce Coleman Ltd: Ed Ross. 137 Douglas Faulkner. 138 *Artist*, Michael Woods, after B. B. Rae 'The Lemon Sole' Fishing News, 1965. 139 Ben Cropp/Tom Stack and Associates. 140 *Artist*, Michael Woods: *artist*, Hargrave Hands, after N. Wickler 'Mimicry in Plants and Animals' Weidenfeld and Nicolson, 1948. 140–1 Flip Schulke/Black Star. 142 *Artist*, Hargrave Hands. 143 Valerie Taylor/Ardea London: Warren Williams/Seaphot: Pat Morris: Ed Ross: Dick Clarke/Seaphot: H. Hille/Zefa: Valerie Taylor/Ardea London: Bill Wood/N.H.P.A.: Chris Newbert/Bruce Coleman Inc. 144–5 Oxford Scientific Films. 144 Oxford Scientific Films. 145 *Artist*, Michael Woods, after J. E. McCosker 'Flashlight fishes' Scientific American, March 1977: Peter David/Seaphot. 146 Jeff Foott/Bruce Coleman Ltd. 146–7 M. Stouffer/Animals Animals. 147 Jeff Foott/Bruce Coleman Ltd: David Attenborough: Jeff Foott/Bruce Coleman Ltd.

6. THE INVASION OF THE LAND

148–9 Dmitri Kessel/Life/© Time Inc. 1958. 150 S. Cordier/Pitch. 150–1 Heather Angel. 153 Museum fur Naturkunde, Berlin, GDR: Peter Scoones/Seaphot. 154–5 Tom Stack/Tom Stack and Associates: Donald Baird. 155 S. M. Andrews. 156–7 *Artist*, Peter Barrett. 158 Jane Burton/Bruce Coleman Inc. 159 Dr F. Sauer/Bavaria Verlag. 160 A. van den Nieuwenhuizen: Adrian Warren/Ardea London. 161 A. van den Nieuwenhuizen: A. van den Nieuwenhuizen: A. van den Nieuwenhuizen: Zig Leszczynski/Animals Animals/Oxford Scientific Films: Zig Leszczynski/Animals Animals/Oxford Scientific Films. 162 François Gohier: Adrian Warren/Ardea London: Adrian Warren/Ardea London. 163 Ed Ross. 164 Alan Blank/Bruce Coleman Inc. 165 Leonard Lee Rue III/Bruce Coleman Inc.: Leonard Lee Rue III/Bruce Coleman Inc.: Leonard Lee Rue III/Bruce Coleman Inc.: John Shaw/Bruce Coleman Inc. 166 Oxford Scientific Films. 167 Oxford Scientific Films. 168 Jane Burton/Bruce Coleman Ltd. 169 Udo Hirsch/Bruce Coleman Ltd: Ed Ross: Oxford Scientific Films. 170 Adrian Warren: Oxford Scientific Films: Oxford Scientific Films. 171 David Attenborough.

7. A WATERTIGHT SKIN

172–3 Emil Schulthess/Black Star. 174 *Artist*, Michael Woods. 175 David Attenborough. 176 State Natural History Museum, Stuttgart: British Museum (Natural History). 177 Dr M. G. Bassett. 178–9 *Artist*, Charles Raymond. 180 British Museum (Natural History). 181 David Attenborough. 182–3 *Artist*, Tom Adams. 184–5 David Attenborough. 186 Jonathan Blair/Susan Griggs Agency. 187 Jonathan Blair/Susan Griggs Agency. 188 Jonathan Blair/Susan Griggs Agency. 189 Gunter Ziesler: *artist*, John Norris-Wood. 190 John R. Brownlie/Bruce Coleman Ltd: Gary Milburn/Tom Stack and Associates: Mantis Wildlife Films: Jane Burton/Bruce Coleman Ltd: Zig Leszczynski/Animals Animals/Oxford Scientific Films: Mantis Wildlife Films. 191 Alan Blank/Bruce Coleman Inc.: Mantis Wildlife Films: David Hughes. 192 Rod Rorland/Bruce Coleman Inc. 193 Loren McIntyre. 194 Anthony Bannister/N.H.P.A.: *artist*, John Norris-Wood. 195 Carol Hughes/Bruce Coleman Inc. 196 Adrian Warren: Tom McHugh/Photo Researchers Inc. 197 Mark Boulton/Bruce Coleman Ltd. 198 Tom McHugh/Photo Researchers Inc. 199 Nina Leen/Life/© Time Inc. 1963.

8. LORDS OF THE AIR

200–1 David Cavagnaro. 202 Museum fur Naturkunde, Berlin, GDR. 203 Tierbilder Okapia: Museum fur Naturkunde, Berlin, GDR: Tierbilder Okapia. 204 G. R. Roberts: Thau/Roberz/Zefa: Adrian Warren. 205 Australian Picture Library: Gunter Ziesler. 206 M. P. Kahl/Bruce Coleman Inc. 207 D. Botting. 208–9 Fote Eugen Schuhmacher, Munchen-Grunwald: Gunter Ziesler. 210 Jennifer Fry/Bruce Coleman Ltd. 211 Stephen Dalton/Bruce Coleman Ltd. 212 Gunter Ziesler/Bruce Coleman Ltd: Jen and Des Bartlett/Bruce Coleman Ltd. 212–13 Stephen Dalton/Bruce Coleman Ltd: 213 Walter E. Harvey/National Audubon Collection/Photo Researchers Inc. 214–15 M. P. Kahl. 215 Bob and Carla Calhoun/Bruce Coleman Inc. 216 Gunter Ziesler. 217 Gunter Ziesler: Gunter Ziesler: Gunter Ziesler: Jacana. 218 Pat Morris/Ardea London. 219 Erwin A. Bauer: Gunter Ziesler. 220 *Artist*, Peter Barrett. 221 Dr G. Konrad. 222 Graham Pizzey/Bruce Coleman Ltd: *artist*, Richard Bonson, after A. J. Marshall 'Bower Birds' Scientific American, June 1956. 223 Barry Ranford. 224 *Artist*, Michael Woods. 225 *Artist*, Sean Milne: Gunter Ziesler. 226 David Parer. 227 David Parer. 228–9 *Artist*, Charles Pickard. 230 Pat Morris/Ardea London. 231 Adrian Warren.

9. EGGS, POUCHES AND PLACENTAS

232–3 J. Dominis/Life/© Time Inc. 1957. 235 Jean-Paul Ferrero. 241 Bob Gossington/Bruce Coleman Inc.: Lois and George Cox/Bruce Coleman Inc. 242 Ed Ross. 243 Hans and Judy Beste/Ardea London: Tom McHugh/Photo Researchers Inc. 244 Hans and Judy Beste/Tom Stack and Associates. 245 Stanley Breeden. 246 Jean-Paul Ferrero: *artist*, Barry Driscoll. 247 Jean-Paul Ferrero/Ardea London. 248 A. G. Wells/Oxford Scientific Films. 250 Jacana. 251 Jean-Paul Ferrero.

10. THEME AND VARIATIONS

252–3 C. B. Frith/Bruce Coleman Inc. 254 Hans Reinhard/Bruce Coleman Inc. 255 Charles Mohr/National Audubon Collection/Photo Researchers Inc.: Oxford Scientific Films. 256 Ed Ross. 257 Gerard/Jacana. 258 Gary Milburn/Tom Stack and Associates. 259 Ed Ross. 260 Tierbilder Okapia: Des Bartlett/Bruce Coleman Ltd: Des Bartlett/Bruce Coleman Ltd. 261 Warren Garst/Tom Stack and Associates. 262 C. B. and D. W. Frith/Bruce Coleman Ltd: Zig Leszczynski/Oxford Scientific Films: Heather Angel: Bavarian State Collection for Palaeontology and Historical Geology, Munich. 263 P. Ward/Bruce Coleman Inc.: Tony Beamish/Ardea London. 264 George Holton/Photo Researchers Inc. 266 Nina Leen/Life/© Time Inc. 1968. 266–7 Nina Leen/Life/© Time Inc. 1968. 269 Nina Leen/Life/© Time Inc. 1968. 270 Stanley Breeden: Stanley Breeden: Jane Burton/Bruce Coleman Ltd: Roy P. Fontaine/Photo Researchers Inc.: S. C. Bisserot/Bruce Coleman Ltd: S. C. Bisserot/Bruce Coleman Ltd. 271 Nina Leen/Life/© Time Inc. 1968. 272–3 Al Giddings/Sea Film Inc.: Charles Nicklin/Sea Film Inc.: R. Kinne/Photo Researchers Inc. 274 Al Giddings/Sea Film Inc. 275 Gordon Williamson/Bruce Coleman Ltd. 276 Wometco Miami Seaquarium. 276–7 Tom Walker/Tom Stack and Associates. 278 Douglas Faulkner: George Holton/National Audubon Collection/Photo Researchers Inc. 279 Jen and Des Bartlett/Bruce Coleman Ltd.

11. THE HUNTERS AND THE HUNTED

280–1 Thomas Nebbia/Woodfin Camp and Associates. 282–3 *Artist*, Charles Pickard. 284 Minoru Takedatsu/'Fox Family' Weatherhill/Heibonsha, Tokyo 1979. 285 Minoru Takedatsu/'Fox Family' Weatherhill/Heibonsha, Tokyo 1979. 286 Andrew Laurie. 287 Andrew Laurie: Chas. J. Ott/Bruce Coleman Ltd: Varin-Visage/Jacana. 288–9 Rolf O. Peterson. 290 Tom McHugh/Photo Researchers Inc. 291 Fred Baldwin/National Audubon Collection/Photo Researchers Inc.: Dick Robinson/Bruce Coleman Ltd. 292 Gunter Ziesler. 293 Stan Wayman/Life/© Time Inc. 1965. 294–5 Erwin and Peggy Bauer. 296 Sven-Olof Lindblad/National Audubon Collection/Photo Researchers Inc. 297 Andrew Laurie. 298 M. Austerman/Animals Animals/Oxford Scientific Films: Allan D. Cruickshank/Photo Researchers Inc. 299 Charlie Summers/Tom Stack and Associates. 300–1 *Artist*, Tom Adams. 303 Carol Hughes: Peter Davey/Bruce Coleman Ltd. 304 Erwin A. Bauer: Klaus Paysan. 304–5 P. Montoya/Pitch. 306–7 Hugo van Lawick. 308 John Dominis/Life/© Time Inc. 1967: Erwin and Peggy Bauer. 309 Andrew Laurie. 310–11 Sylvio Fresco/Bruce Coleman Inc. 311 Hugo van Lawick. 312–13 Hugo van Lawick. 314 J. Pearson/Bruce Coleman Ltd. 315 Hugo van Lawick.

12. A LIFE IN THE TREES

316–17 Loren A. McIntyre. 318 Christian Zuber/Bruce Coleman Ltd. 318–19 Russ Kinne/Photo Researchers Inc. 320–1 Norman Myers/Bruce Coleman Ltd. 322 Mantis Wildlife Films: Stanley Breeden: Ivan Polunin/N.H.P.S. 324 Christian Zuber/Bruce Coleman Ltd: J. H. Carmichael Jnr/Bruce Coleman Inc. 325 Nina Leen/Life/© Time Inc. 1971: Rod Williams/Bruce Coleman Ltd: Rod Williams/Bruce Coleman Ltd: Rod Williams/Bruce Coleman Ltd: Rod Williams/Bruce Coleman Ltd: Rod Williams/Bruce Coleman Ltd: Rod Williams/Bruce Coleman Ltd: George Harrison/Grant Heilman Photography ©. 326 Wolfgang Bayer/Bruce Coleman Inc.: *artist*, Barry Driscoll. 327 Rod Williams/Bruce Coleman Ltd: M. Freedman/Bruce Coleman Inc.: Norman Myers/Bruce Coleman Ltd. 328 Belinda Wright. 329 Norman O. Tomalin/Bruce Coleman Inc.: F. Erize/Bruce Coleman Inc. 330–1 C. Rentmeester/Life/© Time Inc. 1970. 332 David Attenborough. 333 David Attenborough. 334 Andrew Laurie. 335 M. P. Price/Bruce Coleman Ltd: *artist*, Barry Driscoll. 336 *Artist*, Barry Driscoll, after Ralph Morse photograph, courtesy Animal Talent Scout Inc. and Time Life Books: Rod Williams/Bruce Coleman Ltd. 337 *Artist*, Barry Driscoll: Jean-Paul Ferrero. 338 Dian Fossey/Bruce Coleman Ltd. 339 David Attenborough. 340–1 David Attenborough: John Sparks. 342 David Attenborough. 343 David Attenborough.

13. THE COMPULSIVE COMMUNICATORS

344–5 Simon Trevor/Bruce Coleman Ltd. 346 Alan Hutchison Library: B. and C. Alexander: B. and C. Alexander. 347 B. and C. Alexander: Derek Fordham. 348–9 David Attenborough. 350–1 Yan/Rapho/Photo Researchers Inc.: Giorgio Gualco/Bruce Coleman Ltd. 352 David Attenborough. 353 David Attenborough. 354 David Attenborough. 355 David Attenborough. 356 David Attenborough. 357 Maureen Bisilliat. 358 Loren McIntyre. 359 Per-Olle-Stackman/Tiofoto AB. 360 Giraudon: Dr Georg Gerster/John Hillelson Agency. 361 *Artists*, Ikuo Ota: Jeffery Matthews.